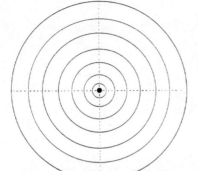

SEARCH AND SCREENING

General Principles with Historical Applications

Bernard Osgood Koopman

MILITARY OPERATIONS RESEARCH SOCIETY

Alexandria, Virginia

This book has been reprinted in its entirety.
Not one word has been changed from the original edition.

Search and Screening: General Principles with Historical Applications.
Koopman, Bernard Osgood
Pergamon Press published the First Edition, 1980.

ISBN 0-930473-08-6. Library of Congress catalog card number 99-63839. All rights
reserved. No part of this book may be reproduced or utilized in any form or by any
means, electronic or mechanical, including photocopying, recording, or by an information
or storage retrieval system, without permission in writing from the publishers. Printed in
the United States of America.

FOREWARD

The Military Operations Research Society (MORS) has established as one of its twelve goals "to preserve the heritage of military operations research." This heritage is an important avenue for the development of our junior analysts. Therefore, MORS is providing a series of "heritage" books that have been key elements in the development of the operations research profession, so that our junior analysts can learn from the "fathers" of our profession. This book is the second in our Heritage Series and is directly related to the first volume titled *Methods of Operations Research*, written by **Philip M. Morse** and **George E. Kimball**. The Operations Evaluation Group, now a major component of the Center for Naval Analyses, published in 1946 several reports summarizing key analytical lessons learned from World War II. This book, *Search and Screening*, written by **Bernard O. Koopman**, and *Methods of Operations Research*, by Morse and Kimball, represent two of the three volumes published.

The MORS heritage committee uses two basic criteria for the selection of books to be reprinted: (1) the publication has enduring value, and (2) the author has played a significant role in the military operations research profession.

This publication has enduring value because as stated in the preface of this book, even though this volume has long been out of print, "extracts and translations of parts of it are being used both in the United States and in many other nations giving scientific naval instructions." Since its original print, it has continually been updated. One of the individuals mentioned in preface who has "helped make important improvements" is CAPT **Wayne Hughes**, USN, (Ret) (MORS Past President, MORS Fellow and Wanner Award recipient). MORS' roots are truly evident in this book.

Dr. Bernard O. Koopman has played a significant role in the military operations research profession. Along with Dr. Kimball, co-author of our first classic, he helped to pioneer the modern theory of search as applied in World War II and designed many naval operating plans. In 1979, he became the second recipient of the MORS **Vance R. Wanner Memorial Award**, presented to those who have played a major role in strengthening the profession.

MORS firmly believes this "classic" provides the correct mix of mathematical theory, scientific approach and practical illustrations of operations research. For the "old timers," this will be a good review. We ask that each mentor buy or share this book with our rising analysts in the operations research profession, so we may continue to "Develop our Junior Analyst."

Dennis R. Baer
CDR, USN (Ret.)
MORS President, 1998-1999

Dedicated to the Memory of

George Elbert Kimball

Colleague and Friend
and Fellow Pioneer in the Theory of Search

Contents

Appendix

SEARCH AND SCREENING

Preface

The theory of search, as a scientific discipline uniting physical and operational facts through mathematical concepts and theorems, may fairly be said to date from World War II, and to have received its major impulse from various phases of the war at sea, in particular, those involving the submarine. At the center of the development of this new branch of operations research was the group of scientists assigned during 1942–1945 to the Commander in Chief, U.S. Fleet, designated first by the name Anti-Submarine Warfare Operations Group (ASWORG); later, Operations Research Group (ORG). After 1945, it became the Operations Evaluation Group (OEG), and is now a subgroup of the Center for Naval Analyses (CNA).

At the close of the war, it was decided that the OEG should publish those parts of its work of general scientific or historical interest in three volumes: *Methods of Operations Research* (P. M. Morse and G. E. Kimball) [6], *Summary of ASW Operations in World War II* (Allan Thorndyke) [9], and *Search and Screening* (B. O. Koopman) [4]. In each case, the authors named had many collaborators, too numerous to list. These books were published by the Summary Reports Group of the Columbia University Division of War Research under contract OEMsr-1131 with the Office of Scientific Research and Development, and printed and bound by the Columbia University Press. *Search and Screening* was designated as Volume 2B of Division 6 in the series of Summary Technical Reports of the National Defense Research Committee. Originally entitled OEG Report 56 and Confidential, it was later declassified.

Search and Screening contained no references to the scientific literature on search: none existed. During the ensuing third of a century, research and publications on the theory of search and its various military and civilian applications have grown enormously and would fill many library bookshelves. Moreover, the advances in research and development of the systems of detection, their platforms and targets, have been so great that an entirely new picture is presented, both to the military and the civilian applications of the scientific theory of search. And finally, progress in the mathematical theory bearing on search, and making itself all the more effective by using modern computers, has given its own impetus to the subject.

For these reasons it has seemed to the author and to many of his colleagues that a new and updated edition of *Search and Screening* is desirable; a very practical reason being that the original volume was issued in limited numbers and has long been out of print—in spite of the fact that extracts and translations of parts of it are being used both in the United States and in many other nations giving scientific naval instruction.

Having decided to publish such a new edition, many difficult questions are raised: To what extent should the contemporary scene influence the treatment? What balance should be struck between the three cardinal factors: (1) physics and engineering developments; (2) mathematical theory; (3) practical recommendations and illustrations ("how to . . . ")? The decision was reached to stay close to the original format: to produce a *textbook* on search (in the sense that we speak of a "textbook" of electromagnetism, of radio engineering, of advanced calculus). It was not intended to produce a learned compendium involving all fields of search, of the order of the *Handbuch der Physik* with its many volumes.

Regarding the proper balance between its parts, there is, first, the natural tendency of engineers and experimental physicists to put the instrumentalities of search (the sensors) and the physical properties of the target and its environment (the medium) at the center of the stage, and to reduce to a secondary role *the operation of search as an organic whole having a structure of its own—more than the sum of its parts.* The original book had three chapters on the technological factors in search of thirty years ago: Visual Detection, Radar Detection, and Sonar Detection, which were, in a sense, separate from the main stream of the work. These, in a re-edited and updated form, have been relegated to appendixes in the present text, but the main burden of the new technology has been noted more by its implications than by its elaboration. Among other advantages, this avoids classified or proprietary material, as well as a requirement of too specialized knowledge on the part of the reader.

The second danger is overemphasis on immediate practical answers to all kinds of questions of how to plan searches—rules without scientific explanation. There are manuals for this purpose, but they must be based on knowledge and reasoning (often mathematical): to supply such a basis has in fact been the intention both of the first and the present edition of this textbook. On the other hand, every textbook must include a wealth of concrete illustrations, motivated by practical problems, and applying the theoretical results. These are of a very general and simple form in the first seven chapters. In the last three, the practical implementations of the theory developed earlier have been illustrated in greater detail by examples drawn from World War II, principally from the war at sea, although a mathematical framework is given for more modern applications. The three reasons for this choice are that they are *available* (neither classified nor proprietary), they are *detailed* and were put to the actual tests of practice (few similarly detailed examples are available), and they have the *historical* importance of examples of theoretical scientific reasoning that achieved success.

The third danger facing a textbook on search is the inappropriate handling of the mathematics. At one extreme, there is often an impulse to leave it out as such. But since in most cases the essential reasoning concerns the structural and quantitative aspect of the question—viz., concerns essentially mathematical factors—to leave out the mathematics is to leave out the essential reasoning. Those parts of the mathematics that can be separated from the reasoning without destroying it and which are somewhat technical and lengthy are best relegated to appendixes (the first four of the present textbook are such) or, when reasonably accessible, by reference to the literature. At the opposite extreme, there is the danger of elaborating the mathematical treatment to a degree of generality and abstraction that is not needed, either practically or theoretically, by the applications. Most of the mathematics used in our text is contained in the familiar first two undergraduate years of calculus and algebra, conventionally required of students of physics and engineering, together with some introductory probability. At points where more is required, its motivation and explanation in intuitive terms are given. The four mathematical appendixes are only somewhat more demanding.

In order to emphasize the link between the world of abstractions and that of physical reality, we have been uncompromising in requiring that all the terms and quantities introduced be given an *operational definition* in the sense of P. W. Bridgman [1]. While this notion will be elaborated in the definition of "event" in Appendix A, of "compatibility of observations" in Chapter 1, and in "density of searching effort" in Chapters 6 and 7, and in many other places, we may recall that it is the requirement that the physical preconditions and method of observation or measurement used in defining any quantity entering the mathematical formulas must be stated explicitly—unless these are already known, or derivable by a validated process from known ones.

In conclusion to the questions of methodology, a word should be said concerning the impact of modern computers on problems of search. When the computers *add* their powers to those of the scientific mind, with its reasoning based on experience, special knowledge, and mathematical concepts and theorems, they are often capable of greatly extending the range of problems that can be solved. But computers are no substitute for the rational process. It is indeed for the furtherance of the latter that this book has been written—its results to be implemented, as appropriate, by the former. At many places in this work such an implementation has been noted. Thus, in target localization by least squares (Chapter 4, Section 8, and Appendix B), the theory has led to computer programs used by the U.S. Navy. And we frequently point out in Chapters 8, 9, and 10, the possibility that speed and efficiency might have been increased had computers been available. For example, in calculating hit probabilities of "browning shots," computer simulation is clearly indicated. But modern computers, along with so many modern improvements in sensor and signal processing technology, have been relegated to a minor position in the book.

Turning from these historical and expository generalities to the topics covered, the first chapter is introductory and qualitative, being a general survey of the various classes of problems demanding a scientific study of search. The ubiquitous presence of probability is emphasized and typical questions leading to its use are outlined. Even on this simple qualitative level, the important issue of the observer's changing what he is observing, forces itself upon the reasoning. This matter, dealt with at length in Appendix A (on probability), along with the related issue of the compatibility of trials, has found little space in conventional works on the subject.

Chapter 2 deals with the simple geometry and motion (absolute and relative) of objects moving in a plane, either at constant velocity or, in the case of a statistical ensemble, in the simplest types of random. In the main, it follows Chapter 1 of the 1946 edition, but adds the kinematics of "sprint and drift," required by certain modern tactics.

Chapter 3 deals with the probabilities involved in the detection of an object of search ("*target*"), under a variety of simplifying assumptions regarding its visibility and relative motion. The chapter includes the material of Chapter 2 of the 1946 edition, in which formulas were developed that have had wide application. The presentation is brought up to date and some new material added. Our intention has been, not only to present known facts, but also to emphasize the incompleteness in our knowledge, with the hope of stimulating further research yielding applicable and verifiable results. Further gaps in our knowledge of the quantitative aspects of detection are made evident in the last three appendixes.

Chapter 4, on target localization, covers new ground, not in the 1946 edition. The reason is that ranges of detection have grown to such an extent in the intervening decades and the process has become so indirect that even when a target is detected, a considerable uncertainty often remains as to its precise location. The problem, under the usual simple assumptions, becomes one of *inverse probability*, requiring the updating of previous estimates of probable positions by Bayes's formula. Under modern conditions, the data often form a complex of pieces of different kinds and must be handled by computers.

Chapter 5 deals with the problem, often very difficult, of predicting future positions of a target after a first detection and a more or less precise localization have been made. The prediction must be based on an appraisal of the factors influencing the target's motion. A number of illustrative cases are examined, ranging from simple predictability, through various orders of random, often compounded by evasive maneuvers. Because of its practical importance, the problem of moving targets has been intensively treated in the literature, but much more work needs to be done. This chapter attempts only to introduce and illustrate the problems, covering ground not touched in the 1946 edition. In practical situations, computer updates in "real time" may be essential, but their adequate consideration would go beyond the scope of this book.

Chapter 6 deals with the problem of optimal search: the most effective application of a limited amount of searching effort. It contains in amplified form the material first developed by the author and presented in Chapter 3 of the 1946 edition and reproduced later [4, 5]. It has had many practical applications and has been generalized in various directions, ranging all the way from concretely useful to theoretically mathematical. For our purposes it will suffice to note the references to the literature given by J. M. Dobbie [3] and L. D. Stone [8].

Chapter 7 continues with the study of optimal search, but instead of assuming that all the searching is committed at once, the author considers searches performed progressively as a sequential operation, a point of view first set forth by Dobbie [2]. When the search is by "successive dichotomies" the theory of numerical *information* automatically introduces itself, and the problem coincides with that of optimal coding in communications engineering. With other types of search there is still a generalized sort of numerical information on the part of the searcher, taking the form of the "degree of jeopardy"—to a target not wishing to be detected.

Chapter 8 gives the practical methods of implementing the theory of the search for targets in transit, by screens, barriers, and retiring searches. It is taken almost entirely from Chapter 7 of the 1946 edition, a major part of which was contributed by three colleagues of the author at OEG: Drs. J. M. Dobbie, J. A. Neuendorffer, and J. J. Steinhardt. Under the direction of the latter, the barrier across the South Atlantic had been established during World War II, leading to the detection and destruction of five German blockade runners carrying important strategic materials to the Third Reich. In their present form, this and the two following chapters owe many improvements to Captain Wayne P. Hughes, Jr. (U.S.N.), both in adding new material and imparting a more up-to-date point of view.

Chapter 9, on surface screens for the defense of convoys against approaching submarines, is mainly a reproduction of Chapter 8 of the 1946 edition. In addition to the three colleagues cited above, Drs. R. E. Beatty and J. K. Tyson (of OEG/CNA) were instrumental in its writing. In view of the revolutionary changes in technology, the present chapter has chiefly illustrative and historical interest. Even without such changes, modern computers would, as noted before, have improved the methods of evaluation. Only Section 7 is new, applying the *isochrons* introduced in Chapter 3 to the design of "sprint and drift" screens. Again, in many parts of this chapter, Captain Hughes helped us in important improvements.

Chapter 10 treats the aerial escort of convoys, as it was used in the period in which submarines had to approach in a surfaced condition, submerging only at closer ranges. Visual and radar systems were effective means of detection; the least they could do was to "keep the subs down" and so deny them much maneuverability. All this has changed, but the principles of applying kinematics and probability to similar problems have not. Therefore, this chapter reproduces Chapter 9 of the 1946 edition. Many of the methods are based on the *tactical zones* composing the (moving) regions about the defended formation. Others use the *polar diagram* of a screen: the radial plot of the probabilities of its undetected penetration at various angles of relative approach, which provides an "x-ray picture" of its weak points. This method, introduced by the author during the war, was used extensively in the design and improvement of screens. We wish to emphasize that had modern computers been available, many of the lengthy and cumbersome steps described in obtaining the polar diagrams might have been avoided. In carrying out the applications of the methods, many of the colleagues mentioned before made valuable contributions to the original chapter. And again Captain Hughes has helped in an important manner in the present version.

Particular mention should be made of Fig. 10-4, which was produced by the late Dr. Walter Albertson of OEG, who accompanied a transatlantic convoy on an escort carrier during the war and, in order to compare the flights actually made by the escorting aircraft with the flight plans attempted, measured their positions by radar observations at frequent intervals. The comparison between plan and actuality should serve as an object lesson.

The four mathematical Appendixes, A through D, were added to the first edition to supply the reader who wishes to go somewhat more deeply into the mathematical side, with a presentation of certain conventional subjects from a point of view most appropriate to the theory of search. In particular, the "events" in the theory of probability are defined physically rather than abstractly; the distinction of compatible versus incompatible trials is emphasized; those situations in which the method of least squares for target localization is applicable are characterized in all detail and distinguished from those in which it can give false results; the question, besetting many problems of operational research, of evaluating unknown probability distributions, is examined and illustrated by the case of variations of target detectability; the applicability of the methods of minimizing the logarithmic information (maximizing the entropy) of a distribution are analyzed; the contrast between the so-called "subjective" (intuitive) point of view of the *meaning* of probability and the objective nature of the methods of determining its *values* is emphasized. Many similar matters are treated. All these touch everywhere on the theory of search, but the appendixes can be omitted without serious impairment to the understanding of the book.

Appendix E, on visual detection, was written by Betsy Jo Constantine (of Arthur D. Little, Inc.), and is a modernized version of Chapter 4 of the 1946 edition, written by E. S. Lamar (then in OEG). In spite of the numerous investigations of the eye and of vision, dating back to the dawn of science, we found ourselves during World War II without enough information to evaluate, in even rough quantitative terms, its performance under the various conditions of search. Since at that time visual detection of air and surface targets played a major role, it was imperative to fill this gap. During a liaison visit to the United Kingdom during the war, E. S. Lamar came in contact with the late K. J. W. Craik and his experimental work (unpublished), which suggested investigations that Lamar carried out shortly in S. Hecht's laboratory at Columbia University. The results were brought together in the original Chapter 4. The evolution of the whole subject since the war was examined by B. J. Constantine and is a basis of Appendix E. A perusal of its seventy references shows how strongly the subsequent investigations were influenced by the early ones mentioned above.

Appendix F on radar and electromagnetic detection was written by Gordon Raisbeck (Vice President at Arthur D. Little, Inc.). It completely replaces Chapter 5 of the 1946 edition. At that time, radar was in its early stages of development and its very name came under security classification. Now there exist a large number of highly detailed and sophisticated texts and articles on all its phases. Probably the most useful treatment from the point of view of the present book is the one by Skolnik [7]. Actually, Appendix F is greatly indebted to many of the expository parts of the latter. As an outline it should be sufficient for our treatment of search; for more details, the reader is referred to Skolnik.

Appendix G, on sonar detection, was written by George Miller (of Arthur D. Little, Inc.) and is a greatly modified replacement of Chapter 6 of the 1946 edition. The whole subject—the hydroacoustic sensing devices and signal processing methods, the characteristics of emitted or reflected sounds, and the complex acoustic properties of the sea—forms such a vast range of subjects that they could be treated only in bare outline in this appendix. It should, however, be sufficient as a basis for understanding the treatment of search in the present book.

This preface, as well as that of the 1946 edition, should make amply clear how greatly the colleagues of the author have contributed both to the development of the subject and to its presentation, in both editions. As we go to press, it is fitting to recall with thanks the names of those most recently involved in helping us to improve it: Captain Hughes, who has read every page of the text; Dr. Gordon Raisbeck, who has contributed both material and administrative support; Dr. J. M. Dobbie, who has worked with me as a colleague ever since the middle of World War II and has made important advances in the theory of search; and, finally, many other members of the Arthur D. Little staff. From this rather inadequate acknowledgment of the help received from fellow scientists, both civilian and military, I turn to a larger view of the contributors: the mighty hosts of those who risked or gave their lives during the grim events that stimulated this department of human knowledge.

The present work was made possible by the Office of Naval Research and the ASW Systems Project Office under Contract N00014-75-C-1096. For this generous support and for the personal encouragement and involvement of Mr. J. Randolph Simpson, ONR, and of CDR Frank Quigley, ASWSPO, we wish to express our deep appreciation and thanks.

The author is exclusively responsible for the statements of opinion contained in this work.

REFERENCES

1. Bridgman, P. W. 1927. *The logic of modern physics*. New York: Macmillan.
2. Dobbie, J. M. 1963. Search theory: a sequential approach. *Naval Research Logistics Quarterly* 4: 323–334.
3. Dobbie, J. M. A survey of search theory. *Operations Res.* 16, 525–537.
4. Koopman, B. O. 1946. *Search and screening, OEG Report No. 56*. The Summary Reports Group of the Columbia University Division of War Research (Contract OEMsr-1131 of the OSRD).
5. Koopman, B. O. 1957. The theory of search, part III: The optimum distribution of searching effort. *Operations Res.* 5: 613–623.
6. Morse, P. M. and Kimball, G. E. 1951. *Methods of operations research*. Cambridge, Mass.: M. I. T. Press and New York: Wiley.
7. Skolnik, M. I. 1962. *Introduction to radar systems*. New York: McGraw-Hill.
8. Stone, L. D. 1975. *Theory of optimal search*. New York: Academic Press.
9. Thorndyke, Allan. 1946. *Summary of ASW operations in World War II*. NDRC Summary Report.

Preface to the 1946 Edition

As the Operations Research Group was at work investigating one question after another in the course of its service to the Commander-in-Chief of the United States Navy, in World War II, it became progressively more apparent that large classes of problems were united by common bonds and could be handled by common methods, that there was indeed unity in diversity. And as in other fields of scientific endeavor, where the clarifying influence of general ideas and methods can form a body of isolated facts into a powerful theory—once they exist in sufficient number—so in the work of the Group, methods borrowed from the mathematician and mathematical physicist showed their power and usefulness in those classes of problems in which the body of practical information had sufficiently accumulated. In this regard, one field was pre-eminently ripe for mathematical treatment: the field involving problems of *search*.

In every question of search there are in principle two parts. One involves the targets, and studies their physical characteristics, position, and motion; since from the very nature of the problem the latter are largely unknown to the searcher, a branch of the science of probability is applied, sometimes so simple as to be trivial, at other times involving developments comparable to statistical mechanics. The other part involves the searcher, his capabilities, position, and motion; inasmuch as detection is an event fraught with manifold uncertainties, this part of the question will also appeal to probability, specifically studying the probability laws of detection. But the study does not stop here: having gained fundamental knowledge as to these two parts of the question and their interrelation, it is necessary to make application to the tactical matters in which search is an essential component, such as hunts, barriers, and those defensive types of search known as *screens*.

The book treats these questions from the point of view and in the order indicated above. It is intended to be scientific and critical in spirit and mathematical in method, and while the data upon which its theory rests are practical and experimental and the ultimate application of its conclusions is to naval warfare, the book itself is not a manual of practical information for naval officers. Rather it is intended to serve as a theoretical framework and foundation for more immediately practical studies and recommendations. In particular, it stands in this relation to Volume 3 of the present series (*A Summary of Antisubmarine Warfare Operations in World War II*) [1]. On the other hand, its relation to Volume 2A (*Methods of*

Operations Research) [2] is in furnishing systematically developed examples, on the analytical side, of the possibilities of operations research foreshadowed in that volume. It is intended for a reader having an interest of a scientific order in the matters treated. While nothing beyond undergraduate physics and mathematics (calculus) is required, a willingness to follow theoretical reasoning of a sometimes rather involved nature is assumed.

The work has been to such a degree the result of a majority of the Operations Research Group that to render adequate acknowledgment would almost be tantamount to giving the roster of the Group; requirements of brevity confine us to the names of those who have been directly involved in writing parts of the book. We wish to express our thanks to Dr. E. S. Lamar for the chapter on visual detection, to Mr. T. E. Phipps for the chapter on radar detection, to Mr. A. M. Thorndike for the chapter on sonar detection and for a part of the chapter on sonar screens, to Dr. J. Steinhardt for important help in the chapter on radar detection and for material on barrier patrols and defense of a landing operation in Chapter 7, to Dr. J. M. Dobbie for material on square searches in the latter chapter, to Mr. Milton Lewis for material on sonar screens, to Mr. J. A. Neuendorffer for material on aerial escort. Finally, it is our great pleasure to vouchsafe our indebtedness to Dr. G. E. Kimball, the pioneer in the theory of search, without whose help and inspiration this enterprise might never have been undertaken.

REFERENCES

1. Thorndike, Allan. 1946. *Summary of antisubmarine warfare operations in World War II.* NDRC Summary Report.
2. Morse, P. M. and Kimball, G. E. 1951. *Methods of operations research.* Cambridge, Mass.: M. I. T. Press and New York: Wiley.

Chapter 1
The General Operation of Search

In any military attack, the object to be attacked must first be found. It is true that in the classical battles of the past, the two opposing forces were often lined up in plain view of one another, each seeking a trial of strength, victory being determined by superior force, skill, and luck. But whenever concealment is used as a tactical measure by one or both sides, finding the enemy—the operation of *search*—becomes an essential part of the battle—as does its counterpart: hiding and evasion, camouflage and decoys, and similar maneuvers.

With the increasing power and accuracy of modern weapons, revealing one's presence is ever more dangerous. Ground forces emphasize a low profile and camouflage of the mechanized equipment, as well as hiding and night operations. Aircraft depend on speed and evasive maneuvers and the use of clouds, night, and low flights to avoid detection. Naval forces add to similar methods that one which has so radically changed the nature of war at sea: concealment by total immersion —the submarine. Thus it follows that the operation of search—in all its phases and aspects, and under its manifold circumstances—has become essential to modern warfare.

All this has long been self-evident to the military and to their technical staffs. What had been less evident before World War II was that the *operation of search has a structure* of such a nature as often to require scientific analysis for its real understanding—as well as for its most effective performance. Up to that time, the scientific aspects of search that had drawn most attention were the invention and design of detecting equipment: optical and photographic devices; radar and infrared sensors; instruments for detection by sound, both listening and echo-ranging; and, of course, the various methods of signal processing, recording, and communication. These subjects belong to applied physics (and psychophysics) and come under the heading of advanced engineering. So in fact does the analysis of the various emanations and echoes from the objects being searched, as well as the study of the medium and other vital features of the physical environment. The knowledge and technology so developed are *necessary* conditions for success in modern warfare; the new thing added—most conspicuously during World War II

—was that they may not be *sufficient*: the physical systems and men using them form a whole greater than the sum of its parts, an "organism" with a specific structure and obeying laws of its own. This observation, and the possibility and practical usefulness of its exploitation, are what started the development of the theory of search as a branch of applied science.

Throughout this book the term *region* is used to mean a geometric figure, such as a part of a surface being searched; whereas *area* is used exclusively as a number of square units of a region. In the earlier simple cases, both may be denoted by the same letter. In the more complicated ones later in the work, the use of different type is necessary; thus A, dM, etc., are the areas of the respective regions $\mathcal{R}$, $d\mathcal{M}$, etc.

1. SEARCH AS A GENERAL OPERATION IN PRACTICAL LIFE

The history of the development of operational research in general and of its military applications to various fields, including search, has been too well documented to require any general discussion in this place. On the other hand, it may be enlightening and help to place our subject in perspective to direct attention briefly to nonmilitary situations, noting how the problems of search pervade other more or less organized practical efforts.

A first example is the *search for mineral deposits* such as oil, metals, or gems. Here the geological features of the region lead to the selection of promising localities. These are first examined by broad-area methods, such as producing echoes by explosive charges, noting magnetic or gravitational anomalies by means of airborne equipment, and similar not excessively expensive procedures. Finally, on the basis of positive indications from these, such far more costly methods of search as drilling or excavation are applied.

A second example is *search in police operations*, not only for presumed perpetrators of crimes but for missing persons. This class of example is in one respect most akin to military search in that the people searched do not want to be found, and may be driven away from the region searched by any betraying sign that the police are seeking them. On the other hand, the missing person may be lost and want to be found and act cooperatively. All this adds an essentially different factor from anything in our first example: the mineral deposit does not try to baffle or aid our attempts to find it.

A third example is in *searching for a pattern* among electronic recordings: information retrieval, code-breaking, and various counter-intelligence operations. While in the latter cases it may be part of a military operation, its high degree of technical complexity and specialized nature will, among other reasons, lead us to limit ourselves, for the most part, to its mere mention.

A fourth example is in the *search for sources of disease or contamination*. This is an important part of the activities of departments of public health. In such cases the infective agents are of a known kind, make no attempt at evading our search, and have revealed themselves by being found in samples or by having infected certain members of the community.

A fifth example is in *medical diagnostics*: a patient must be searched for all likely causes of his apparent indisposition. There is no evasion by the disease agent, but there may be deception; special circumstances may give rise to false indications. Moreover, there may be a multicausal situation and a chain of successively triggering reactions. Finally, certain diagnostic procedures may impede others.

Our sixth and final example is in the *search for markets*, either on the part of the seller or of the buyer. Here another factor may enter: rivalry between sellers, which may cause one of them to use his information that another is exploring such and such a potential market, to move into it himself. This application of search to business and advertising has been a popular topic of recent operational research.

In concluding this list of examples of search, we emphasize one cardinal restriction: the search considered is always for a thing of known sort or a cause of known kind. As soon as the search is for an as yet unknown cause of observed effects—as in the study of baffling diseases—it becomes *research*: the search for new knowledge. Such matters are quite beyond the scope of the present work.

2. TARGET RECOGNITION

The thing for which a search is undertaken, called the *object of search*, is in its military context called the *target*. But in all cases, military or of the civilian sort exemplified in Section 1, the act of its *recognition* is essential: what the searcher perceives is a set of sensory impressions which he must *interpret* before he knows what is causing them. When the object is in plain view its recognition is so immediate that this may hardly seem to take place; but in the typical problems of search, recognition can easily be a matter of real difficulty. Everyone is familiar with the task of finding a friend in a poorly lighted place. It may be easy to see various passing figures dimly; but recognizing the person sought is a very different matter. With detection equipment, what is perceived is a set of appearances on a scope, or sounds in an ear-phone, or similar indications, and it is necessary to interpret them (in the light of specific knowledge) to decide whether they are actually caused by the target sought. The standard military term of this process is "*target classification*" (evidently an abbreviation of: "assigning a target-like impression to one of the two classes: target, nontarget).

Three factors are involved in this act of recognition:

* First, factors of a physical order, such as the nature and properties of the target, those of the detecting equipment, and also those of the medium of propagation and similar environmental elements.
* Second, in cases involving conflict (military or police operations), such general factors as its time, place, and purpose; the presumed intentions, capabilities, and tactics of the enemy; and any light cast on the action by recent events.
* Third, and at once most subtle and important, that psychological capability, possessed by us all in varying degree, of being able to "recognize"—as in the recognition of a face.

Whereas technology is providing more and more aids, methods of filtering out signals which can be objectively identified as caused by false targets, improvements in signal processing, image formation, adjustable scales, etc., it must be realized that these merely move the boundaries between what can and what cannot be recognized by the human observer. If only one side of a conflict could make such improvements, its engineers might be supposed to provide it with equipment which moves the threshold of recognizability beyond that of the other side: the first would detect the second without being detected by him. Such a situation could only be temporary; and we must realize that we will be forced to operate in a situation in which *recognition must take place under marginal conditions*. This can be accepted as a principle in the scientific study of search.

These three factors have long been understood, but in recent times the engineering community, in its attempts to supplant the human observer—with all his frailties—by more reliable automatic devices, has emphasized the decibel measure of the *ratio of signal to noise*. (We recall that its value is $10 \log_{10}$ [signal power/noise power].) This can be obtained by straightforward, if not always easy, power observations and calculations. It is, moreover, an essential element in detection and recognition: when much below a certain level, these are impossible; when much above, they are very easy, and thus their chance of success is strongly influenced by the decibels of signal to noise.

On the other hand, it is a common misapprehension to assume that the probability of successful detection depends *only* on this quantity—i.e., that it is a *function* of signal to noise. (It may be unnecessary to recall that y is said to be a function of x if for the determination of the value of y it is *sufficient* to give that of x. While loose usage often implies that in the above, "sufficient" is replaced by "necessary" ["y varies when x varies"], the whole body of mathematical analysis is based on the former definition, not the latter.) In the operations required by many military situations, each side is forced to deal with signals in the twilight zone between high and low signal to noise ratio. Then the success of detection is driven by the "*pattern*" or "*configuration*" of the target's signal and of the background. The ease of recognizing a face in a crowd is not determined by the relative amounts of lighting, although in extreme cases it is influenced by this factor. In just about every nontrivial case of search, whether in a military or in a civilian operation, the object of search does not show itself by a single intensity but by a pattern of intensities, and the background is not the pure "noise" familiar to engineers in circuit theory, but usually involves in addition a deceptive pattern of appearances.

We shall return to these matters in Section 6.

3. TARGET POSITION AND MOTION

The mere perception and identification of an object of search is not enough for most practical applications, neither in the military cases nor in the civilian ones exemplified in Section 1. It is usually necessary to know where it is and, in the case of moving targets, to gain information concerning its speed and course. "*Target localization*" is the military term for the former; "*prediction*" applies to the main results of the latter. Both are needed whenever action is to be taken, and the accuracy required in estimating them must be matched to the nature of the action. When the target is detected by being directly seen by those taking the action, their distances must be so close as to give little difficulty to localization—or to prediction, unless the target is moving at high speed in a variable course. Under modern conditions, the more usual case is for the target to be observed indirectly with the aid of detection equipment, and for the distances to be great.

Localization and prediction become, under the latter conditions, technical problems in themselves, often as difficult as they are important. The methods will depend on all the physical factors involved: the target, detecting equipment, medium, and so on.

It must be emphasized that the two processes, recognition on the one hand and localization and prediction on the other, are usually interdependent, going in practice hand in hand. Often an essential factor in the recognizability of the target is its position and motion. The *Doppler* effect of a moving target is one example of this sort.

Probability, which has entered rather implicitly in Section 2 as the probability of successful recognition, enters in a more elaborately technical way in the present subject, which cannot be treated with precision without it. We return to this point in Section 6.

4. MULTIPLE SEARCH

In the great majority of problems in which search is an essential feature, more than one mechanism of detection, recognition, localization, etc. has to be applied in the same or in related operations. This is because under the difficult conditions of practice, whether military or civilian, a single piece of detecting equipment is forced to make a "tradeoff" between the two desirable features: broad coverage (searching wide areas) and precision of data when it detects (good localization). We have already described in the first example of Section 1 how various methods may be applied in succession in the search for mineral deposits. Similar progressively narrower searches enter into police operations. This is true also in the medical examples of search for sources of contamination or in diagnostics, and so on.

The multiple search in military operations is exemplified in naval warfare against submarines when the use of wide-area *surveillance*, which can cover a great expanse of ocean but is poor in localizing what it detects, is followed by a narrower search by means of more precise equipment. This second search will be concentrated in regions indicated by the former broad coverage search. Finally, before an attack can be made, a still narrower examination is made on the basis of the data provided by the second stage of the search. Some *fire control* systems may be regarded as the agents of this third phase.

More precise discussion of the quantitative aspects of multiple search involves probability in an essential manner and is deferred to Section 6.

5. PASSIVE AND ACTIVE OBSERVATIONS: TARGET ALERTING

In the scientific study of search the *actions* taken for detecting the target must be analyzed. It then turns out that they fall into two quite different classes, depending on whether they are acts of pure observation, leaving the target and its environment unaltered, or whether they require actions which materially alter these factors, e.g., in military cases, when they betray information to the enemy. We will call the two types *passive* and *active*, respectively.

In the examples of nonmilitary search given in Section 1, that for mineral deposits involved two processes that can be regarded as acts of pure observation, since they cause no material change. The third (drilling or digging) on the contrary changes the environment, and this can mean that a repetition of the process is done under altered conditions. The search in police operations of the second example is a highly active one when identifiable agents are sent into the field, since their presence can alert those sought. (This may, of course, give it a defensive or deterrent value, even with no detection.) On the other hand, when effectively disguised secret agents are searching, or when an examination of police records is made, the observation is passive. In the medical searches, that for contamination is a passive observation when it involves records of the incidence of disease or the examination of samples. Diagnostic procedures performed on an individual may be either passive or active observations—the latter, in cases of exploratory operations, catheterization into the heart through arteries, and such-like.

The use of German *search receivers* on the U-boats to detect search radar emanations in World War II is a classical example. Before their installation, long-range radar, particularly at night, corresponded to a passive observation —which became an active one after the search receivers were used. Search for naval mines by echo-ranging is a passive observation; mine-sweeping is an active one. On the other hand, echo-ranging against hostile submarines is an active observation when they are equipped to hear it. Similar examples of the two types could be multiplied indefinitely.

While the distinction between passive and active observations may be regarded as an utter truism, the *quantitative* differences, showing themselves in particular by the quite different ways in which probability has to be applied in the two cases, have not been sufficiently appreciated. Errors and controversies have been the result. While this subject will be carried further in the next section, it may give perspective to consider an exactly parallel case of slowness in realizing the quantitative implications of active versus passive observations, drawn from theoretical physics.

The traditional view of the positions and motions of material objects regarded them as objective properties, possessed by the objects as they exist in the external world. After Einstein had emphasized the role of the observer in showing that there are no logical grounds for preferring Newtonian mechanics to relativistic, positions and motions of objects were defined as what the observer measures. But even then his observations were passive. His own position and motion determined a frame of reference, but he did not physically change what he observed; if he immediately repeated his observations he would get the same results (within the accuracy of the method of observation). In this sense, positions and motions could again be regarded as objective properties of the objects, differing only when expressed in terms of different frames of reference. This point of view remains valid in dealing with large inanimate objects.

In the case of elementary particles (of atomic or subatomic dimensions), neither Newtonian nor relativistic mechanics could be made to fit the observations. Heisenberg and N. Bohr once again invoked the role of the observer, but this time recognizing his observations of the position and motion of particles as *active* ones. Thus after measuring a particle's position and then its momentum, the second process did such violence to the particle that the earlier readings of its position were no longer valid; viz., reproducible on immediately performing a second measurement of position. This fact, and the formula derived from quantum mechanics for the lower limit of the product of the errors (standard deviations) of a measured position and conjugate momentum of the elementary particle, was called the *Ungenauigkeit Princip* and *Unbestimmtheitsrelationen*, known in English as the "principle of uncertainty." (These are ambiguous terms which suggest that the position and momentum are meaningful properties of the particle—apart from observation—but are not determined: i.e., have a scattering of their "actual" values. This has led to many misdirected notions.)

The differences in the application of probability formulas in the cases of active and passive observations in search theory will be noted in the next section.

6. THE ROLE OF PROBABILITY IN THE THEORY OF SEARCH

Every operation involved in search is beset with uncertainties: it can be understood quantitatively only in terms of the concepts and laws of the scientific theory of probability. This may now be regarded as a truism; but it seems to have taken the developments in operational research of World War II to drive home its practical implications. The reason for the lateness in taking full advantage of this theory has undoubtedly been the simple nature of most of the earlier operations of search, the short ranges involved, and the power of the human eye at such ranges. These factors made a "deterministic" approximation satisfactory: "When a thing is there and I look at it without anything in front of it, I see it; otherwise I don't." Approximations of this sort are still useful, but they must be validated by more realistic analysis, based on probability, among other things.

The specific applications of probability to search will form the major part of the present work, and the more technical details of the theory of probability as such will be outlined in Appendix A. In the present section we shall note, in a brief, qualitative way, how probability enters into the matters cited in preceding sections and comment on the issues raised.

Before a search is undertaken, e.g., in its planning phase, assumptions are always made, often implicitly, concerning the probable *positions* of the object of search, or, when it is not fixed, of the *times* of its probable appearance in various positions.

Such assumptions acquire a precise form in terms of the *probability distribution* of the target before the search (its *a priori* distribution). In the case of a moving target, a one-parameter family of such distributions is implied, the time (epoch *t*) being the parameter. In practice, it is rarely possible to know such distributions exactly; in any actual calculation it has to be approximated or "boxed up" between two extremes, as in "limiting arguments." But this does not alter the fact that the *concept* of a probability distribution is a perfectly precise one and is a necessary basis of any logical deduction.

In the examples of Section 1, no rational prospector would search a region for mineral deposits unless a geological study, or the experience of previous prospectors, showed a sufficiently high probability of their presence. Police will patrol localities of high incidence of crime. Public health officials will have ideas in advance of the likely sources of infection and will examine them first. In diagnostics, the age, sex, previous history, and recent exposure of the patient will determine what examinations are made at the outset. Advertising is placed where there are most targets (possible customers with wants and money).

In military search, the geographic nature of the region (land or sea) in which the target is apt to be found, the times when it may enter various sub-regions, and the motives of the enemy in placing it there are all taken into account in planning a search. They are expressed precisely in terms of a priori probability distributions. Chapters 2–5 illustrate various methods for finding such distributions, as well as their evolution in time, by combining simple probabilistic assumptions with elementary geometry and kinematics, procedures quite similar to those used in elementary statistical mechanics.

Section 2 must have made it clear that under the conditions of practical search, where the facilities of perception are marginal, target recognition is an uncertain event. The most precise statement that can be made about it is to give its (approximate) probability, and to see how this is affected by the various conditions, external and internal. We have already noted the use of the signal-to-noise ratio for this purpose, as well as its limitations. The following application will illustrate both.

Suppose that an observer at a position *O* is using a long-range detection device (e.g., radar or underwater sound). From knowledge of the environment, the characteristics of the detection device, and the target, it may be possible to calculate a good approximation to the signal-to-noise ratio for each position *P* of the target. If, further, a lower limit of signal-to-noise is known below which it is impossible to detect, and an upper one above which detection is certain, one could divide the region of possible positions of *P* into three zones: that in which detection is impossible; that in which it is practically certain; and an intermediate one, in which—being unpredictable—detection is a *random event*. If the intermediate zone were of insignificant area, or of minor tactical importance, this use of signal-to-noise would give very valuable indications of the capabilities of the observer at *O*. Unfortunately, in many of the most important tactical situations, this is not true. The intermediate zone is large and highly relevant to the operation. Of course its size would be further increased by any physical fluctuations and other uncertainties of the environment, and corresponding shrinkage of the pure zones of impossibility and of certainty.

We are accordingly forced to a more detailed study of the *probability of detection* (used without qualification, "detection" means true detection with identification) when various visual or auditory patterns are presented to the observer. We have noted a first step: to assume that this probability is a *function* of (i.e., determined by) signal-to-noise. The nature of this function has been studied on the basis of statistical data making use of many observers, under as standardized conditions as possible, and its general trend under such conditions has been found, with somewhat crude precision. Reasonable analytic expressions have sometimes been given for it. Another approach has been to find the value of the signal-to-noise for which, on the average, detection occurs half the time; this is termed the *recognition differential*. A further simplification is to regard detection as impossible or certain, according as the signal-to-noise is less or greater than this threshold quantity, so that the intermediate zone on the ocean disappears as an area. Since no experience conforms to such a situation, the recognition differential itself is sometimes regarded as a random quantity. Various adjustments therefore of the "model" are tried but, up to this time, with minimal consideration of the quantitative effects of the *pattern* or *configuration* of the signal-and-background complex, which, as we have seen, may contribute a decisive factor. Evidently much research is called for on this important subject. We cannot equate the magnitude of these effects to the magnitude of our knowledge concerning them!

The problem posed in Section 3 may be restated as follows: Given that a target has been detected (and recognized as such), where is it? As we have noted, this question does not come into everyday experience, which can be described in the words of the old hunter who declared, "When I see ducks, I shoot at the ducks." In most of the examples of Section 1 as well as in modern military cases, detection is done indirectly, through the use of some form of detecting equipment. Such equipment, as noted in Section 4, is forced to make a compromise between *coverage* (the extent of target positions exposed to its detection) and *precision* (the degree of accuracy of the true positions when detected).

To consider an extreme case, with maximum coverage but minimum precision, let us return to the application of signal-to-noise mentioned above to divide the region searched into three zones. Suppose further that the detecting equipment can give no indication of position of a detected target beyond what could be inferred from the presence or absence of the signal on the scope. How can inferences of position be drawn? Evidently if it is detected it cannot be in the nondetectable zone; if not detected, no such target could be in the zone of certain detectability. In the simple case of the vanishing intermediate zone, this is the only sort of conclusion that we can draw: a detected target is somewhere in the zone of sure detectability. Just where it is in this zone, this observation does not tell us; but as we shall see, inferences could be drawn by combining the fact of detection with our possible knowledge of the target's probability distribution *before* detection. In the more realistic case, the intermediate zone not only is present but can dominate the whole situation, and we shall have to know more about the probability of detection at various positions in this zone. Clearly we must draw conclusions "after the event" (of detection)—and in the light of prior knowledge. The methods are just as easy to describe in the more general case, to which we now turn.

The general situation in target localization is typified by the case in which the target is at some point P (unknown to the searcher) of a region (of the ocean, land, air, etc.), and when it is assumed that the searcher knows the following two quantities (with some acceptable degree of approximation): first, the a priori distribution of the target, i.e., the probability (before detection) that it will be in any given part of the region, and second, the detection probability as a function of the target's position in that region. Then the inferred knowledge of target position after detection must, in all but the simplest cases, take the form of another set of probabilities: the *a posteriori probability distribution*, giving the probabilities, after the event of detection, of the various subregions in which the target could be.

In the technical language of the theory of probability, this is a straightforward problem of *inverse probabilities*, solved by *Bayes's formula* (published in 1763). This expresses the required a posteriori probability density in terms of our data: the a priori probability density and the *conditional probability* of detecting a target given to be at a point P of the searched region. Since there are as many of these probabilities as there are points P, they form a *family* of values (a two-parameter family, if P has two coordinates). Bayes's formula gives the a posteriori (or *up-dated*) probability as the product of the a priori one times the probability of detection at P, all divided by the integral of this product over the whole region (thus introducing a "normalizing factor"). In the simple two-zone case described above, the a posteriori probability density is zero on the nondetectable zone, and is proportional to the a priori density on the zone of sure detectability (the factor of proportionality arising from the division of the latter by its own integral taken over this zone).

The above conditional probability of detecting a target of a certain type, given to be at P, will, when there are several different observers stationed at different points O_1, O_2, etc., depend on them as well as on P: a function of the observer's position (coordinates) as well as of the target's. On a plane surface it will thus be a four-parameter family of probabilities. In a systematic plan, two factors may influence the positioning of O_1, O_2, etc. One is that they be so placed (within geographic constraints) as to increase the accuracy of localizing a target, once detected. This implies facilities for rapid intercommunication, so that combined detection data can lead to triangulation by a *cross-fix*. The mathematical aspects of this will be examined in Chapter 4.

A second factor in the positioning of the intercommunicating observers O_1, O_2, etc. becomes important when a fairly definite and unchanging a priori probability density of the targets of interest can be established, and when we have a high degree of flexibility in the choice of positions. Then it is natural so to place these that the probability of initial detection of a target by the *system* $\{O_1, O_2, \ldots\}$ *as a whole* is greatest. This is a special case of a very general and important problem, that of the optimal use of a given amount of searching facility (here, the limited number of observers O_i). In its various mathematical forms, it is the subject of Chapters 6 and 7. Practical applications that have been made of the results are contained in various parts of Chapters 8, 9, and 10. In many cases, the quantity optimized is *earliest detection*. Sometimes the constraints involve diminishing the danger to the searcher. As a general class, these problems belong to the calculus of variations involving inequality (*unilateral*) constraints, among others. (This type of problem has entered into post-World War II economics and operational research under the new name of "nonlinear programming.")

Up to this point, the examples of probability in search have implied such long ranges and clandestine operation that they involve no alerting of hostile targets: that detection is a *passive* observation, in the sense of Section 5. Most of the nonmilitary examples of Section 1 are of this sort. But suppose, on the contrary, that the operation of detection involves an *active* observation, as in radar against targets provided with search receivers, or echo-ranging against submarines equipped to hear the sound. Does Bayes's formula apply as before, and if not, does a modified form of it apply?

This whole subject, which is analyzed theoretically in Appendix A, will be examined on the basis of concrete cases in Chapters 6 and 7, and in the practical applications in the last three chapters.

7. OPERATIONAL DEGRADATION AND HUMAN FACTORS

Anyone living in the world of practical applications of the results of science and technology knows that systems usually fall short of their specified or physically possible capabilities, even when these are calculated with all allowance for predictable decrease in performance. Under wartime conditions, and even in peacetime tests, a weapons system seems inevitably fated to do decidedly less well than the engineers who designed it and the planners of the operation often expect. The causes of this *operational degradation* may be roughly divided into two classes: those pertaining to the physical system and its environment; and those due to the human factors involved. They all apply to search as well as to other operations.

That the physical systems may not be up to their designed standard was shown every day in World War II, as well as in subsequent operations. The statistics of torpedo failures were notorious, often running to 40%—and not confined to one side! The antiaircraft five-inch shells introduced later in that war had at best an *operability factor* of 80% (20% failing); and this was usually nearer to 70%. For reasons never completely understood, in a systematic set of tests soon after the close of the war, it fell toward 60%. The causes for operability factors so markedly lower than 100% have only in part been understood: maintainance; insufficient quality control at the factories; ill-advised features in the design; and insufficient time to "debug" the system. But whatever their cause, the operability factors have one curious feature, their being roughly the same for a large class of quite different operations, somewhere between 60% and 70%. This purely statistical observation has led certain nations (e.g., the United Kingdom) to include a standard factor of this sort in many plans and designs.

The operational degradation due to *human factors* is becoming increasingly well known, although again only some of its causes are well understood and it is a subject of continuing research. (NATO has sponsored conferences on this side of operational research, and the second 1975 meeting of the Military Operations Research Society [MORS 36] had this problem as its central theme. This desirable turn of events contrasts with the too exclusively physical orientation of the earlier period of operational research.) Obvious causes of the variability of human effectiveness are *training* and *motivation*, as well as the *selection* of physically competent operators. As far back as World War II, consideration was given to the optimum time that a radar or sonar operator should spend on a watch, so that his attention and acuteness of perception should be at its reasonable best. Furthermore, training devices began to be developed. There has, unfortunately, been a continued insufficiency of research in that branch of psychophysics that deals with the use of the sense organs under operational conditions (e.g., looking for ships at sea, blips on a scope, or traces on a gram). Reinforcement of audio presentation of target echoes with simultaneous visual ones has been noticed, but apparently not examined systematically.

As already emphasized, pattern recognition may play an essential role in target detection, in the important marginal cases. Individuals differ markedly in this ability, just as they do in other perceptions and in marksmanship. Training can improve such abilities, although personnel selection may be an essential in securing high performance.

We shall return to this subject in the appendixes devoted to special instrumentalities for detection, in particular, in visual search.

8. CONCLUSION—SEARCH AS A COMPONENT IN A LARGER OPERATION

While it is convenient to examine the many aspects of search in themselves and in some degree of isolation, it would be fatally misleading if, in so doing, one were to fall into the trap of those specialists who, in developing one part of a whole, ignore the rest and its relation thereto. Splendid work has been done in medical research by detailed examination of one disease or one physical function, but such results must be integrated into the whole human system if they are to serve effectively. A brief perusal of the examples in Section 1 will indicate the bearing of these remarks, which should be truisms.

The search for mineral deposits is not undertaken lightly, but only when the conditions are such that, if found, the mineral can be *economically extracted and transported* to processing points and markets. Further, there must be an economic need for the products. Finally, the cost of extraction and processing must include losses of environmental amenities, with all the concomitant lawsuits and political action.

Search in police operations is related to the whole sociological state of affairs connected with crime, the prevailing legal climate, and attitude of judicial bodies. In more important cases, the political environment must be taken into account.

Search of a pattern among electronic recordings is so basically related to the circumstances that it is hardly necessary to belabor the point.

Search for sources of disease or contamination is not only related to such obvious factors of public health in the community as water supply, drainage, and sanitary measures affecting food marketing, but to the possible presence of new arthropod or other animal vectors, new elements entering the community from distant parts where a disease is prevalent, possible breakdown of prophylactic measures, mutant strains of infective organisms, and even changes in lifestyles.

Medical diagnostics has already been mentioned as a focal point of many considerations. We may add the sociological and psychological effects, bearing not only on the patient but on the physician.

The reader can easily make his own list of factors affecting the search for markets, this isolated component of all of business, finance, economics, and sociology.

The military operations in which search plays an important part will never be lost to view, and will often be explicitly noted, in the development of the theory of search in the following chapters. While in the earlier ones the main emphasis will be on mathematical treatments of the various special cases, in later chapters the practical applications actually made during World War II and in some later engagements will be noted: screening a surface formation, hunter-killer groups, barrier patrols, air escort of convoys, etc. These examples will make the point that search is a part of an organic whole. And if these examples seem somewhat antiquated, it is not because more modern ones are lacking, but because they could not be published in a textbook of the present type.

For an extensive bibliography of recent investigations of many of the civilian applications of search theory noted in this chapter (e.g., search for minerals and in medical diagnostic surveys, etc.), see Peter Kolesar, "On searching for large objects with small probes: a search model for exploration " *Operations Res*. 1980 (in press).

Chapter 2

Position, Motion, and Random Encounters

The first step in the quantitative study of search is the establishment of precise terms for the description of the positions and motions of the searcher and the object of search: the target. The basic case is the simplest one, that in which both the searcher and the target are moving at constant speeds along straight paths. Then their positions and motions are completely determined by their constant *vector velocities* and their positions at any given initial time (the *initial epoch*). This is as true when the motion is in space (e.g., in the air or under the sea) as when it is confined to a plane or spherical surface, land or ocean. In plane or space, all the information that may be required concerning the individual and relative positions and motions is easily obtained by the elementary formulas and methods of two- or three-dimensional analytic geometry. The methods can be simplified and put in the form of graphical constructions when the motion is on a plane surface. These constructions are often carried out on the *maneuvering board*. The present chapter is confined to this case of motion in a plane, the first section defining the descriptive elements and their relations.

Even in this simple case of one searcher and one target moving on a surface at constant velocities, there are some tactically important geometrical deductions, marking out as impossible certain types of approach, escape, or attack. They follow solely from kinematic relations, and form the subject of Sections 2 and 3.

When the observer is faced with many targets instead of a single one, the *objective* description of the situation simply repeats the one given above, applying it to each individual target. On the other hand, the situation as it occurs *in the mind of the searcher*, who characteristically does not have precise knowledge of the numbers, positions, or motions of the individual targets but only general knowledge of their possible positions and motions, requires a *statistical* description: the observer has to replace the actual and unknown set of targets by a *statistical ensemble*. The present chapter considers the simplest case of such an ensemble,

25

corresponding to the minimum knowledge on the part of the searcher, who assumes that the targets are distributed at random, uniformly and independently, throughout the set of possible positions, directions, and similar characteristics. Sections 4 and 5 deal with this subject. Other more specialized target distributions will be considered in various later chapters.

Note the precise distinction between "region" and "area" defined in the introduction to Chapter 1.

1. MOTION AT FIXED SPEED AND COURSE

When the searcher and target are both moving at a constant speed and direction (course), i.e., with constant velocity vectors, their relative motions and positions are most easily found by vector constructions. Let

v = speed of observer in knots (ocean or true speed),
u = speed of target in knots (ocean or true speed),
w = speed of target relative to observer in knots.

The relationship of w to u and v is best shown by drawing the *vector* velocities **u**, **v**, **w**, whereupon it is seen that **w** is simply the vector difference $\mathbf{w} = \mathbf{u} - \mathbf{v}$ (Fig. 2-1). For, **w** being the target's velocity with respect to a reference system, itself

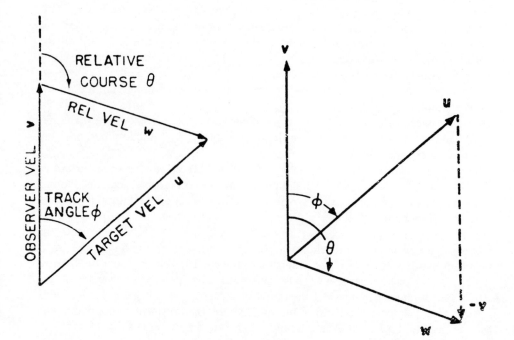

Fig. 2-1. True and relative velocities and angles.

moving over the ocean at velocity **v**, the vector sum **w** + **v** must equal the target's ocean velocity **u**; hence the above equation. Fig. 2-1 also shows two important angles, the target's *track angle* ϕ and *relative course* θ, with respect to the observer, where

ϕ = angle between **v** and **u** measured from the former to the latter in the clockwise sense;

θ = angle between **v** and **w** measured from the former to the latter in the clockwise sense.

Throughout the present chapter, and later unless the contrary is explicitly stated, these angles are measured in *radians* and zero $\leqslant \phi < 2\pi$, zero $\leqslant \theta < 2\pi$.

A convenient method for showing the dependence of the relative quantities **w** and θ upon the angle ϕ (the speeds u and v remaining fixed) is by drawing the circular diagrams (A), (B), and (C) of Fig. 2-2, corresponding to the cases $v < u$, $v = u$, and $v > u$, respectively. In each case the radius of the circle around which the extremities of **u** and **w** move is u, and the distance of its center from the origin O of **w** (the extremity of **v**) is v. As ϕ goes from zero to 2π, **v** stays fixed, **u** rotates with its length remaining constant, and **w** changes both in length and direction. It is to be noted that while in case (A) ($v < u$) all directions of **w** are possible ($0 \leqslant \theta < 2\pi$), in the other cases ($v \geqslant u$) this is untrue, and we have:

$$\text{When } v = u, \frac{\pi}{2} \leqslant \theta \leqslant \frac{3\pi}{2};$$

$$\text{when } v > u, \pi - \sin^{-1}\frac{u}{v} \leqslant \theta \leqslant \pi + \sin^{-1}\frac{u}{v}.$$

This corresponds with the fact that when the searcher is faster than the target, relative approach of the latter to the former is restricted (see Section 2). When $v > u$, two values of w correspond to general values of θ for which approach is possible, one for the target approaching the observer, the other for the overtaking of a target headed away from the observer. When $\theta = \pi \pm \sin^{-1} u/v$, there is just one value of w; for other θ's, no value.

The relative speed w can be found from the law of cosines or else by projecting **v** and **u** on **w** and using the law of sines; similarly for ϕ. This expresses relative quantities in terms of true:

(1)
$$w = \sqrt{u^2 + v^2 - 2uv \cos \phi},$$
$$= -v \cos \theta \pm \sqrt{u^2 - v^2 \sin^2 \theta},$$
$$\sin \theta = \frac{u}{w} \sin \phi.$$

In addition to the speeds and angles just considered, it is necessary to have further quantities to specify a particular contact between observer and target; one must be able to state the position of the target relative to the observer at any given instant of time (epoch) t. One method of accomplishing this is to give the *target range* r and *relative bearing* β; these are shown in Fig. 2-3 (at the arbitrary epoch t),

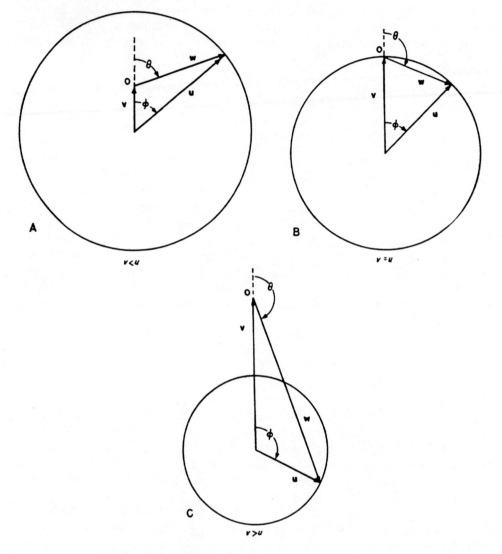

Fig. 2-2. Circle of relative velocities.

together with the *target angle* α, which depends on quantities previously introduced. The definitions are as follows (throughout, a "mile" shall mean a "nautical mile"; in numerical examples, a nautical mile is taken as 2,000 yards):

$\mathbf{r}$ = vector from observer to target,
r = length of $\mathbf{r}$ in miles,
β = angle from $\mathbf{v}$ to $\mathbf{r}$ measured clockwise,
α = angle from $\mathbf{u}$ to $-\mathbf{r}$ measured clockwise.

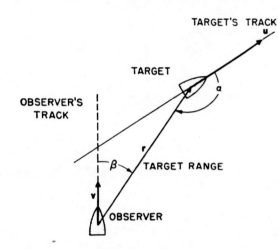

Fig. 2-3. Geographic tracks, ranges, and bearings.

As usual, angles are in radians and lie between 0 and 2π, except when in later chapters the contrary is explicitly stated. It is evident that when the rôles of target and searcher are interchanged, those of β and α are likewise, vector $\mathbf{r}$ being replaced by the reversed vector $-\mathbf{r}$.

The situation relative to the observer is given in Fig. 2-4, which shows the target's track, etc., in a plane in which the observer is fixed and which moves over the ocean with the velocity $\mathbf{v}$. It is seen that (r, β) are the polar coordinates of the target referred to observer's position and heading. The target's track is altogether different from his geographic track of Fig. 2-3; it is described with the velocity $\mathbf{w}$, but the target's heading is in the direction of $\mathbf{u}$ and hence not along its relative track. It is seen that with the particular angles of Fig. 2-4, $\alpha = \pi + \beta - \phi$. It is sometimes convenient to use rectangular coordinates (ξ, η), the η axis being along the observer's heading. ξ and η are in miles; they are related to (r, β) by the equations

(2) $$r^2 = \xi^2 + \eta^2, \qquad \xi = r \sin \beta, \qquad \eta = r \cos \beta.$$

In the course of time (as t increases) $\mathbf{u}, \mathbf{v}, \mathbf{w}, u, v, w, \phi, \theta$ stay constant, while $\mathbf{r}, r, \beta$ (and α) change. If at the epoch $t = t_0$, $\mathbf{r}, r, \beta$ have the values $\mathbf{r}_0, r_0, \beta_0$, their values at a general epoch t are found by noting that relative to the observer the target undergoes the vector displacement $(t - t_0)\mathbf{w}$, and thus

(3) $$\mathbf{r} = \mathbf{r}_0 + (t - t_0)\mathbf{w},$$

from which the equations expressing (r, β) in terms of $(r_0, \beta_0, t - t_0)$ are found by trigonometry, and similarly for α. Equation (3) or its equivalent in terms of (r, β) are the equations of the target relative to the observer. In the very special case when target and observer have the same speed and direction, i.e., when $\mathbf{u} = \mathbf{v}$ so that $\mathbf{w} = 0$, equation (3) reduces to $\mathbf{r} = \mathbf{r}_0$, corresponding to the fact that the target

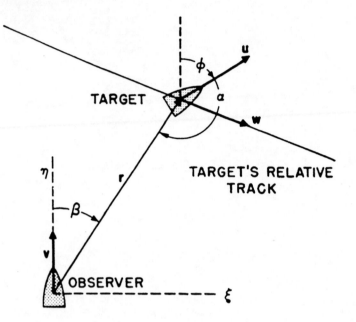

Fig. 2-4. Target's track relative to observer.

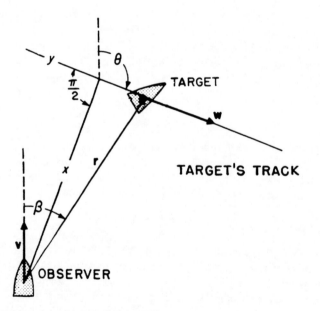

Fig. 2-5. Lateral range of the target.

remains fixed relative to the observer. In all other cases, there is a least distance between the target and the observer. This distance is called the *lateral range* of the target.

Let x = lateral range of the target in miles, and
y = distance in miles traveled by the target relative to the observer since its closest approach (negative prior to closest approach).

If t_0 is now used to denote the epoch of closest approach, evidently $y = (t - t_0)w$. Figure 2-5 shows the relation between x, y and the earlier quantities. Clearly $r^2 = x^2 + y^2$, and with the particular angles of Fig. 2-5, $\beta = \theta - \cot^{-1}(y/x)$.

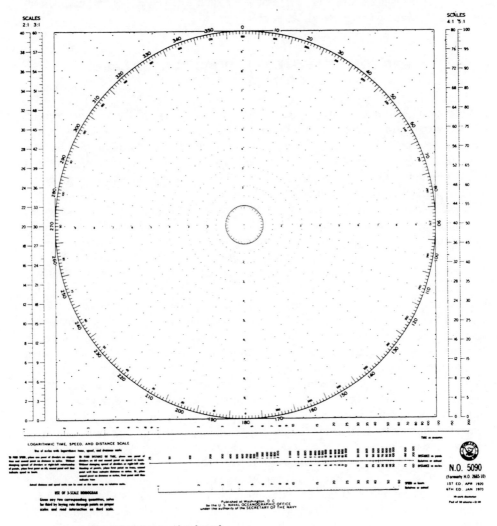

Fig. 2-6. Maneuvering board.

Thus it appears that, in addition to u, v, ϕ (and their dependent w, θ), in order to specify a particular contact we can use either (r, β) (at a standard epoch) or (x, t_0) (or, indeed, any convenient independent functions of either pair); (r, β) can be found where (x, t_0) are given, and vice versa, and either pair can be used as independent variables. On the other hand, only one quantity is needed to specify a *type* of contact, for example, x. Given u, v, ϕ and the range of closest approach x, the configuration (searcher and target and their tracks) is determined, but not the time at which the contact occurs.

Graphical constructions and nomogran methods of quick calculation are conventionally performed on the *maneuvering board*, which contains a polar coordinate diagram showing angles in degrees and methods of adjusting scales of distances. A reduced picture is shown in Fig. 2-6. For a detailed explanation of its methods of use, see the "Maneuvering Board Manual."

2. REGIONS OF LIMITED APPROACH UNDER SPEED CONSTRAINTS

A naval unit (searcher or target) seeking to reach a second unit that is proceeding at fixed speed and course and is without knowledge of the first, can always reach the latter if there is no physical constraint in its velocity or time limitation for this purpose. But even when it has all the time in the world but is forced to move at a lesser speed than the unit that it wishes to approach, it can succeed only when its starting point is favorably situated.

In Fig. 2-7(A), A is a plane region fixed with respect to the observer; A, then, is moving straight ahead over the ocean surface with the velocity **v**. It may or may not be possible for a target capable of moving with the speed u and starting outside A to enter A. It is understood that the target is restricted to the *speed* u but can choose any *direction*, and has all the time it needs to try to enter A. Evidently if $u > v$, the target can always enter A; but if $u \leqslant v$ this is no longer necessarily true, as for example when the target starts behind A. In order to be able to enter A the target must have its starting point in a certain region B called the *region of approach*. Of course B is also attached to the observer and moves over the ocean with the velocity **v**. Figure 2-7(A) shows the construction of B; when **v** points up the page, a line inclined at the angle $\sin^{-1} u/v$ with the vector **v** to the right is drawn to the right of A and is moved toward A until it touches A; the part of the line above the lowest point of contact forms the right-hand boundary of B. Similarly for the left-hand boundary, the inclination being to the left and the contact occurring on the left of A. The rear boundary is the forward boundary of A between the two rear points of contact (for targets not starting within A).

The justification of this construction is based on Fig. 2-7(B). During the time t a point starting at P and moving with the observer's velocity will arrive at Q, $PQ = vt$; the circle centered at Q and of radius ut is the locus of positions from which the target must start if it is to close this point after the time t. By considering all positive values of t and observing how the circle varies in both center and radius, it

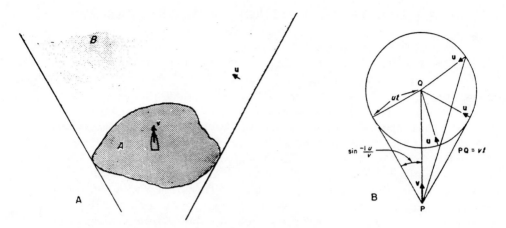

Fig. 2-7. Construction of the region of approach.

is seen that it will sweep out the whole angular region between the two (fixed) tangents drawn from zero. Thus the whole upper angular space between the two tangents to the circle is the locus of all starting positions of the target if it is to close the moving point at *any* time after the latter leaves P. B is constructed by letting P take on all positions in A, whereupon the upper angular space attached to P sweeps out B (in addition to A itself).

When $u = v$, the tangents coalesce into a horizontal line tangent to A in the rear, and B is above it. When $u > v$, there is no limiting boundary.

An important naval application of the region of approach is to submarine warfare, where v is the speed of the convoy and A the region within which a weapon (torpedo, missile, or such) must be fired to be in range of a ship of the convoy. What we have been terming the "target" may be thought of as a submerged submarine having the underwater speed $u < v$. Then evidently the submarine must be in B in order that it may be able to approach, submerged, for weapon firing. This simplified case is only illustrative. A hostile target may base its choice of range of approach on such considerations as hit *probability*, the chance of repeated attack on the same or another ship in the moving formation.

The angle $\sin^{-1} u/v$ is called the *limiting approach angle*—the "limiting submerged approach angle" in the example of the submarine of restricted underwater speed.

During World War II, the limitation of u was due to the fact that the submarines of that period were very restricted in their underwater speed. Since then, technological improvements have largely removed this mechanical restriction. However, moving at such greater speeds usually incurs the disadvantage of generating greater underwater sound, thus risking the revelation of their presence. The previous construction may still be valid if u is taken as the maximum *quiet* speed, and not necessarily the maximum *possible* speed.

3. REGIONS OF APPROACH UNDER TIME CONSTRAINTS

In Section 2 we have considered only the limitations of approach due to relative positions and velocities, but without regard to the length of time necessary to make an approach even when it complies with these conditions. While this is usually an important side of the subject, another often equally important one is the case of constraints in *time*. Two cases will be considered: one in which the constraint arises from the limited endurance of the target, and another due to limited periods of time when the target is free to approach without danger of detection.

Returning to the construction of limited approach regions given above, it is seen that quite a different figure for B is obtained if the target is assumed to have a *limited time* (T hours) to make its approach to A. Then even when $u > v$ approach is not always possible. The construction of B in such a case is given in Fig. 2-8(A) and (B), when $u > v$; Fig. 2-8(B) shows a circle of radius uT centered at Q and vT units ahead of the starting point P; the circular region is the locus of starting positions from which the target can close the point P within the time T. From the circular boundary the target just reaches P at the end of this time (the object at P then having moved to Q). Now move the circular figure (B) so that the point P takes all positions in A: this will sweep out B (as well as A), the envelope of the circles giving the outer boundary of B. A similar construction is made when $u < v$, where the starting point region is that bounded by the two tangents as well as the larger intercepted arc of a circle disposed as in Fig. 2-7(B).

It will be seen at once that this region B could have been obtained in two steps. *First*, construct B' (not shown in Fig. 2-8) as the envelope of circles of radii all equal to uT, as their center Q moves along the contour of A; *second*, translate B' upward by the amount vT (i.e., as determined by the vector $\mathbf{v}T$). This construction also is valid in the cases $u = v$ and $u < v$, except that in the latter, the rearward circular arcs are replaced by segments of the limited approach times.

We turn next to the case in which there are a succession of intervals of time, of common length D, during which the target is exposed to detection by a hostile force, with all the dangerous consequences that this would entail. These periods of exposure alternate with intervals of common length I during which the target is almost or completely undetectable. The further assumptions are that the target cannot make itself less detectable (once it has chosen its greatest quiet speed) and that it must approach to a certain range R of its objective, a unit or formation of units, moving at constant velocity $\mathbf{v}$, as in Section 2.

This situation occurs when the searcher, which is escorting the formation, uses the tactic of *sprint and drift*: stays still or almost still during a period D while its detection equipment is in operation; then, during the next period I, is not using this equipment, but is employed in attaining a new position, so that it can keep up with the defended formation: its *mean speed of advance* (SOA) must equal v.

The isochrons. The key to the tactics of this situation—both from the point of view of the approaching target and of the defended and searching formation—is given by reference to *curves of constant approach time*, or isochrons. We have already given the construction of such a curve in Fig. 2-8: the outer boundary of

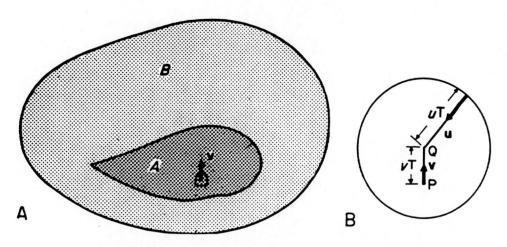

Fig. 2-8. The region of approach with limited time.

the region B is the isochron for the given period of time T needed for approach to the outer boundary of A—which in the case $u > v$ is also the inner boundary of B. In that figure, A is the locus of points from which the moving formation is vulnerable. It has been given a "general" and therefore a "peculiar" shape, to convey the idea that the method of construction of B applies to any shape.

A useful specialization of the construction of isochrons is shown in Fig. 2-9. This corresponds with the case in which the range R from the target's objective is so much larger than the dimensions of the latter that the region A of Fig. 2-8(A) may be taken as a circle of radius R centered at a reference point 0 in the formation, which circle moves (up the page) with the constant velocity **v**. The radius R is the range of the target's torpedo or missile, possibly increased to take the spread of the formation into account.

Applying the two-step method of constructing B, we see that B', being the envelope of circles of radii uR centered on the circumference of the circle A, is itself a concentric circle of radius $R + uT$; B is this circle translated upward the distance vT: its center is at G where $\overrightarrow{OG} = \mathbf{v}T$.

Fig. 2-9 shows the isochrons in the three cases: when (a) $u > v$ and the isochron encloses A; (b) $u = v$, it is outside A but is tangent to it in the rear; and (c) $u < v$, the limited approach lines exist and are tangent to the isochron circle (the isochron is itself the forward arc intercepted by these tangents). In all cases the target's track (with respect to the ocean) **u** is directed to G, the center of B; while its relative track is directed to a point L at the rear of O by the distance $OL = Rv/u$. When $u < v$, L is outside A and is the intersection of the limited approach lines. When $u = v$, these lines coincide and are the common tangent to the circles A and B at the point L. When $u > v$, L is inside A and there are no limited approach lines. All these facts are shown by the elementary geometry of similar triangles, indicated in Fig. 2-9. (For their practical application, see Chapter 9, Section 7, Fig. 9-27.)

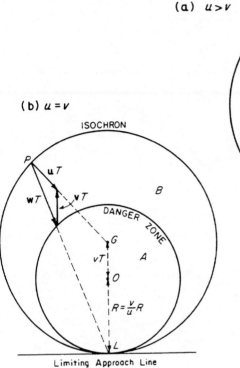

(a) $u > v$

(b) $u = v$

(c) $u < v$

In all cases, triangles PGL and one
determined by $\mathbf{u}T$, $\mathbf{v}T$, $\mathbf{w}T$ are similar,
with $OL = R\frac{v}{u}$, $OG = vT$, $GP = R + uT$.
Isochron is a circle, center G, radius $R + uT$;
but in case $v > u$, consists of forward arc
between points M, N, of tangency with
limiting approach lines. Boundary of B
includes in addition, MM', NN', and rear
arc of A.

Fig. 2-9. Isochrons in circular case.

4. CONTACTS IN A RANDOM DISTRIBUTION OF TARGETS

In the preceding sections the motion of observer and target were given or precisely
specified and the conclusions were exact. In Section 1 one observer and one target
of stated speeds and tracks were assumed; in Sections 2 and 3 the same was true
for the observer and for the target's speed, but a precisely defined class of targets

(those which enter A) was considered in defining B (the locus of their starting points) and the conclusion was the precise one: "*The target can enter* A *if and only if it starts in* B." Fundamentally different is the state of affairs in the present section, in which the notion of *random* is introduced and conclusions are stated in terms of *probability*. Instead of saying, "Under such and such conditions the target will necessarily do so and so," we shall be saying, "Under such and such conditions the probability that the target will do so and so has this value," or, equivalently, "This percentage of targets will on the average do so and so." The importance of arriving at probabilities and statistical results in naval matters should be self-evident; it has been discussed at length in Chapter 1, Section 6.

To specify a target (always assumed in this chapter to be moving at constant speed and course) it is necessary to give its speed and heading (the vector **u**) and also its position at a particular epoch (i.e., when $t = t_0$). This requires in principle four independent quantities, such as u, ϕ, r, β. By a *random distribution* of targets is meant either of the two following situations:

I. There are present a very large number of different targets, and what is known is not their velocities and positions, but the *proportion* or *percentage* which have the various possible velocities and positions.

II. There is present only one target; its velocity and position are not precisely known, but the *probabilities* that it has the various possible velocities and positions are known.

In these statements, the proportion or probability of targets "having such and such a velocity and position" must be interpreted to mean "having a velocity and position within a stated closeness of such and such a velocity and position." (Such probabilities might all be zero. With many distributions the probability that the target will be exactly at a prestated position is necessarily zero. It is the probability that it will lie in a prestated *area* that is of interest.) Thus if the above choice of quantities is made, it is the proportion or probability of targets having a speed between u and $u + du$, track angle between ϕ and $\phi + d\phi$, range between r and $r + dr$, and bearing between β and $\beta + d\beta$ which is in question. In many cases (but not all, as seen below) it can be represented to terms of first order in the differentials by $p(u, \phi, r, \beta) \, du \, d\phi \, dr \, d\beta$, and the function $p(u, \phi, r, \beta)$ is the mean *relative density* (I) or *probability density* (II) of the distribution. Then the proportion or probability for a large class of velocities and positions is obtained by integrating $p(u, \phi, r, \beta)$ over all values of the class considered—a quadruple integration in the "space" of the "coordinates" (u, ϕ, r, β).

While the situations in (I) and (II) above appear to be quite different, they are in reality equivalent, or, rather, either one leads to the other. Thus from the very large number of targets in (I) we can think of an individual target chosen at random, all targets having the same chance of being chosen; this target will then be the single target to which the situation (II) applies. Reciprocally, if a very large number of targets is constituted from individual targets, to each of which the state of affairs of (II) applies *independently*, the resulting swarm will be as described in (I). The mean relative density in (I) and the probability density in (II) are equal. All this is a consequence of the *law of large numbers* in the theory of probability. Situation (I) is generally used to give a pictorial representation of (II) which might otherwise seem too abstract. But (I) has the disadvantage of being rather unrealistic; if so many targets were actually all present they would be apt to interfere with one another physically! For further details, see Appendix A.

What we have termed a *random distribution* should more properly be called a *known random distribution*, to distinguish it from the case where the values of the *probabilities* are partly or wholly unknown; in fact a frequent problem of importance in operational analysis is to find them by theoretical calculations or statistical methods. It is discussed in Appendix A.

One of the simplest and most important cases of random distribution of targets is that of the *uniform distribution* of targets of given speed u. It is one which complies with the three following requirements:

a. The probability that the track angle ϕ will be between ϕ_1 and ϕ_2 is proportional to $\phi_2 - \phi_1$ [and hence is equal to $(\phi_2 - \phi_1)/2\pi$ when $\phi_1 < \phi_2$].
b. The probability that at any chosen epoch the target will be in the area A (fixed in the ocean or else fixed relative to the observer; the two situations are here equivalent) is proportional to A (and hence, if the target is known to be in some larger area B containing A, the probability that it will be in A is A/B).
c. The event of ϕ being between ϕ_1 and ϕ_2 on the one hand and the event of the target being in A on the other are *independent events*. If one of them is known to have occurred, the probability of the occurrence of the other is the same as before such knowledge.

In the case of such a distribution, the probability density will (when the target is given to be in B) have the value $p(\phi, r, \beta) = r/2\pi B$; this is because $r\, dr\, d\beta$ is the element of area corresponding to a position of range and bearing between r and $r + dr$ and β and $\beta + d\beta$ respectively. It is to be noted that the probability is $p(\phi, r, \beta)\, d\phi\, dr\, d\beta$ and not $p(u, \phi, r, \beta)du\, d\phi\, dr\, d\beta$, as in the earlier example; i.e., neither u nor du occurs: this is because the value of the target's *speed* is supposed to be known.

The case considered is of importance in naval operations, since it corresponds to the situation in which the target is an enemy unit presumed to be running at the known speed of about u knots, but is in such a large area of ocean with so many possible intentions that nothing concerning its position or heading can be regarded as known. The chances that the observer will make various kinds of contacts with such a unit are studied in the following section. The u is generally taken as the maximum *sustained* speed.

It is noted that in the foregoing example the language of (II) is used. This is permissible in view of the equivalence of (II) with (I), and there is manifestly no difficulty in rewording things to correspond to (I). Whichever of the two terminologies will be employed in the succeeding pages will be purely a matter of convenience: this involves absolutely no inconsistency.

5. RANDOM ENCOUNTERS WITH UNIFORMLY DISTRIBUTED TARGETS

When an observer is progressing on course at the constant velocity v among a uniform random distribution of targets of speed u, it is frequently important to know the proportions of targets that pass within the stated range of R miles of the observer. In some cases R may be the range within which the observer can sight the target (horizon distance); in others, the range within which the target can detect the observer's presence; again, R may be effective weapon range of observer against target, or vice versa. If a circle of radius R is pictured centered on the observer and moving along with it at velocity **v** over the ocean, the question becomes that of the proportion of targets entering the circle; or entering it at various specified bearings; or the chance that a target of given starting point shall enter the circle—a question of *probability*, in contrast with that of Section 3, which was one of *possibility*. The three problems will be solved in turn.

Problem 1. Let there be on the average N targets per square mile (N will usually be far less than unity; it is an "expected value" in the sense of probability). On account of the uniform distribution of track angles and their independence of position [(a) and (c) of Section 4 above], the average number with track angle between ϕ and $\phi + d\phi$ will be $N\, d\phi/2\pi$. Fixing our attention exclusively on targets of a particular track angle ϕ, it is easy to find how many enter the circle per unit time. The relative speed and course are found as in Section 1 and the circle of radius R is drawn about the observer as shown in Fig. 2-10. Since the target is moving at velocity **w** with respect to the observer, if it is to enter the circle in a unit of time (one hour) it must be in the large shaded region of Fig. 2-10 between the circle and the circle moved through the displacement $-\mathbf{w}$, and between their tangents parallel to **w**. The area being $2Rw$, it is seen that the number of targets of track angle between ϕ and $\phi + d\phi$ that enter the circle per unit time is (to quantities of first order in the differential) $2RwN\, d\phi/2\pi$. Hence the total number N_0 is given by integration:

(4)
$$N_0 = \frac{2RN}{2\pi} \int_0^{2\pi} w\, d\phi,$$

$$= \frac{RN}{\pi} \int_0^{2\pi} \sqrt{u^2 + v^2 - 2uv \cos \phi}\; d\phi,$$

$$= \frac{4RN}{\pi} (u + v) \int_0^{\pi/2} \sqrt{1 - \sin^2 \sigma \sin^2 \psi}\; d\psi,$$

$$= \frac{4RN}{\pi} (u + v) E(\sigma), \quad \sin \sigma = \frac{2\sqrt{uv}}{u + v}.$$

Here the second equation results from equation (1), the third by introducing σ and the new variable of integration $\psi = (\pi - \phi)/2$, and $E(\sigma)$ is the complete elliptic integral of the second kind.

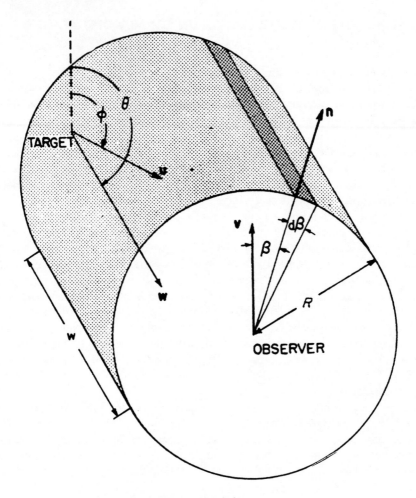

Fig. 2-10. Area of targets entering a circle.

Note that equation (4) is left unchanged if u and v are interchanged. This corresponds with the fact that whenever the target comes within range R of the observer, the observer automatically comes within this range of the target, etc.

As an example, if there are 20 vessels distributed at random in an area of 10,000 square miles, so that $N = 0.002$, if they are cruising at 10 knots in various directions and if the observer is traveling at 15 knots, the number per hour arriving within the range of $R = 25$ miles of the observer is found to be 1.67, contrasted with 1.5, which would be the number in case the targets remained stationary. That the first number is greater than the second is due to the fact that the target's motion tends to bring more of them into the range than escape from getting within range—a fact that would not have been evident without calculation.

The preceding example illustrates the general principle that the contact rate on the random targets increases with increase of the motion of the targets. To show this, we have but to prove that $\partial N_0/\partial u$ is positive. Using the second form for N_0 in (4), but with the integral taken over half the interval of integration and doubled (a permissible change, in view of the symmetry of the integrand),

$$
\frac{\partial N_0}{\partial u} = \frac{2RN}{\pi} \frac{\partial}{\partial u} \int_0^\pi \sqrt{u^2 + v^2 - 2uv \cos \phi} \; d\phi,
$$

$$
= \frac{2RN}{\pi} \int_0^\pi \frac{u - v \cos \phi}{w} \; d\phi,
$$

$$
= \frac{2RN}{\pi} \int_0^\pi \cos \omega \; d\phi,
$$

where ω is the angle between the vectors $\mathbf{u}$ and $\mathbf{w}$ (cf. the various cases of Fig. 2-2, with obvious constructions). The integrand is always positive when $v \leqslant u$ (cases [A] and [B]), so that the required inequality $\partial N_0/\partial u > 0$ is evident. To show that this continues to be the case when $v > u$ (case [C]), decompose the interval of integration $(0, \pi)$ into the two halves $(0, \pi/2)$ and $(\pi/2, \pi)$, and then replace the variable of integration in the second half by the supplement of the ϕ of the first, thus recombining the integrals

$$
\frac{\partial N_0}{\partial u} = \frac{2RN}{\pi} \int_0^{\pi/2} (\cos \omega + \cos \omega') \; d\phi;
$$

here ω' denotes the value which ω assumes when ϕ is replaced by its supplement. Since a simple construction based on Fig. 2-2(C) shows that ω' is less than the supplement of ω, we have $\cos \omega' > - \cos \omega$; i.e., $\cos \omega + \cos \omega' > 0$, and hence $\partial N_0/\partial u > 0$, as was to be proved. Application: If an enemy is passing in our vicinity but along an unknown path, we must cut our speed until he passes, if we wish to improve our chances of remaining undetected.

Problem 2. Find the number of targets that enter the circle considered above between the bearings β and $\beta + d\beta$, per unit time. [We note that this has turned out to be one of the most useful tactical calculations.] Their number is given by an expression of the form $N_0(\beta) \, d\beta$, where $N_0(\beta)$ is a density related to N_0 by the equation

$$
(5) \qquad\qquad N_0 = \int_0^{2\pi} N_0(\beta) \, d\beta.
$$

To find $N_0(\beta)$, again we begin by considering only those targets of a particular track angle ϕ. They can enter the circle only if the direction of the vector $\mathbf{w}$ points *into* the circle, i.e., if the angle γ between the reversed vector $-\mathbf{w}$ and the unit vector $\mathbf{n}$ normal to the circle and pointing outward is *acute* (γ is defined as measured between 0 and π). Figure 2-10 shows that in this case the targets in question all come from the small heavily shaded region of area $Rw \cos \gamma \, d\beta = (-\mathbf{w} \cdot \mathbf{n})R \, d\beta$ where $(-\mathbf{w} \cdot \mathbf{n})$ denotes the scalar product. The number per unit time is obtained by multiplying this expression by the density $N \, d\phi/2\pi$. Hence, finally, the number $N_0(\beta)$ for targets of all track angles is given by

(6) $$N_0(\beta) = \frac{RN}{2\pi} \int (-\mathbf{w} \cdot \mathbf{n}) \, d\phi,$$

where the integration is over all those values of ϕ between 0 and 2π for which the integrand is *positive*.

For the evaluation of (6), observe that in view of the vector equation $\mathbf{w} = \mathbf{u} - \mathbf{v}$, (Section 1.2) we have

$$-\mathbf{w} \cdot \mathbf{n} = \mathbf{v} \cdot \mathbf{n} - \mathbf{u} \cdot \mathbf{n}$$
$$= v \cos \beta - u \cos(\phi - \beta).$$

It remains to insert this value into (6), then to determine those values of ϕ for which $v \cos \beta - u \cos(\phi - \beta) > 0$, and finally to integrate over such values. The details of this straightforward computation are omitted. As a result, the following expressions are obtained.

(7)   When $v \leqslant u$:

$$N_0(\beta) = \frac{NR}{\pi} \left[v \cos^{-1}\left(-\frac{v}{u} \cos \beta \right) \cos \beta \right.$$
$$\left. + \sqrt{u^2 - v^2 \cos^2 \beta} \, \right].$$

When $v > u$:
$$N_0(\beta) = NRv \cos \beta, \quad \text{when } -\cos^{-1}\frac{u}{v} \leqslant \beta \leqslant \cos^{-1}\frac{u}{v};$$

(8) $$N_0(\beta) = \frac{NR}{\pi} \left[v \cos^{-1}\left(-\frac{v}{u} \cos \beta \right) \cos \beta \right.$$
$$\left. + \sqrt{u^2 - v^2 \cos^2 \beta} \, \right],$$

when $$-\cos^{-1}\left(-\frac{u}{v} \right) \leqslant \beta \leqslant -\cos^{-1}\left(\frac{u}{v} \right)$$

or when $$\cos^{-1}\left(\frac{u}{v} \right) \leqslant \beta \leqslant \cos^{-1}\left(-\frac{u}{v} \right);$$

$$N_0(\beta) = 0,$$

when $$\beta \leqslant -\cos^{-1}\left(-\frac{u}{v} \right)$$

or $$\beta \geqslant \cos^{-1}\left(-\frac{u}{v} \right).$$

This result can be stated in terms of probabilities. Suppose that it is known that a target has entered the circle; *where* is it likely to have entered? If $p(\beta) \, d\beta$ is the probability that it entered between the bearings β and $\beta + d\beta$, the expected number $N_0(\beta) \, d\beta$ which enter per unit time is the number entering in unit time N_0

times the probability $p(\beta)\, d\beta$; thus

(9)
$$
p(\beta) = \frac{N_0(\beta)}{N_0}
$$
$$
= \frac{\pi N_0(\beta)}{4RN(u+v)E(\sigma)},
$$

in virtue of equation (4). Thus equations (7) and (8) give $p(\beta)$ at once.

Figure 2-11 gives the polar diagram showing the dependence of $p(\beta)$ on β for different values of u/v. At one extreme, $u/v = 0$: The targets are at rest and the dependence on β is as the cosine, and the diagram is a circle with the observer at the circumference. At the other extreme $u/v = \infty$: the targets move but the observer is at rest; in this case the number entering at all bearings is the same and

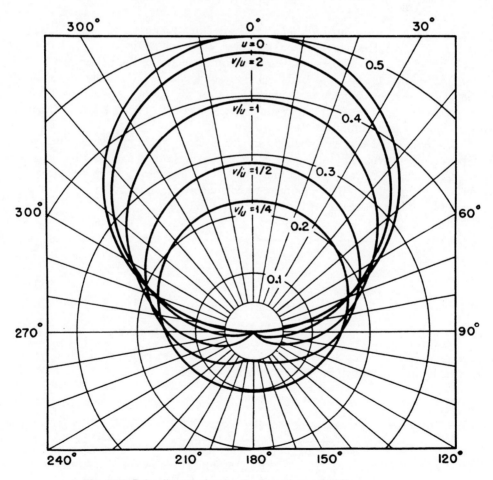

Fig. 2-11. Polar diagram showing the dependence of $p(\beta)$.

we have a circle centered at the target. In the intermediate cases, as long as target speed u is less than observer speed v, there is a certain angular range aft over which no contacts are made. As u becomes greater than v, however, the number of contacts made aft increases rapidly until in the limit as many are made aft as ahead.

There is a sort of inverse to this problem which it is useful to consider. Suppose that a contact has actually been made at the known bearing β (and range R), what is the distribution of values of the track angle ϕ? In other words, we have seen the target; what is its heading likely to be? This is essentially a problem in the "probability of causes" and is solved by Bayes's formula of *inverse probability* (see Appendix A):

$$\Pi_\beta(\phi) = \frac{\tilde{\omega}(\phi) f_\phi(\beta)}{\int \tilde{\omega}(\phi) f_\phi(\beta)\, d\phi},$$

where $\tilde{\omega}(\phi)\, d\phi$ is the *a priori probability* (i.e., as estimated before the contact was obtained) of a track angle between ϕ and $\phi + d\phi$; $f_\phi(\beta)$ is the "productive probability" of the effect observed (i.e., of a contact between the bearings β and $\beta + d\beta$), given that the target actually has the track angle ϕ; and, finally, $\Pi_\beta(\phi)\, d\phi$ is the *a posteriori probability* (i.e., as estimated after the contact at bearing β has been observed) that the target's track angle lies between ϕ and $\phi + d\phi$. In other words, $\Pi_\beta(\phi)$ is the quantity we want.

As before, $\tilde{\omega}(\phi) = 1/2\pi$. To obtain $f_\phi(\beta)\, d\beta$, observe that it equals the average number of targets detected in unit time between bearings β and $\beta + d\beta$, divided by the average number detected in unit time at all bearings (both averages for targets of given track angle ϕ). This quotient is calculated at once by means of the reasoning used before (based on Fig. 2-10); it has the value

$$\frac{(-\mathbf{w} \cdot \mathbf{n})\, d\beta}{2w} = \frac{v \cos \beta - u \cos(\phi - \beta)}{2w}\, d\beta.$$

Thus

$$\Pi_\beta(\phi) = \frac{(-\mathbf{w} \cdot \mathbf{n})}{\int (-\mathbf{w} \cdot \mathbf{n})\, d\phi},$$

where the region of integration must be determined as in problem 2, since here again values of ϕ for which the integrand is negative are excluded. The results are,

when $\qquad\qquad\qquad\qquad\qquad\qquad v \leqslant u,$

$$\Pi_\beta(\phi) = \frac{1}{2} \cdot \frac{\cos \beta - \dfrac{u}{v} \cos(\phi - \beta)}{\cos^{-1}\left(-\dfrac{v}{u} \cos \beta\right) \cos \beta + \sqrt{\left(\dfrac{u}{v}\right)^2 - \cos^2 \beta}};$$

when $$v > u,$$

$$\Pi_\beta(\phi) = \frac{1}{2\pi}\left[1 - \frac{u}{v}\cdot\frac{\cos(\phi-\beta)}{\cos\beta}\right],$$

when $$-\cos^{-1}\frac{u}{v} \leqslant \beta \leqslant \cos^{-1}\frac{u}{v};$$

$$\Pi_\beta(\phi) = \frac{1}{2}\,\frac{\cos\beta - \dfrac{u}{v}\cos(\phi-\beta)}{\cos^{-1}\left(-\dfrac{v}{u}\cos\beta\right)\cos\beta + \sqrt{\left(\dfrac{u}{v}\right)^2 - \cos^2\beta}},$$

when $$-\cos^{-1}\left(-\frac{u}{v}\right) \leqslant \beta \leqslant -\cos^{-1}\frac{u}{v},$$

or when $$\cos^{-1}\frac{u}{v} \leqslant \beta \leqslant \cos^{-1}\left(-\frac{u}{v}\right).$$

Detection is impossible when

$$\beta \leqslant -\cos^{-1}\left(-\frac{u}{v}\right)$$

or

$$\beta \geqslant \cos^{-1}\left(-\frac{u}{v}\right).$$

6. RANDOM ENCOUNTERS, GIVEN INITIAL TARGET POSITION*

Problem 3. Still assuming that the speeds u and v are known constants and the direction of $\mathbf{u}$ random, let the target's relative position (r, β) at the epoch t be given. Find the probability P that the target will enter the circle of radius R centered on the observer. Graph the equiprobability curves.

Evidently P depends on (r, β): $P = P(r, \beta)$, and $P = 1$ if $r \leqslant R$. When $r > R$ the target will enter the circle if, and only if, its vector relative velocity $\mathbf{w}$ points into the circle (i.e., when $\mathbf{w}$ is produced in the direction it is pointing). The situation is illustrated in Fig. 2-12(A) $(v > u)$ and (B) $(v < u)$, which show the angular range of vectors $\mathbf{w}$ pointing into the circle, i.e., the range of angles θ. Corresponding to this angular range of θ the angular range of ϕ is constructed immediately (shaded angle in Figure 2-12). On account of the uniformity of the distribution [in particular, of Section 4, (a) and (c)], the probability that ϕ will lie in this angular range is the magnitude of the range divided by 2π. This is the required value of $P(r, \beta)$. The problem is thus reduced to the geometry of Fig. 2-12, and the formula for $P(r, \beta)$ is

---

*This problem, contributed by J. M. Dobbie, provides a rather complicated example of random encounter. It is applied only at the end of Chapter 10, in planning predark sweeps ahead of a convoy. Its study may be postponed.

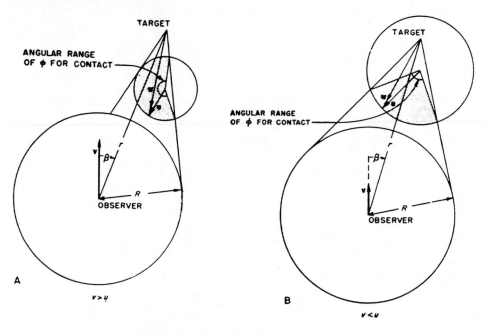

Fig. 2-12. Probability of entering circle.

obtained by straightforward trigonometry. There are, however, a number of different cases to be considered. For example, in Fig. 2-12(B) the angular range of θ is between the two tangents from the target to the circle of radius R, while in Fig. 2-12(A) it is between one such tangent and the tangent to the velocity diagram circle, corresponding to the restricted orientations of **w** when $v > u$ (limiting approach angle); moreover, in this case the θ range counts multiply: To one θ there are two ϕ's, one for the target moving toward the observer and the other for the target moving away and being overtaken. There are other cases not shown in Fig. 2-12.

The expression of $P(r, \beta)$ is as follows:

$$P(r, \beta) = \frac{\Phi(r, \beta)}{2\pi},$$

where $\Phi(r, \beta)$ is the total radian length of the range or ranges of values of $\phi(0 \leqslant \phi < 2\pi)$ that satisfy the inequality

$$r^2[u \sin(\beta - \phi) - v \sin \beta]^2 \leqslant R^2[u^2 + v^2 - 2uv \cos \phi],$$

subject to the condition

$$u \cos(\beta - \phi) \leqslant v \cos \beta.$$

The second of the above inequalities is needed to insure that the target will enter the circle of radius R after the reference epoch t. It is automatically satisfied for those values of ϕ which satisfy the first inequality when $v \geqslant u$.

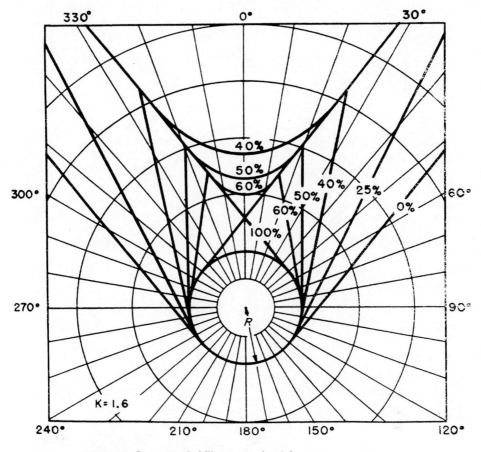

Fig. 2-13. Contact probability curves. $k = 1.6$.

The curves of constant probability are symmetrical with respect to the course of the observer. In the following discussion, only the half plane to the right of the observer's course is considered. First, consider the case when $v \geqslant u$ and $k = v/u$ (Fig. 2-13). Outside the circle of radius R and between the tangents to this circle which are inclined to the right and the left of the course of the observer at the limiting approach angle $\sin^{-1} u/v$, the curve of constant probability P is a straight line tangent to the circle and inclined to the observer's course at the angle $\sin^{-1}[(u/v) \cos \pi P]$. When $v = u$, this latter angle reduces to $(\pi/2)(1 - 2P)$. On and below the lower tangent line inclined at the angle $\sin^{-1} u/v$, $P = 0$.

Above the upper tangent line inclined at the angle $\sin^{-1} u/v$, the equation of the curve of constant probability P is

$$r^2 = \frac{R^2 v^2 \csc^2\left(\dfrac{\pi P}{2}\right)\left[\sin^2 \beta - \cos^2\left(\dfrac{\pi P}{2}\right)\right]}{v^2 \sin^2 \beta - u^2 \cos^2\left(\dfrac{\pi P}{2}\right)}.$$

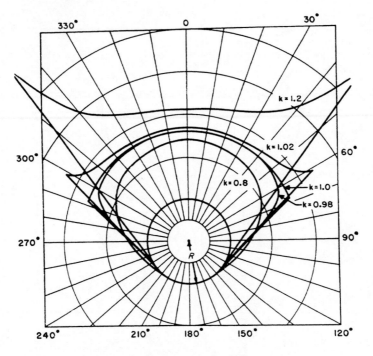

Fig. 2-14. Contact probability curves. $k = 2/3$.

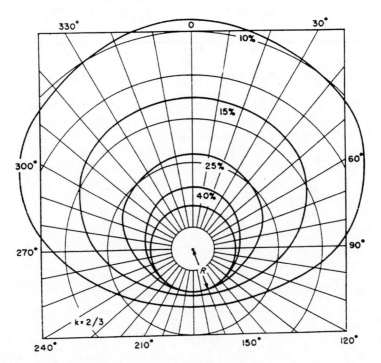

Fig. 2-15. 25 per cent contact probability curve.

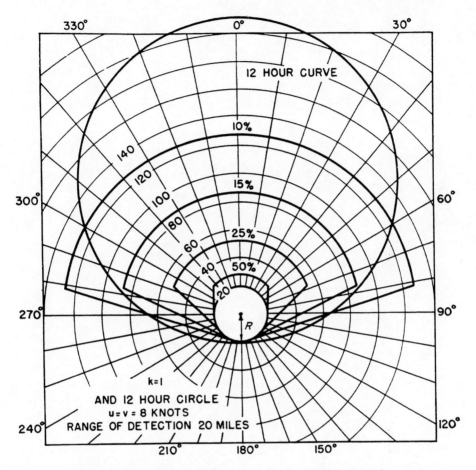

Fig. 2-16. Contact probability curves. $k = 1$, and 12 hour circle. $u = v = 8$ knots. Range of detection 20 miles.

When $v = u$, this equation reduces to $r = R \csc(\pi P/2)$.

Second, consider $v < u$ and $k = v/u$ (Fig. 2-14). Outside the circle of radius R, the equation of the curve of constant probability P is

$$v^2 \sin^2 \beta \left[\cos^2(\psi + \pi P) - \cos^2 \psi \right] = \sin^2(\psi + \pi P) \left[u^2 \cos^2(\psi + \pi P) - v^2 \cos^2 \psi \right],$$

where ψ is the positive acute angle $\cos^{-1}(R/r)$. Figure 2-15 shows how the equiprobability curve $P = 0.25$ varies with $k = v/u$. Figure 2-16 is for later reference.

Chapter 3

Target Detection — Individual and Cumulative

In Chapter 1 various aspects of the detection, identification, and localization of an object of search (target) have been discussed, together with the concept of probability in relation with such events. The stress has been on the qualitative aspects of these matters. In the present chapter their quantitative formulation will be undertaken. Chapter 2 has involved the geometrical and kinematic relations between searcher and target, but has left entirely out of consideration the act or process whereby the observer gains knowledge of the presence and position, etc., of the target. Contacts have been considered purely as geometrical events taking place in the course of time, and their probabilities have been based solely on the chance that the target will reach specified positions in relation to the searcher. Since, as emphasized in Chapter 1, even when the relative positions of searcher and target are such that a detection is physically possible, it may or may not occur. It is in general a *random event*, a fact which poses the problem of finding its *probability* of occurrence under the various conditions of practical importance.

Closely connected with the probabilities of target detection is the manner in which the probabilities build up with the exposure of the target during more or less extended periods of time, the *cumulative* effects of continued search. This is the point at which the detection problem and the tracking problem of Chapter 2 combine into a single operation. It is also the point at which the issue discussed in Section 5 of Chapter 1 is raised: whether the method of search involves a succession of passive or of active observations. The simplest case is of course the former. It will occur, as we have seen, when the physical acts involved in detection neither change the environment nor give evidence that could alert the target and lead him to alter his motion or detectable features. *The present chapter will be confined to this case.* We may then apply the laws of probability in their familiar classical form. (The alerting case is studied later, as occurring under special tactical situations.)

Before a definite answer can be given to questions involving the cumulation of detection probabilities (even in the case of passive observations), another matter must be settled. We must know whether the act of detection could be performed quickly, or whether on the other hand the nature of its mechanism requires a more extended period—an *integration time*—to form and present to the human observer a stimulus to which he could respond by a detection.

The former situation is typified in the familiar case of seeing or hearing. We may or may not be successful in seeing a target that is actually visible, or hearing its emitted sound when it is physically audible, but it needs only a brief moment to be successful, and therefore successive attempts can (under natural assumptions) be treated as *repeated independent trials*, to which the traditional methods of *survival probabilities* can be applied. The second situation occurs when human awareness of the target is not by direct perception by sense organs, but indirectly, by examining a display built up by electronic means, requiring the reception of radiant energy during a period of time (the integration time). One instance is in the use of the chemical recorder which builds up a pattern from processed acoustical signals, e.g., sound from an underwater source. A second example is the process whereby photographs of planets were taken by satellites that scanned the latter and transmitted the results to earth, "bit by bit." The integration time in the former case could be an hour or a good fraction thereof, while in the latter case it could take days or weeks.

During and for a while after World War II, even mechanisms of indirect detection, such as radar or acoustic listening or echo-ranging, required no appreciable integration time. They could be treated probabilistically in the same manner as in the case of direct visual detection; whatever time was needed by the process was so brief a period that successive attempts could be combined as independent trials. *The present chapter will confine itself to this situation.* Cases in which the integration time plays an essential role are appropriately examined in connection with the specific characteristics of the detection equipment: cf. Section 11 below, and Appendixes E, F, and G.

This order of treatment allows a large and important class of cases to be studied by simple methods; it also leads quite naturally to the introduction of various general concepts of search theory on an elementary basis. Such concepts will later be extended, with appropriate modifications, to the cases involving integration time.

We continue to maintain the distinction between the terms "region" and "area" defined in the introduction of Chapter 1.

1. THE ASSUMPTION OF INDEPENDENCE

In addition to the assumption that the searches considered here are by passive (nonalerting) observations and require no appreciable integration time, as explained above, we shall frequently make use of a further one: that when two attempts at finding the target are made, the failure of one does not alter the probability of failure or success of the other. They are in this sense "independent trials" as in elementary probability. Consequently no Bayesian "update" of probabilities is required to take account of the previous failure. It is essential to realize that there are situations in which this assumption of independence is illegitimate, and to distinguish them from those in which it is legitimate.

The assumption of independence would be false if made by an observer having any real uncertainty concerning the physical condition of the environment (the medium, air or water, through which the target's signal must pass), of his detecting equipment, or of the target. A previous failure would lead him to increased pessimism with regard to these physical factors and thus to readjust downward his evaluation of the chance of success on the second trial. We shall return to this effect in later connections.

Even when there is no uncertainty concerning the conditions of these physical factors, a Bayesian update of the target's probability distribution after a first failure must be made by the searcher when all that he knows concerning the target's position is its a priori probability distribution. Then he will have to replace this distribution by an a posteriori one given by Bayes's formula (see Chapter 1, Section 6), with a consequent updating of the probabilities in the second trial. Inasmuch as all that a normal searcher knows about the target is its a priori distribution, it might be asked how the independence assumption can ever be used.

The answer is that the assumption is in fact legitimate—and important—when applied to *conditional probabilities* of detection: probabilities calculated on the basis of *postulated* positions and motions of the target. Thus the probability that a searcher will detect a target on a stated relative course (as defined in Chapter 2, Section 1) would be a case in point. The "tightness" of a screen of detectors is calculated on the postulation that a target take this or that specified path through it. In fact the main body of the present chapter is concerned with such conditional probabilities.

There is another case, specialized but important, in which the assumption of independence may be applied, and to an unconditional probability: the case of *random search* examined in Section 6 below. In that model the relative motions of searcher and target have such a disorderly and changeable character that all coherence between different outcomes is lost (as in catching a jumping flea in the dark). Then, virtually *by definition* of "random search," the assumption of independence is applicable.

Returning to the conditional probabilities, we must stress the fact that the postulated target positions and motions, on the one hand, and the postulated law of detection and its results, on the other, must not be logically inconsistent. This could occur, for example, in some applications of the *definite range law* given in the following sections and examined in this respect in Section 6. It could also occur with its generalization, the *definite detection law* examined in Section 9.

If we have dwelt in some length on these conditions of validity of the concepts and formulas now to be developed, it is because after their introduction during World War II, their scope has been much too often misunderstood, with resulting errors. This danger is all the more insidious when such misapplications have been incorporated into the "software" of computer programs, so apt to conceal the underlying assumptions.

2. INSTANTANEOUS CONDITIONAL PROBABILITIES OF DETECTION

The three assumptions discussed earlier in this chapter having been made, we proceed to derive their first consequences. These assumptions, to repeat, are passive observations, zero integration time, and independence of successive trials at detection (when they are not broken off).

Suppose that the physical conditions (distances, etc.) remain fixed and that the observer is looking for the target (by "looking" shall be meant trying to detect with the means considered, visual, radar, sonar, etc.). There are two possibilities. First, the observer may be making a succession of brief "glimpses"; a typical case is in the echo-ranging procedure in which each sweep or scan affords one opportunity for detection (glimpse), successive ones occurring two or three minutes apart. Second, the observer may be looking continuously; a typical case is the observer fixing his eyes steadily on the position where he is trying to detect the target. The case of radar is intermediate; on account of the scanning it would belong to the first case, but if the scanning is very fast, and especially when there is persistency of the image on the scope, it may be treated as in the second. Likewise, visual detection by a slow scan through a large angle belongs to the first rather than the second case. Very often the decision to regard a method of detection in the first or in the second way depends simply on which affords the closest or more convenient approximation. This will be made clear on the basis of examples in succeeding chapters.

In the case of separated glimpses, the important quantity is the *instantaneous probability g of detection by one glimpse*. When n glimpses are made under unchanging conditions, the probability p_n of detection is given by the formula

$$(1) \qquad p_n = 1 - (1 - g)^n.$$

This is because $1 - p_n$ is the probability of failing to detect with n glimpses, and for this to occur the target must fail to be detected at every single one of the n glimpses; each such failure having the probability $1 - g$ and the n failures being independent events, we conclude that $1 - p_n = (1 - g)^n$; hence equation (1). When $g = 0$, obviously $p_n = 0$; but if $g > 0$ and even if g is very small, p_n can be made as close to 1 as we please by increasing n sufficiently. In other words, once the physical conditions give some chance, however small, of detecting on one glimpse, enough glimpses under the same conditions will lead with practical certainty to eventual detection.

To find the mean or expected number $\bar{n}$ of glimpses for detection, we must first find the probability P_n that detection shall occur precisely at the nth glimpse (and not before). This is the product of the probability that it shall not occur during the first $n - 1$ glimpses, $(1 - g)^{n-1}$, times the probability that a detection shall occur on a single glimpse g (the nth). It is accordingly $P_n = (1 - g)^{n-1}g$. The required mean number $\bar{n}$ is, according to the theory of probability, $1P_1 + 2P_2 + 3P_3 + \cdots$, and thus

(2)
$$\bar{n} = \sum_{n=1}^{\infty} n(1 - g)^{n-1}g$$
$$= g + 2(1 - g)g + 3(1 - g)^2 g + \cdots$$
$$= -g \frac{d}{dg}\left[1 + (1 - g) + (1 - g)^2 + \cdots\right]$$
$$= -g \frac{d}{dg} \frac{1}{1 - (1 - g)}$$
$$= -g \frac{d}{dg}\left(\frac{1}{g}\right)$$
$$= \frac{1}{g}.$$

Turning to the case of continuous looking, the important quantity is the *probability $\gamma\, dt$ of detecting in a short time interval of length dt* (as always with differentials, "to quantities of higher order"). The quantity γ is called the *instantaneous probability* density (of detection). When the looking is done continuously during a time t under unchanging conditions, the probability $p(t)$ of detection is given by

(3)
$$p(t) = 1 - e^{-\gamma t}.$$

To prove this, consider $q(t) = 1 - p(t)$, the probability of failure of detection during the time t. For detection to fail during the time $t + dt$ [probability $= q(t + dt)$], detection must fail both during t [probability $= q(t)$] and during dt (probability $= 1 - \gamma dt$), and multiplying these probabilities of independent events we obtain

$$q(t + dt) = q(t)(1 - \gamma\, dt)$$

which is equivalent to the differential equation

$$\frac{dq(t)}{dt} = -\gamma q(t).$$

The solution of this equation on the assumption that $q(0) = 1$ (no detection when no time is given to looking) is $q(t) = e^{-\gamma t}$: whence (3). Again it is true that if there is the least chance of detection in time dt (i.e., if $\gamma > 0$) the chance of detection increases to virtual certainty as the looking time t becomes sufficiently large.

To find the mean or expected time $\bar{t}$ at which detection occurs, observe that the probability $P(t)\, dt$ of detection between t and $t + dt$ (when looking has been continuing from the initial time 0) is the product of probability of no detection before t times probability of a detection during dt, i.e., $P(t)\, dt = e^{-\gamma t}\gamma\, dt$. $\bar{t}$ is found

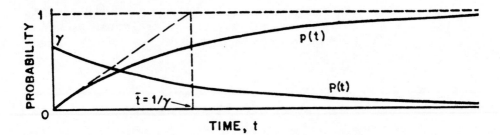

Fig. 3-1. Probabilities of detection under fixed conditions.

by integration

(4)
$$\bar{t} = \int_0^\infty t e^{-\gamma t} \gamma \, dt = \frac{1}{\gamma}.$$

Figure 3-1 shows the graphs of the probability $p(t)$ of detection *during* the time t and $P(t)$ of detection *at* the time t and gives the construction of $\bar{t}$ as the abscissa of the intercept with the horizontal line of unit ordinate of the tangent to $p(t)$ at the origin.

Since equation (3) reduces to equation (1) when (with $\log = \log_e = \ln$) $\gamma = -\log(1 - g)$ and $t = n$ (glimpses one unit of time apart), Fig. 3-1 serves to show the quantitative behavior of p_n and P_n: the difference is that only discrete points $(t = 1, 2, 3, \ldots)$ on the curve are used, and $\bar{n}$ is no longer given by the tangent intercept but rather by a secant intercept.

Having thus treated the case of fixed conditions, we now turn to that in which they vary during the search, when, as usually occurs during actual search, the distances, etc. (and hence the probabilities g or γ) change as time goes on. Then (1) must be replaced by

(5)
$$p_n = 1 - \prod_{i=1}^n (1 - g_i) = 1 - (1 - g_1)(1 - g_2)$$
$$(1 - g_3) \cdots$$

which takes into account the fact that g will change from glimpse to glimpse: g_i is the probability of detection for the ith glimpse. And (3) must be replaced by

(6)
$$p(t) = 1 - e^{-\int_0^t \gamma_t \, dt},$$

where in γ_t the possible change in the probability density of detection as time goes on is put into evidence by the subscript. The reasoning leading to these equations is precisely similar to that in the earlier case. But the probabilities p_n, $p(t)$ do not necessarily approach unity as n or t increases. Thus when $\int_0^\infty \gamma \, dt$ is finite, the chance of detection $p(t)$ never exceeds

$$1 - e^{-\int_0^\infty \gamma_t \, dt} < 1.$$

The instantaneous probability quantities g and γ depend, as we have said, on the sum total of physical conditions. For example, in visual detection, γ depends on the range r from target to observer, on the meteorological state (illumination and haze), on the size and brightness of target against the background, on the observer's facilities, altitude, etc. Corresponding lists can be made out for radar and sonar detection. Throughout most of the remainder of the present chapter, only the dependence on range will be explicitly considered, and we shall write

$$(7) \qquad\qquad g = g(r), \qquad \gamma = \gamma(r).$$

It will be legitimate to apply the results either when all the other conditions remain practically unchanged during the operation considered, or when the other conditions have been shown not to influence the results to the degree of approximation that is accepted.

Since the instantaneous probability quantities tend to decrease to zero as the range r increases and to be large when the range is small, their graph against r will be of the character shown in Fig. 3-2. Case A is when the instantaneous probability density reaches a finite maximum at zero range (as when the probability of detecting the target when flying over the target is less than unity). In case B this maximum is infinite (as when the probability of detection when flying over the target is unity). In case C the effect of sea return on radar diminishes the probability of detection when over target. In case D, the instantaneous probability is *infinite* when $r < R$: detection is sure to occur as soon as the target gets within this critical range R.

The last case, while not altogether realistic, often gives results not very far from the truth (taken literally, it may be inconsistent with the assumption of independence, as explained in Section 1). A very useful rough approximation is to assume

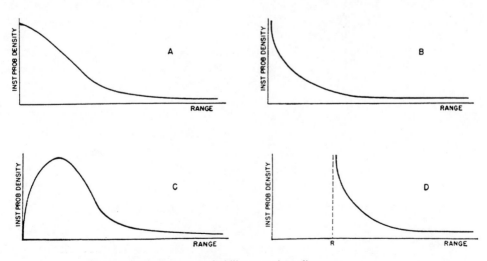

Fig. 3-2. Instantaneous probability at various distances.

further that the instantaneous probability is *zero* for $r > R$. Then detection is sure and immediate within the range R and is impossible beyond R. This assumption shall be called the *definite range law of detection*. It will be extended later to the *definite detection law*, another useful approximation.

An example of the possibility of explicitly calculating the quantities in (6), and providing useful results that fitted the rough data gathered during World War II, is based on the following assumptions:

1. The observer is at height h above the ocean, on which the target is cruising on the surface.
2. The observer detects the target by seeing its wake.
3. The instantaneous probability of detection γ is proportional to the solid angle subtended at the point of observation by the wake.

The calculation of the solid angle is shown in Fig. 3-3 for an area of ocean which is a rectangle of length a toward the observer and width b perpendicular to the

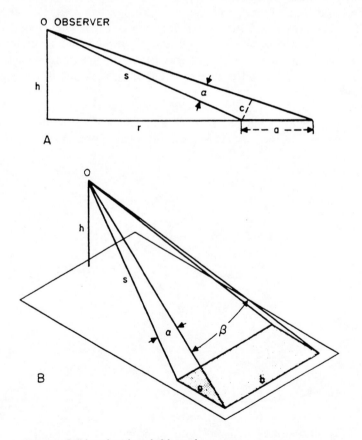

Fig. 3-3. Solid angle subtended by wake.

direction of observation (perpendicular to the page in Fig. 3-3A). The infinitesimal solid angle is the product of the angle α subtended by a, and the angle β subtended by b. The radian measure of α is c/s. By similar triangles, $c/a = h/s$ and hence $\alpha = ah/s^2$. And the radian measure of β is obviously b/s. Hence solid angle $= \alpha\beta$ $= abh/s^3 =$ area of rectangle times h/s^3. The actual area A of the target's wake is not rectangular, but can be regarded as made up of a large number of rectangles like the above, the solid angle being the sum of the corresponding solid angles. Hence, when the dimensions of A are small in comparison with h, r, and s, we have the formula

$$\text{(8)} \qquad \text{Solid angle} = \frac{Ah}{s^3} = \frac{Ah}{(h^2 + r^2)^{3/2}}.$$

Since γ is assumed to be proportional to the solid angle, we obtain

$$\text{(9)} \qquad \gamma = \frac{kh}{s^3} = \frac{kh}{(h^2 + r^2)^{3/2}},$$

where the constant k depends on all the factors we regard as fixed without introducing explicitly, such as contrast of wake against ocean, observer's ability (number of lookouts and their facilities), meteorological conditions, etc.; and of course k contains A as a factor. Dimensionally, $k = [L^2 T^{-1}]$. In the majority of cases r is much larger than h, and (9) can be replaced by the satisfactory approximation

$$\text{(10)} \qquad \gamma = \frac{kh}{r^3}.$$

Formulas (9) and (10) lead to cases A and B respectively of Fig. 3-2; the property of detection that they express shall be called the *inverse cube law* of sighting. When the subject of vision is studied in Appendix E it will be found that many changes in this law have to be made to obtain a high degree of approximation under the various conditions of practice. Nevertheless the inverse cube law gives a remarkably useful approximation. Its use in the present chapter is chiefly as an illustration of the general principles.

As an historical footnote, we add that formulas derived, as in succeeding sections, from the inverse cube law have been used with some success as "curve-fitting" devices to operational results obtained from certain early forms of radar, etc. Further, if the solid angle is that subtended by the actual solid hull of the target, perfectly tractable mathematical formulas are obtained, but they give results inconsistent with the operational data on surfaced submarine sightings of World War II. This confirms the experience of naval aviators that the most visible feature of surfaced craft is the wake rather than the hull.

3. DEPENDENCE OF DETECTION ON TRACK

When the observer and target are moving over the ocean in their respective paths, which may be straight or curved and at constant or changing speeds, the continuous change in their relative positions constantly changes the instantaneous probability of detection. We have to deal with the functions g_t and γ_t and calculate probabilities of detection by means of formulas (5) and (6). It is convenient to draw the target's track C (Fig. 3-4) relative to the observer. The latter need not be moving in fixed course and speed over the ocean, although this is very often the case. The coordinates used have been described in Chapter 2, Section 1 (see Fig. 2-4 and equation (2) of that chapter).

The target is at (ξ, η) at the time t, so that the equations of the target's relative motion are

(11) $$\xi = \xi(t), \qquad \eta = \eta(t),$$

where initially $(t = t')\xi_0 = \xi(t')$, $\eta_0 = \eta(t')$, and finally $(t = t'')\xi_1 = \xi(t'')$, $\eta_1 = \eta(t'')$. The target describes the relative track C. Accordingly, (7) becomes [writing $\xi^2(t)$ for $\{\xi(t)\}^2$]:

(12) $$g = g\left(\sqrt{\xi^2(t) + \eta^2(t)}\right) = g_t$$
$$\gamma = \gamma\left(\sqrt{\xi^2(t) + \eta^2(t)}\right) = \gamma_t.$$

Hence, according to equations (5) and (6), the probabilities p_c of detection are

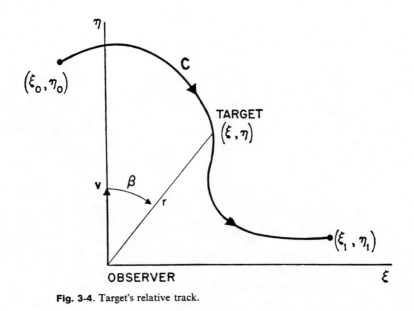

Fig. 3-4. Target's relative track.

given by either of the following

(13)
$$p_C = 1 - \prod_{i=1}^{n} \left[1 - g\left(\sqrt{\xi^2(t_i) + \eta^2(t_i)}\,\right)\right],$$

(14)
$$p_C = 1 - \exp\left[-\int_{t'}^{t''} \gamma\left(\sqrt{\xi^2(t) + \eta^2(t)}\,\right) dt\right].$$

In (13) t_i is the time (epoch) of the ith "glimpse" or scan, and n the number of glimpses between t' and t'':

$$t' \leqslant t_1 < t_2 < \cdots < t_n \leqslant t''.$$

In (14), the integral is actually a *line integral* along C. If w is the relative speed (not necessarily constant), we may write [with $s = $ arc length along C from (ξ_0, η_0)]:

(15)
$$p_C = 1 - e^{-\int_C \gamma(r)\, ds/w}.$$

Formulas (13) and (14) may be united into

(16)
$$p_C = 1 - e^{-F[C]},$$

where for the case of *separate glimpses*

(17)
$$F[C] = -\sum_{i=1}^{n} \log\left[1 - g\left(\sqrt{\xi^2(t_i) + \eta^2(t_i)}\,\right)\right],$$

and in the case of *continuous looking*

(18)
$$F[C] = \int_C \gamma(r)\frac{ds}{w}.$$

This quantity $F[C]$ shall be called the *sighting potential*. It has the important property of *additivity*: If C_1 and C_2 are two tracks and $C = C_1 + C_2$ is their combination or sum, and if $p_C = p_{C_1 + C_2}$ is the probability of sighting on at least one track, $p_{C_1 + C_2}$ is still obtained by formula (16) and

(19)
$$F[C_1 + C_2] = F[C_1] + F[C_2].$$

This is an immediate consequence of the usual equation for combining probabilities of events which may not be mutually exclusive:

$$p_C = 1 - (1 - p_{C_1})(1 - p_{C_2}) = p_{C_1} + p_{C_2} - p_{C_1}p_{C_2}.$$

This additivity applies, of course, to the sum of any number of paths. One application is to the calculation of p_C when C is complicated but made up of a sum of simple pieces such as straight lines. Another application is in the case of two or more intercommunicating observers: C_1 can be the path of the target relative to the first and C_2 that relative to the second, etc.

A most important case, and one which will chiefly concern us in this book, is when both observer and target are moving at constant speed and course. The results of Chapter 2 become applicable. Track C is a straight line, and the speed w is a constant (as long as C is not turned). It is convenient to make the calculations with the aid of the coordinates (x, y) of Chapter 2 (Fig. 3-5), where x is the lateral range. The equations of motion that take the place of (11) are $x =$ constant, $y = wt$, where t is measured from the epoch of closest approach and where, furthermore, the positive direction of the y axis is that of the target's relative motion; this convention is used throughout this chapter. The potential $F[C]$ is given by the appropriate one of the formulas

(20)
$$F[C] = - \sum_{i=1}^{n} \log\left[1 - g\left(\sqrt{x^2 + w^2 t_i^2}\right)\right],$$

$$= - \sum_{i=1}^{n} \log\left[1 - g\left(\sqrt{x^2 + y_i^2}\right)\right];$$

(21)
$$F[C] = \int_{t'}^{t''} \gamma\left(\sqrt{x^2 + w^2 t^2}\right) dt,$$

$$= \frac{1}{w} \int_{y'}^{y''} \gamma\left(\sqrt{x^2 + y^2}\right) dy,$$

where y_i is the distance of target at the ith glimpse to its closest position, and (x', y') and (x'', y'') are the extremities of $C : x' = x'' = x =$ constant, $y' = wt'$, $y'' = wt''$.

In the case of the inverse cube law (9),

(22)
$$F[C] = \frac{kh}{w} \int_{y'}^{y''} \frac{dy}{(h^2 + x^2 + y^2)^{3/2}}$$

$$= \frac{m}{h^2 + x^2} \left(\frac{y''}{\sqrt{h^2 + x^2 + (y'')^2}} \right.$$

$$\left. - \frac{y'}{\sqrt{h^2 + x^2 + (y')^2}} \right).$$

And for (10),

(23)
$$F[C] = \frac{kh}{w} \int_{y'}^{y''} \frac{dy}{(x^2 + y^2)^{3/2}} = \frac{m}{x^2} \left(\frac{y''}{r''} - \frac{y'}{r'} \right)$$

$$= \frac{m}{x^2} (\sin \omega' + \sin \omega''),$$

where in each case

(24)
$$m = \frac{kh}{w},$$

and where r' and r'' are the ranges of the extremities of C, and ω' and ω'' the angles they subtend with the normal to C.

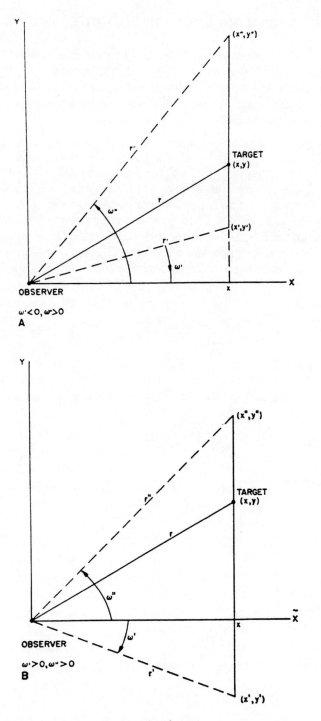

Fig. 3-5. Detection at fixed speed and course.

4. THE LATERAL RANGE DISTRIBUTION: SWEEP WIDTH

When the observer and target are on their straight courses at constant speeds for a long time before and after their closest approach, the probability $p(x)$ of detection is a function of the lateral range x (defined in Chapter 2, Section 1). The graph of $p(x)$ against x is called the *lateral range curve* and expresses the *distribution in lateral range*. In consequence of (16), $p(x)$ is given by

$$(25) \qquad\qquad p(x) = 1 - e^{-F(x)},$$

where $F(x)$ is the value of $F[C_x]$, C_x being an infinite straight line at the perpendicular distance x from the observer. The value of $F(x)$ is found by applying equation (20), summing over all integral values of i, or equation (21) with $y' = -\infty$ and $y'' = \infty$, in the glimpse or the continuous looking cases, respectively.

With continuous looking, (21) applies. For the definite range law, $p(x) = 1$ or 0 according as $-R < x < R$ or not, and the lateral range curve is shown in Fig. 3-6A. It is obtained by direct reasoning, (25) being inapplicable (cf. Section 1, end).

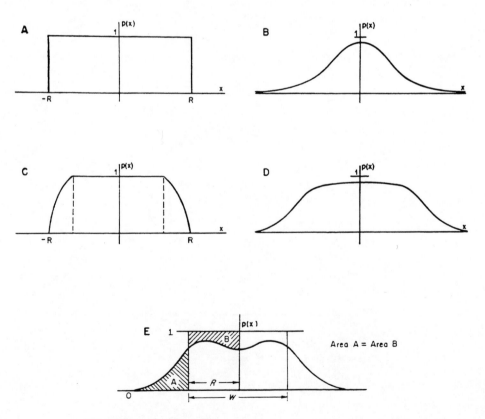

Fig. 3-6. Lateral range curves.

For the inverse cube law,

(26) $$p(x) = 1 - e^{-2m/(h^2 + x^2)} \quad \text{or} \quad p(x) = 1 - e^{-2m/x^2},$$

according to whether (22) or (23) is used. The curve is shown in Fig. 3-6B in the former case.

With intermittent glimpses taking place T units of time apart, equation (20) applies. For the definite range law, $p(x) = 0$ when $x > R$ or $x < -R$, and $p(x) = 1$ when the length $2\sqrt{R^2 - x^2}$ of relative track during which the target is within range R of the observer is greater than wT, i.e., when

$$-\sqrt{R^2 - w^2 T^2/4} \leqslant x \leqslant \sqrt{R^2 - w^2 T^2/4} \; ;$$

but $$p(x) = \frac{2\sqrt{R^2 - x^2}}{wT}$$

in intermediate cases, this being the probability that the target be glimpsed while within range R. The lateral range curve is shown in Fig. 3-6C.

Other typical lateral range curves are those of Fig. 3-6D and 3-6E. The dip at $x = 0$ in Fig. 3-6E shows the effect of sea return (radar) or pinging over the target (sonar).

The area W under the lateral range curve is called the *effective search (or sweep) width*:

(27) $$W = \int_{-\infty}^{+\infty} p(x) \, dx.$$

It has the following interpretation. If the observer moves through a swarm of targets uniformly distributed over the surface of the ocean (N per unit area on the average) with either all at rest or all moving at the same vector velocity u, the average number N_0 detected per unit time is

(28) $$N_0 = NwW.$$

For suppose that t is such a long period of time that the length of time during which a target is within range of possible detection is small in comparison with t. Then the number of targets passing during the period t through detection range (i.e., exposing themselves to detection) and having the lateral range between x and $x + dx$ is $Nwt \, dx$ (since such targets are in an area of $wt \, dx$ square miles). On the average $p(x)Nwt \, dx$ of these will be detected. Hence the average total number detected is

$$\int_{-\infty}^{+\infty} p(x)Nwt \, dx.$$

Dividing this by t and applying equation (27), equation (28) is obtained. Since for continuous looking with a definite range law, $W = 2R$, we may describe W as follows:

> The effective search width is twice the range of a definite range law of detection, which is equivalent to the given law of detection in the sense that each of the two laws detects on the average the same number of uniformly distributed targets of identical velocity.

The product wW is called the *effective search or sweep rate*. It is the mean number of targets detected per unit time for the previous example. See Fig. 3-6E.

For a useful approximation to visual ranges R (at various levels of probability) when the meteorological visibility, target size, and intrinsic contrast are given, see Appendix E, Section 2 (end). When enough of these are obtained, numerical integrations can yield $p(x)$ and W; otherwise the cruder approximation of the definite range law is used.

When the distribution of targets is uniform in the sense of Chapter 2, Sections 4 and 5 (when their speed is given but their course is not), w has to be replaced by its average $\bar{w}$ (taken as uniformly distributed in track angle ϕ); we must write $\bar{w} = 1/2\pi \int_0^{2\pi} w \, d\phi$, so that an equation corresponding with (28): $N_0 = N\bar{w}W$, may hold ($W = 2R$). [See Chapter 2, equations (1) and (4)].

In the case of the simplified inverse cube law, equations (26) and (27) give, by carrying out the integration (see below):

$$(29) \qquad W = 2\sqrt{2\pi m} = 2\sqrt{\frac{2\pi kh}{w}} \, ,$$

so that the search width is proportional to the square root of the altitude and inversely proportional to the square root of the target's relative speed. Furthermore, if there are n aircraft flying the same path without mutual interference (or if there are n observers having the same facilities operating independently of one another in the same aircraft), W is replaced by $W\sqrt{n}$.

This results from the additivity of the potentials, Section 3, which has the effect that k is replaced by nk in equations (22) and (23), and thus that m is replaced by nm [see (24)]. Thus the statement that W is replaced by $W\sqrt{n}$ is a consequence of equation (29).

The integration leading to (29) is performed by introducing equation (26) into (27) and changing to the new variable of integration:

$$z = \frac{\sqrt{2m}}{x} \, ;$$

and then integrating by parts. Use is made of the well-known equation

$$\int_0^\infty e^{-z^2} \, dz = \frac{\sqrt{\pi}}{2} \, .$$

As another footnote to history, the change from W to $W\sqrt{n}$ was the first answer given in World War II to the question, "How can the advantage of having n

observers on the same searching aircraft instead of one be quantified?" It is given above in terms of the effect on the search width, but the answer reposes on the special assumption of the inverse cube law.

In the more general cases the answer has to be derived from the additivity of potentials: $F(x)$ in (25) being replaced by $nF(x)$ and then (27) applied. One may note a trend toward exponential saturation, but more exact results would require more specific assumptions, and possibly mechanical integration. Finally, in the case of the definite range law ("infinite potentials") the answer reduces to triviality.

By its definition, $p(x)$ is the probability (*not* probability density) that a target given to have the lateral range x will be detected. On the other hand, $p(x)\,dx/W$ is the probability that a target known to have been detected will have a lateral range between x and $x + dx$ (in this case $p(x)/W$ *is* a probability density). This fact (actually a consequence of Bayes's theorem in probability) is easily seen, as follows: The detected target may be thought of as chosen at random from the set of all detected targets; the chance that its lateral range will be between x and $x + dx$ is equal to the proportion of targets in this set which have such a lateral range; from the previous calculations, this proportion is seen to be

$$\frac{Nwp(x)\,dx}{NwW} = \frac{p(x)\,dx}{W}.$$

5. THE DISTRIBUTION IN TRUE RANGE

Again we suppose that the observer makes constant speed and course and that the targets do likewise and are distributed uniformly over the surface of the ocean with the density N (average number per unit area). Relative to the observer, the targets all move parallel to the y axis in the direction of increasing y. *How many targets are detected on the average per unit time in the small region of area dx dy of Fig. 3-7?* The number will be proportional to N and to $dx\,dy$, and may accordingly be represented by $N\rho(x, y)\,dx\,dy$, where $\rho(x, y)$, which may be described as the rate of first contacts at the point (x, y) per unit area and per unit density of targets, is obtained by the argument which follows.

The number of targets entering $dx\,dy$ in unit time is $Nw\,dx$. A given target's probability of being detected therein is the product of the probability that it will fail to be detected before entering this region times the probability that, when not previously detected, it will be detected while crossing $dx\,dy$, i.e., during the time $dt = dy/w$. The former probability is $e^{-F(x,y)}$ in virtue of equation (16), where $F(x, y)$ is given in the case of glimpses by equation (20), with i summed over all values for which $y_i < y$ (with sufficient accuracy we may write $y_i = y - iwT$ and sum for $i = 1, 2, \ldots \infty$); and in the case of continuous looking, by equation (21) with $y' = -\infty$ and $y'' = y$. The latter probability is given by $g(r)\,dy/wT$ (intermittent glimpses, one every T units of time, dy/wT being the probability that a glimpse will occur while target is in $dx\,dy$), or by $\gamma(r)\,dy/w$ (continuous looking).

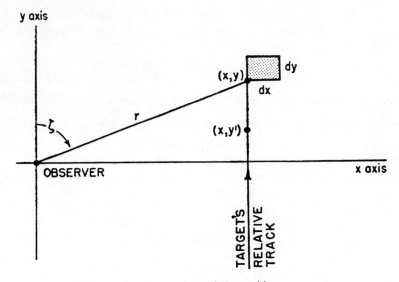

Fig. 3-7. Target detection at given relative position.

Thus the probability is

$$\frac{e^{-F(x,y)}g(r)\,dy}{wT} \quad \text{or} \quad \frac{e^{-F(x,y)}\gamma(r)\,dy}{w},$$

according to whether glimpsing or continuous looking is used. To obtain the mean number of detections per unit time in $dx\,dy$, these expressions are multiplied by the number of targets exposed to such detection, $Nw\,dx$. Hence the answer to the question in the preceding paragraph is supplied by the following expressions for $\rho(x,y)$:

(30)
$$\rho(x,y) = \frac{e^{-F(x,y)}g(r)}{T}$$
$$F(x,y) = -\sum_{i=1}^{\infty} \log\left[1 - g\left(\sqrt{x^2 + (y - iwT)^2}\,\right)\right]$$

for intermittent glimpsing, and

(31)
$$\rho(x,y) = e^{-F(x,y)}\gamma(r)$$
$$F(x,y) = \frac{1}{w}\int_{-\infty}^{y} \gamma\left(\sqrt{x^2 + y^2}\,\right) dy$$

for continuous looking.

It is seen by carrying out the differentiation that in the case of equation (31),

(32)
$$\rho(x,y) = w\frac{\partial}{\partial y}\left[1 - e^{-F(x,y)}\right].$$

In the case of (30), the corresponding formula is

(33)
$$\rho(x, y) = w \, \Delta_y \left[1 - e^{-F(x,y)} \right],$$

where the operation Δ_y applied to a function denotes the result of the following process: first, replace y in the function by $y + \Delta y$, $(\Delta y = wT)$; second, subtract the original value of the function from the new; third, divide by Δy.

If A is a plane region moving with the observer over the ocean, the average number Q_A of targets detected per unit time within A is (by addition of averages)

(34)
$$Q_A = N \iint_A \rho(x, y) \, dx \, dy.$$

In particular, when A embraces the whole plane, equations (32) and (33) lead from equation (34) to the previously obtained expression $N_0 = NwW$ of (28) by straight-forward calculation. When $A = A_R$ is a circle of radius R centered on the observer, (34) expressed in polar coordinates (r, ζ) $(\zeta = $ angle from positive y axis to vector r drawn from observer to target) becomes:

$$Q(R) = N \iint_{A_R} \rho(x, y) \, dx \, dy$$

$$= N \int_0^R dr \int_0^{2\pi} r\rho(r \sin \zeta, r \cos \zeta) \, d\zeta.$$

Now the number of targets detected per unit time at a distance (true range) from the observer between r and $r + dr$ is of the form $N\rho(r) \, dr$ (being proportional to both N and dr), and since its integral from 0 to R must, for every value of R, be equal to $Q(R)$, it follows (by equating the two integral expressions for $Q(R)$ and differentiating through with respect to R, etc.) that

(35)
$$\rho(r) = \int_0^{2\pi} r\rho(r \sin \zeta, r \cos \zeta) \, d\zeta.$$

$\rho(r) \, dr$ may be described as the rate of detection in the range interval $(r, r + dr)$ at unit target density.

If, now, a target is known to be detected but at unknown range, the probability that the range of detection has been between r and $r + dr$ is $\rho(r) \, dr / wW$. For this target may be thought of as chosen at random from the set of all the NwW detected targets, of which there are $N\rho(r) \, dr$ detected at range between r and $r + dr$. Hence the probability that the target be detected at such a range is the quotient

$$\frac{N\rho(r) \, dr}{NwW} = \frac{\rho(r) \, dr}{wW}.$$

The function $\rho(r)$ (or the equivalent functions $N\rho(r)$ or $\rho(r)/wW$) expresses the *distribution in (true) range*, and the graphs of these functions against r are called *range curves*. They fall considerably for small values of r, since relatively few targets come close to the observer by chance, and of these a still smaller number

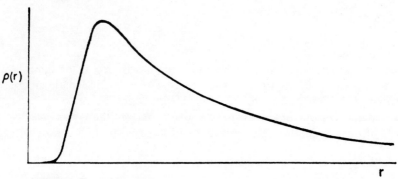

Fig. 3-8. True range curve.

are apt to survive undetected up to a close proximity of the observer. Figure 3-8 shows a typical range curve (actually, for the inverse cube law). As the situation approaches the definite range law, the curve humps up indefinitely about the value $r = R$ of the definite range, and falls to the axis of abscissas elsewhere.

The mean value of the range of detection is given by

(36) $$\bar{r} = \frac{1}{wW} \int_0^\infty r\rho(r)\, dr = \frac{1}{wW} \int_0^{2\pi} r^2 \rho(r \sin \zeta, r \cos \zeta)\, d\zeta$$

in all cases.

In the case of the simplified inverse cube law, we have equation (23), in which we set $\omega' = \pi/2 - \zeta$ and $\omega'' = \pi/2$; we obtain

$$F[C_y] = \frac{m}{x^2}(1 + \cos \zeta) = \frac{m}{r^2}\frac{1 + \cos \zeta}{\sin^2 \zeta},$$

$$= \frac{m}{2r^2}\csc^2\frac{\zeta}{2}.$$

Thus

$$\rho(x, y) = w \exp\left(-\frac{m}{2r^2}\csc^2\frac{\zeta}{2}\right)\frac{m}{r^3}.$$

Hence, as will be shown at the end of this section,

(37) $$\rho(r) = \frac{wm}{r^2}\int_0^{2\pi}\exp\left(-\frac{m}{2r^2}\csc^2\frac{\zeta}{2}\right)d\zeta,$$

$$= 2wm\pi\frac{1}{r^2}\left[1 - \text{erf}\left(\frac{1}{r}\sqrt{\frac{m}{2}}\right)\right],$$

where "erf X" (the "error functions" or "probability integral") is defined as

$$\text{erf } X = \frac{2}{\sqrt{\pi}}\int_0^X e^{-x^2}\, dx.$$

By expressing m in terms of the search width W by means of equation (29), equation (37) is reduced to

$$(38) \qquad \rho(r) = \frac{wW^2}{4r^2}\left[1 - \mathrm{erf}\!\left(\frac{W}{4\sqrt{\pi}\,r}\right)\right].$$

This is the function actually graphed in Fig. 3-8. For values of r not over about 15 miles, it is in reasonable rough agreement with operational data (visual); but farther out it has too high an ordinate.

This and a later formula depend on the evaluation of the following integral, not given in standard tables:

$$\phi(\lambda) = \int_0^{\pi/2} e^{-\lambda\,\csc^2\theta}\,d\theta\,.$$

This is done by the following device: Differentiating with respect to λ,

$$\phi'(\lambda) = -\int_0^{\pi/2} e^{-\lambda\,\csc^2\theta}\,\csc^2\theta\,d\theta$$

$$= e^{-\lambda}\int_\infty^0 e^{-\lambda\,\cot^2\theta}\,d\cot\theta$$

$$= -\frac{1}{\sqrt{\lambda}}\,e^{-\lambda}\frac{\sqrt{\pi}}{2}\,,$$

as is seen on changing to the variable of integration $x = \sqrt{\lambda}\,\cot\theta$, and the use of the formula $\int_0^\infty e^{-x^2}\,dx = \sqrt{\pi}\,/2$. Integrating $\phi'(\lambda)$ with respect to λ, observing that $\phi(0) = \pi/2$, we obtain

$$(39) \qquad \phi(\lambda) = \frac{\pi}{2} - \sqrt{\pi}\int_0^\lambda e^{-\lambda}\frac{d\lambda}{2\sqrt{\lambda}} = \frac{\pi}{2}\left[1 - \mathrm{erf}\sqrt{\lambda}\,\right],$$

as it appears on changing to the variable of integration $\mu = \sqrt{\lambda}\,$.

6. THE LAW OF RANDOM SEARCH

In the last two sections both observer and target were on straight courses at constant speeds, which represents the extreme of simplicity of paths. At the other extreme is the case where both are moving in complicated paths over the ocean and at speeds which may vary in the course of time, a case which is called that of *random search*. If the position of the target is in the area of interest A (which may be many hundred square miles) in which the searcher is moving, and if the latter is without preknowledge indicating that the target is more likely to be in one part of A than in another, a good approximation to the probability p that the observer will make a contact is given on the basis of the following three assumptions:

1. The target's position is uniformly distributed in A.
2. The observer's path is random in A in the sense that it can be thought of as having its different (not too near) portions placed independently of one another in A.
3. On any portion of the path that is small relative to the total length of path but decidedly larger than the range of possible detection, the observer always detects the target within the lateral range $W/2$ on either side of the path and never beyond.

These assumptions lead to the *formula of random search*

(40) $$p = 1 - e^{-WL/A},$$

where A = area in square miles, W = effective search width in miles, L = total length of observer's path in A in miles.

To prove this, suppose that the observer's path L is divided into n equal portions of length L/n. If n is large enough that most of the pieces are randomly related to any particular one, the chance of failing to detect during the whole path L is the product of the chances that detection will fail during motion along each piece. If, further, L/n is such that most of the pieces of this length are practically straight and considerably longer than the range of detection, then in virtue of (3) the latter chance of detection is the probability that the target will be in the area swept (whose value is WL/n square miles), and this probability is WL/nA [assumption (1)]. Hence the chance that along all of L there will be no detection is $(1 - WL/nA)^n$, and hence

$$p = 1 - \left(1 - \frac{WL}{nA}\right)^n$$
$$= 1 - e^{-WL/A} \text{ for large } n.$$

This reasoning assumes, of course, that a large n having these properties exists. This is essentially assumption (2).

The derivation above is based on "target space": a horizontal plane fixed with respect to the target, and in which the searcher does all the moving. It was used in the 1947 edition of this work because it employs a simple picture, as of a person groping for an object in semidarkness. It has given rise to misconceptions, however, such as, for example, an *intentional* randomness on the part of the searcher, quite inconsistent with military or indeed with any other organized operating procedure. Such misconceptions might not have arisen if the picture above had been replaced by one in "searcher space," fixed with respect to the searcher. All the mathematical steps of the derivation would have been identical with the above, and (40) again obtained. It is still true that the objection might be raised that a military target can be assumed to move with some systematic intention and hence not in a random path. This would of course imply that we return to formulas such as those in the previous sections of this chapter. But such a simple procedure would ignore a fundamental fact applying to most of the humanly planned operations in real life: they are always subject to unavoidable random factors. These may come from navigational errors, wind and weather, misunderstandings of the various intention, evasive tactics, and so on through a long list.

The issues raised in the use of the random search law are important enough to warrant a second derivation, based on a minimum of assumptions, and pin-pointing the introduction of randomness, in contrast with an extreme case of its opposite.

Let $q(t)$ as before be the probability that the searcher will fail to detect a target, for which assumption No. 1 above is valid, during a search of duration t. Clearly (by compound probability), $q(t + dt) = q(t)f(t, dt)$, where $f(t, dt)$ is the conditional probability of failure to detect during the short interval $(t, t + dt)$, *given* failure during the interval $(0, t)$. The "randomness" merely assumes the independence of these two events, the first and the second failures. It allows us to equate the conditional probability $f(t, dt)$ to an unconditional one: the chance of failure during $(t, t + dt)$, given no other information—or, equivalently, $1 - \psi \, dt$, where $\psi \, dt$ is the probability of successful detection. This coefficient ψ is dependent on the mechanism of search; it has been the constant Wv/A in the case above, where v is the searcher's speed. The resulting differential equation leads at once to (40). But there are, as will be seen at the end of this section, cases in which things vary with the searcher's position. Then an obvious generalization of (40) is appropriate, with ψ a function of position, etc.

Suppose on the contrary that the searcher has searched a rectangular A by means of equally spaced parallel sweeps as in Fig. 3-10 below, but with a definite range law of range $R = W/2 = S/2$. Then he "sweeps clean" with no overlapping (we are ignoring slight corrections during turns). Failure to detect during the first period of t hours proves that the target is not in the region swept, of area Wvt; so it must be in the remaining part of A, of area $A - Wvt$. Hence the conditional probability $f(t, dt)$ of the subsequent failure is (when $Wvt \leqslant A$)

$$f(t, dt) = 1 - \frac{Wv \, dt}{A - Wvt}, \quad \text{not} \quad 1 - \frac{Wv \, dt}{A}.$$

Evidently the conditional probability is not equal to the unconditional one given in the second expression above; the independence assumption discussed in Section 1 does not apply (a possibility noted there). The differential equation obtained with the above $f(t, dt)$ leads to the solution $p(L) = WL/A$ when $L(= vt)$ is less than A/W; $p(L) = 1$ otherwise. This is graphed as two straight lines in Figs. 3-9 and 3-12. The value of this function could have been obtained as an obvious consequence of the assumptions, but by passing through the differential equation we are able to pin-point the mechanism whereby the randomness can introduce itself in the earlier case: by the target's chance of moving back into the swept regions. This in turn suggests that in real cases some intermediate degree of this effect may occur. The two extremes can be portrayed graphically in Fig. 3-9 and a slight

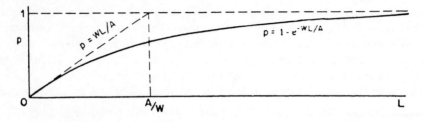

Fig. 3-9. Detection with random search.

modification of the mechanism suggested (mathematically equivalent to the one just given).

If the exponential in equation (40) is replaced by the first two terms in its power series expansion, the equation is replaced by $p = WL/A$. This corresponds to the probability, in the case where L consists of a single straight line or a path so little bent that there is practically no overlapping of swept regions, that the total area swept is WL and the chance of the target being in it is WL/A. The departure from this simple value represents the effect of random overlapping of swept areas.

Figure 3-9 shows the way in which the probability given by (40) increases with the length of observer's path L. For smaller values of L it is closely approximated by its tangent $p = WL/A$. For much larger values, it approaches unity, exhibiting a "saturation" or "diminishing returns" effect.

An important extension of the random search formula (40) will be discussed in detail in Chapter 6, Sections 1 and 2, and generalized further in Appendix C. A still more detailed critique of various generalizations, with references, will be found in [1]. The formula, basic to Chapters 6 and 7, involves the concept of *search density*, outlined as follows.

Let $\lambda(X)$ be the "track density" at point X. It is defined in the following manner, comparable to the exact definition of the number-density N of targets (or of molecules of a gas): Let $\Delta\mathfrak{M}$ be an element of area ΔM containing X, and let ΔL be the total length of track in $\Delta\mathfrak{M}$, which varies irregularly with the position and shape of $\Delta\mathfrak{M}$, and which can be regarded here as a random variable, having an expected value of $\overline{\Delta L}$. The ratio $\overline{\Delta L}/\Delta M$ can, in actual physical cases, be assumed to settle down to a steady "quasilimit" as $\Delta\mathfrak{M}$, always containing X, becomes small enough. This is the track density $\lambda(X)$. When this is true for A itself, we may replace L/A in (40) by $\lambda = \lambda(X)$, X being any point in A.

Furthermore, W may itself depend on the searcher's position X, as when detectability (visibility, sound conditions, etc.) vary from point to point, but with *gradual* variation. The reasoning to establish the generalization proceeds as before, but now gives

(40′)
$$p(X) = 1 - e^{-W(X)\lambda(X)}.$$

(If the visibility depends on other than local factors, (40′) generalizes; see the lemma to Theorem I, Chap. 6, Sect. 3; also Appendix C.)

7. PARALLEL SWEEPS

Search by parallel sweeps is a method frequently employed, and many apparently more complicated schemes turn out to be equivalent to parallel sweeps, either exactly or with sufficient approximation for practical purposes. A target is at rest on the ocean in an unknown position, all equal areas having the same chance of containing it; it is decided to search along a large ("infinite") number of parallel lines on the ocean, their common distance apart, or *sweep spacing*, being S miles; what is the probability $P(S)$ of detection? Or again, the target's speed and direction are known, but the position is uniformly distributed as above. It is possible to search in equally spaced parallel paths *relative to the target* (in the plane moving with the target's motion and in which it appears to be a fixed point), as in the first case. It is immaterial whether all the parallel paths are traversed by the same observer or by different observers having similar observing characteristics.

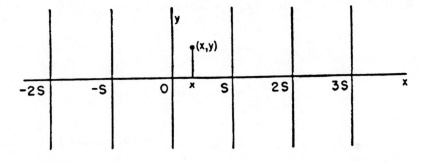

Fig. 3-10. Parallel sweeps.

In Fig. 3-10 the parallel paths are shown referred to a system of rectangular coordinates; the axis of ordinates is along one of the paths and the target's (unknown) position is at (x, y), and $0 \leqslant x < S$. It is observed that this inequality, expressing the fact that the target is in the strip immediately to the right of the axis of ordinates, is a consequence of the method of choice of the axes and implies no restriction in the position of the target.

The first step in calculating $P(S)$ is to write down the lateral ranges of the target from the various observer paths. For paths at or to the left of the axis of ordinates, the lateral ranges are

$$x, x + S, x + 2S, x + 3S, \cdots$$

For those to the right,

$$S - x, 2S - x, 3S - x, \cdots$$

All these cases may be combined into the absolute value formula:

(41) $$lateral\ range = |x - nS|$$

where

$$0 \leqslant x < S \quad \text{and} \quad n = 0, \pm 1, \pm 2, \pm 3, \cdots .$$

Equation (25) is now applied to find the probability $p_n = p$ (nth lateral range) of detection by the nth sweep when the target's position is given as (x, y):

$$p_n = 1 - e^{-F(|x - nS|)},$$

where the potential F is given by the appropriate formula. The probability of no detection by the nth sweep is $1 - p_n$; that of no detection by any sweep is the (infinite) product $\Pi (1 - p_n)$ for all values of n ($< 0, = 0, > 0$); and the probability that at least one sweep will detect a target given at (x, y) is

$$P(x, S) = 1 - \prod_{n=-\infty}^{+\infty} e^{-F(|x - nS|)},$$

or, finally,

$$(42) \qquad P(x, S) = 1 - e^{-\Phi(x, S)}$$

$$\Phi(x, S) = \sum_{n=-\infty}^{+\infty} F(|x - nS|), \quad 0 \leqslant x < S.$$

This is essentially a repetition of the argument proving the additivity of the potentials, Section 3.

It remains to find the probability of detection $P(S)$ when the target's position (the value of x) is not given but has a uniform distribution between 0 and S. An easy probability argument shows that $P(S)$ is the average of $P(x, S)$ over all values of x in this interval:

$$(43) \qquad P(S) = \frac{1}{S} \int_0^S (1 - e^{-\Phi(x, S)}) \, dx$$

$$\Phi(x, S) = \sum_{n=-\infty}^{+\infty} F(|x - nS|).$$

This gives the general solution of the problem.

The *effective visibility* (a concept much less commonly used now than formerly) E is defined as half that sweep spacing for which the probability of detection by parallel sweeps is one half. In other words, E is determined as the solution of the equation

$$P(2E) = \frac{1}{2}.$$

Three cases are of particular interest. The first is that of continuous looking on the assumption of a definite range law. Detection will surely occur if, and only if, the target happens to be within the definite range R of either of the two adjacent sweeps. The chance for this is $2R/S = W/S$ when $S > 2R = W$, and unity when $S \leqslant W$. It is easy to see that the effective visibility $E = W$.

The second case is that of the inverse cube law (which will be taken here in its simplest form). We obtain $\Phi(x, S)$ with the aid of equation (26)

$$(44) \qquad \Phi(x, S) = 2m \sum_{n=-\infty}^{+\infty} \frac{1}{(x - nS)^2}$$

$$= 2m \frac{\pi^2}{S^2} \csc^2 \frac{\pi x}{S},$$

the latter equality resulting from a well-known formula of analysis (obtained, e.g., from the expansion of the sine in an infinite product by taking logarithms and then differentiating twice). Inserting this expression into equation (43), we must find

$$P(S) = \frac{1}{S} \int_0^S \left[1 - \exp\left(-\frac{2m\pi^2}{S^2} \csc^2 \frac{\pi x}{S} \right) \right] dx.$$

This is found by means of equation (38), on setting $\theta = \pi x/S$ and $\lambda = 2m\pi^2/S^2$. The result, which can be transformed by means of equation (29), is

$$(45) \qquad P(S) = \operatorname{erf} \frac{\pi \sqrt{2m}}{S} = \operatorname{erf}\left(\frac{\sqrt{\pi}}{2} \frac{W}{S} \right).$$

We are now in a position to express m and W in terms of the effective visibility E. To find E we solve

$$P(2E) = \operatorname{erf} \frac{\pi \sqrt{2m}}{2E} = \operatorname{erf} \frac{\sqrt{\pi}}{4E} \frac{W}{} = \frac{1}{2}.$$

The tables of the probability integral show that erf $0.477 = 0.5$; hence

$$\pi \frac{\sqrt{2m}}{2E} = \frac{\sqrt{\pi}}{4E} \frac{W}{} = 0.477,$$

i.e.,

$$(46) \qquad m = 0.046 E^2, \quad W = 1.076 E.$$

These values substituted into equation (45) give

$$(47) \qquad P(S) = \operatorname{erf}\left(0.954 \frac{E}{S} \right).$$

A third case is useful to consider, although strictly speaking it is not one of parallel sweeps but of uniform random search. It may be described as the situation that arises when the searcher attempts to cover the whole area uniformly by a path or paths that place about the same length of track in each strip but that operate

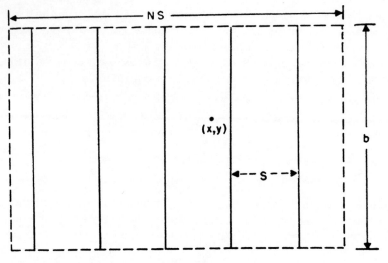

Fig. 3-11. A rectangle of random sweeps.

within a given strip in the manner of the searcher of Section 6. This would occur even when there is no random element in the searcher's path, but much disorder in the target's motion. Let all the strips be cut by two horizontal lines a distance of b miles apart and suppose that the search is for a target inside the large rectangle bounded by these lines and two vertical lines NS miles apart, as shown in Fig. 3-11. The area is $A = NSb$ square miles. Assume that the total length of track is equal to that of all included parallel sweeps, $L = Nb$, apply equation (40), and we obtain

(48) $$P(S) = 1 - e^{-W/S}.$$

It is independent of N and b.

These three cases may be represented by means of a common diagram (Fig. 3-12) by plotting $P = P(1/n)$ where $n = 1/S$ is the *sweep density*, or number of

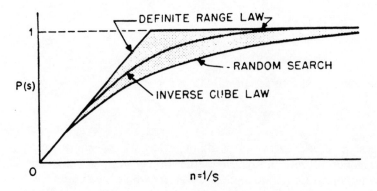

Fig. 3-12. Probabilities with parallel sweeps.

sweeps per mile. At one extreme is the case of the definite range law, at the other the case of random search. All actual situations can be regarded as leading to intermediate curves, those lying in the shaded region. The inverse cube law is close to a middle case, a circumstance which indicates its frequent empirical use, even in cases where the special assumptions upon which its derivation was based are largely rejected.

8. FORESTALLING

When the observer is using two different means of detection simultaneously and independently (i.e., when neither interferes with or aids the other), it is sometimes necessary to know the probability of making a first detection by a particular one of the two means. Since the second means of detection can deprive the first of a chance of initial detecting (by detecting it first) its probability may be lower than if the second means had not been present. We say that the second can *forestall* the first. For example, when both radar and visual detection are possible, in gathering data bearing on the effectiveness of the radar, the possibility of visual forestalling of the radar must be taken into account. This was capable of vitiating operational data in World War II.

Again, when the target is itself capable of detecting the observer, and if it is important to detect the target before it can detect the observer (as when the former is a submarine with detection gear exposed but which itself is subject to detection unless the submarine completely submerges) it is important to find the probability that the observer will detect the target first, before it has been forestalled by the target's detection.

Just as the chance of detection is mathematically equivalent to that of hitting a target continuously exposed to fire (intensity varying in general with time), so the question of forestalling is mathematically identical with that of hitting the target before it hits the searcher, in the case of an enemy continuously firing back.

It will be sufficient to consider the case of continuous looking with the instantaneous probability $\gamma_t \, dt$ for the first means of detection without forestalling (Section 2), the probability $p(t)$ of detection when there is no forestalling being given by equation (6). Let $\gamma_t' \, dt$ and $p'(t)$ be the corresponding quantities for the second means of detection, or for the target's detection of the observer in the second example above.

If $P(t)$ is the required probability of first detection during the interval of time from 0 to t by the first means, we consider the value of $P(t + dt)$. It is the probability of an event that can succeed in either of the following mutually exclusive ways: either by having the required detection between 0 and t, or by having neither means detect during this period, and having a detection by the first means between t and $t + dt$. This leads to the equation

$$P(t + dt) = P(t) + [1 - p(t)][1 - p'(t)]\gamma_t \, dt,$$

whence a differential equation is obtained, the solution of which is

(49)
$$P(t) = \int_0^t \gamma_t \exp\left[-\int_0^t (\gamma_t + \gamma_t') \, dt \right] dt.$$

Precisely the same reasoning leads to the expression

$$P'(t) = \int_0^t \gamma_t' \exp\left[-\int_0^t (\gamma_t + \gamma_t') \, dt \right] dt$$

for the probability of a first detection by the second means in the time interval 0, t.

Note that the sum $P(t) + P'(t)$ is the probability of a first detection either by the first means or by the second, in other words, the probability of a detection by *some* means between 0 and t. The expression obtained by adding the above equations and carrying out one integration is

$$P(t) + P'(t) = 1 - \exp\left[-\int_0^t (\gamma_t + \gamma_t') \, dt \right],$$

which is simply the expression (6) with γ_t replaced by $\gamma_t + \gamma_t'$, the latter being the instantaneous probability when both means of detection act in conjunction (additivity of potentials).

When a large number of independent trials of the detection experiment are made under identical conditions, all cases that have resulted in a first detection by the first means are sorted out, and the precise epochs of this detection are averaged, the result will (statistically) be equal to

(50)
$$\bar{t} = \frac{\displaystyle\int_0^\infty t\gamma_t \exp\left[-\int_0^t (\gamma_t + \gamma_t') \, dt \right] dt}{\displaystyle\int_0^\infty \gamma_t \exp\left[-\int_0^t (\gamma_t + \gamma_t') \, dt \right] dt}.$$

The denominator is proportional to the total number of first detections by first means, and the result of dividing

$$\gamma_t \exp\left[-\int_0^t (\gamma_t + \gamma_t') \, dt \right] dt$$

by the denominator is the proportion of such detections between t and $t + dt$. Thus the expression in equation (50) represents the expected value $\bar{t}$ of t, the epoch of detection by the first means.

As a first application we consider the case of constant instantaneous probabilities of detection, $\gamma_t = \gamma$, $\gamma_t' = \gamma'$. Equations (48) and (49) reduce to

$$P(t) = \frac{\gamma}{\gamma + \gamma'} \left[1 - e^{-(\gamma + \gamma')t} \right],$$

$$\bar{t} = \frac{1}{\gamma + \gamma'}.$$

It is thus seen that the proportion of the total number of first contacts by the first means (as $t \to \infty$) is $\gamma/(\gamma + \gamma')$, and, correspondingly, by the second, $\gamma'/(\gamma + \gamma')$. And the mean time elapsed to the former is the same as for the latter, i.e., $1/(\gamma + \gamma')$. This is different from the mean time $1/\gamma$ when no forestalling had been possible.

As a second application we consider the straight track case of Section 4 and assume that the observer is an aircraft and the target a surfaced submarine. If the observer sights the wake of the submarine, his ability to detect may reasonably be taken as the inverse cube law of equation (10), and if the submarine sights the horizontal surfaces of the aircraft's wing, the same law (with k replaced by a different constant k') can reasonably be assumed for the submarine's detection of the aircraft. If it is assumed that the submarine dives as soon as it detects the aircraft, what is the probability that the aircraft will detect the submarine, as a function of lateral range x? By how much is its effective search width decreased by this new possibility? (Of course the situation described here belongs to an earlier era.)

Equation (10), under the circumstances of Section 4, leads to

$$\gamma_t = \frac{kh}{(x^2 + w^2 t^2)^{3/2}}, \quad \gamma'_t = \frac{k'h}{(x^2 + w^2 t^2)^{3/2}};$$

only in the present case the time interval is from $-\infty$ to t instead of from 0 to t. With these changes, equation (49) leads to the following expression for the probability of sighting the submarine before the time t:

$$P(x, t) = m \int_{-\infty}^{W_t} \exp\left[-\frac{m + m'}{x^2}\left(1 + \frac{y}{\sqrt{x^2 + y^2}}\right)\right] \frac{dy}{(x^2 + y^2)^{3/2}}$$

where $m = kh/w$ and $m' = k'h/w$. The integral can be evaluated explicitly when it is noted that the integrand is proportional to the derivative of the exponential expression, i.e.,

$$\frac{1}{(x^2 + y^2)^{3/2}} \exp\left[-\frac{m + m'}{x^2}\left(1 + \frac{y}{\sqrt{x^2 + y^2}}\right)\right]$$

$$= -\frac{1}{m + m'}\frac{d}{dy}\exp\left[-\frac{m + m'}{x^2}\left(1 + \frac{y}{\sqrt{x^2 + y^2}}\right)\right].$$

The result, on setting $t = +\infty$, gives the following probability of detecting the submarine some time on its whole straight course.

$$P(x, \infty) = \frac{m}{m + m'}\left[1 - e^{-2(m + m')/x^2}\right].$$

To find the value of the search width (which will be denoted by W^*), this expression must be used in place of (26) in equation (27). The answer is obtained from (29) by replacing m by $m + m'$ and then multiplying the result by $m/(m + m')$; it is

$$W^* = 2\sqrt{2\pi m} \sqrt{\frac{m}{m + m'}} = W\sqrt{\frac{m}{m + m'}} \, .$$

Thus the effect of forestalling is to multiply W by a factor less than unity of $\sqrt{m/(m + m')}$. And the probability of detection even when the target is flown over ($x = 0$) is $P(0, \infty) = m/(m + m')$ instead of unity, as it would have been in the absence of forestalling.

For a definite range law, that means of detection which has the greater range will always forestall the other. (Of course this is strictly true only in the case of *continuous looking*.)

9. THE LAW OF DEFINITE DETECTION OR CLEAN SWEEP

Among the various detection laws illustrated in Section 2, the definite range law has been mentioned, reposing on the simplified model of immediate and certain detection of any target within a definite range R of the searcher and the impossibility of detection of any target at greater range. This model, applied to special types of target and searcher under special conditions, has proved to give useful indications in many cases. Moreover, it has served as a standard of comparison, easy to visualize, of various more physically realistic laws of detection, and leads to such concepts as effective sweep width, search rate, and others, illustrated in the preceding sections. Furthermore, this law has been implied in Section 5 of Chapter 2. It was introduced into systematic search theory as serving a purpose similar to the "capture cross-section" of molecules and various elementary particles in physics.

The cumulative behavior of detections under the definite range law is exceedingly simple when the searcher and target are at rest or on fixed speed and course, or when one is at rest and the other in various forms of random motion. In the case of parallel sweeps, Section 7, it leads to the simple motion of "sweeping clean." All this has been set forth earlier.

On the other hand, there are many cases in which the cumulative or joint effects of the definite range law are both complicated and misleading. Thus, when applied literally to sonobuoys in a field, to dunking sonar, or to sprint-and-drift platforms of detection, it has led to complicated patterns of tangent (or restrictedly overlapping) circles of radius R, and to mathematical calculations as elaborate as they are artificial. Effective application of this type of "cooky-cutter" reasoning is an art rather than the result of rigid rules; the dangers of accepting as real mere "artifacts" of an approximating model are particularly severe in such cases.

What is evidently needed is a simplification of the same order of realism as the definite range law, but applying to more complicated spreads of the searched region. Suppose for example that a region $\mathcal{R}$ of the plane is to be searched intensively; an approximate expression of the result is suggested by either of the two following constructions.

First, let us start with n circles of radius R corresponding to the definite range law for n detectors. Then suppose that the circles can be moderately deformed into various other shapes without changing their areas but so that they exactly fit without overlapping onto the region $\mathcal{R}$ of area $n\pi R^2$. Finally, suppose that even in their changed shape they correspond with the same law of detection: everything inside them, nothing outside. Then the region $\mathcal{R}$ is one of "definite detection": to be detected, it is necessary and sufficient for the target to be in this region.

Second (perhaps more scientifically), we may base the construction on the idea of *equivalence* of detecting devices and dispositions with respect to a random distribution of targets—in this case motionless—of uniform density over the searched region. Two motionless detecting systems are regarded as "equivalent" if the expected number of targets they detect is the same. The time factor has of course to be specified in a manner appropriate to the operation considered, "unit time," "relaxation time," "infinite time," or some other. Clearly, the region $\mathcal{R}$ constructed as above from the n deformed circles of radius R is equivalent, in the present sense, to the n circles in their undeformed and nonoverlapping positions. We are thus led to the definition:

A law of "definite detection" or "clean sweep" is an idealized search that detects all targets within a particular region $\mathcal{R}$ and none outside. Any detection system is said to be "equivalent" (under stated conditions) with a particular definite detection law if each detects the same expected number of targets in a uniform random distribution.

The same ideas apply when motions of targets or searchers may occur, although the relation between the n searchers of definite range R and the equivalent region $\mathcal{R}$ may be quite different from that derived in the first construction above. Thus a single definite range searcher in a straight course of length L sweeps an area $2RL$ clean; this is still true when the course is curved, but not enough to produce overlapping bands (as shown as an easy exercise in elementary calculus). This is quite different from the sum of circular areas.

If a region of area B inside A is swept clean (A containing unit density of targets), the expected number of targets detected is B/A. If on the other hand a length of path L is traversed when the law of random search applies, the expected number is $1 - e^{-WL/A}$. On equating these to find the "equivalent area B," and writing $\bar{B} = WL$, we obtain the relation

$$\bar{B} = -A \log(1 - B/A) = B + B^2/2A + \cdots$$

showing the decreased efficiency in applying the area $\bar{B} = WL$ at random in A rather than without random overlapping—a degradation due to the nature of things and by no means necessarily to human factors. All this slightly generalizes the similar results obtained in Section 7.

As an introduction to some of the further applications of the definite detection law, to be given in later chapters, consider the problem of the optimum distribution of searching effort to find a target of known probability distribution, $p(X)\,dM$ being the probability of its being in the infinitesimal region $d\mathfrak{M}$ at X of area dM. This problem was introduced in qualitative terms at the close of Chapter 1, Section 6. An easy geometrical presentation of the solution can be given when the definite detection law is assumed, as we proceed to show.

We first construct the family of "level curves" $p(X) = z$, a constant; and also the family of plane regions $\mathfrak{M}(z)$ bounded by these curves, on which $p(X) \geqslant z$, together with their areas $M(z)$:

(51) $$\mathfrak{M}(z) = \{X : p(X) \geqslant z\}; \qquad M(z) = \text{area of } \mathfrak{M}(z)$$

We next pick that value of z for which the area $M(z)$ equals the available searching effort, as expressed by a given area B. Then if the region $\mathfrak{M}(z)$ for this z is searched clean, it is just about self-evident that the effort B will have been used optimally (consider the result of relocating the search of a piece of the above region to a position outside it). See Fig. 3-13.

After B has been optimally applied as above without detecting the target, Bayes' formula shows that the a posteriori distribution $p'(X)$ is zero inside the $\mathfrak{M}(z)$ searched, and $p(X)/Q$ outside it, where Q is the integral of $p(X)$ over the region outside $\mathfrak{M}(z)$ (it could be described as a normalizing factor).

Suppose now that a second amount of searching effort B' becomes available. Its optimal application would make use of the above construction, but now based on $p'(X)$ and the corresponding regions $\mathfrak{M}'(z)$. It is then not a difficult exercise to show that the regions searched and the resulting probabilities of detection (as estimated at the outset of the whole operation) are just the same as would have

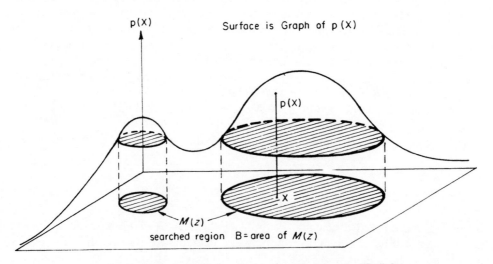

Fig. 3-13. Optimal distribution of given area B, using the "Definite Detection Law."

been derived from the optimal application of an initially given $B + B'$. This is the simplest example of the *sequential additivity property*. It will be extended to the case of random search in Chapter 5, and made a basis for extending information theory to search theory.

10. OPERATIONAL DISTRIBUTIONS: GENERALITIES

Returning to first principles, as set forth earlier in this and in the first chapter, it has been laid down as basic that detection, even when possible, is an *uncertain* event, and the whole course of development of this chapter has been toward the calculation of *probabilities* of detection. But an essential restriction has been imposed in all these calculations, discussed in part in Section 1: The assumption of independence, even in the case of conditional probabilities, implicitly presupposes a further condition in the state of things. It presupposes that the causes of the randomness and uncertainty which have been considered are the human fallibility of the observer and the sudden uncontrollable fluctuations in the physical state of affairs, but not in the random element introduced by unknown, long-term variations in the underlying physical conditions (conditions which may be expressible as parameters). Thus, as we have said in Section 2, under given meteorological conditions of visibility V the observer will have a definite chance $\gamma(r)\, dt$ of sighting a target of given size A and background contrast C, and subsequent deductions have been made on the assumption that while the range r may vary in a given manner in the course of time, the parameters V, A, and C *all remain fixed*. The distributions calculated on this assumption can be expected to agree with the distributions found empirically when the results of a large number of experiments are obtained, all of which are performed under the same conditions of visibility and size and contrast of the target, with only geometrical quantities like r being allowed to vary. But as soon as operational results are compiled that refer to cases in which V, A, and C vary from incident to incident, an altogether different situation is present. The cause of the uncertainty of the event of detection is twofold, being dependent not only on the human fallibility of the observer and short-term fluctuations, and so on, but on the more or less unknown and heterogeneous nature of the underlying physical conditions. And it is important to realize that in many cases this second factor may outweigh the first. When this is judged to be the case, it may well be expedient to employ a highly simplified law of detection, such as the definite range law, and then seek to explain the distributions found in the operational data simply by averaging the calculated results of such laws over different possible values of the parameters. Thus if the definite range law is assumed, mathematical expressions deduced from it will involve this range R. Then it may be considered that in the operational incidents, different values of R are present. By choosing appropriate frequencies for the different values of R and combining or averaging the theoretical results over such distributions of R, a good agreement may often be found with the observations.

It must be emphasized that equations such as (1), (3), (5), and (6) are true only when the first cause of uncertainty alone is present and when the underlying physical conditions remain constant (and are known to be of constant, though not necessarily of known values) throughout the course of the looking. Thus in proving (1), the probability of detection for one glimpse was g; of not detecting, $1 - g$. Now precisely at the point where it was asserted that the probability of failure to detect at each and every one of the first n glimpses is $(1 - g)^n$, the assumption that the n different events are independent was made. This is justified only in two cases: first, when the only uncertainty is in the observer's chance performance so that his different opportunities (glimpses) are regarded as repeated independent trials (as in successive tosses of a coin); second, when there are indeed changes in physical conditions, but of such a rapidly fluctuating character that if no detection is known to occur at one glimpse, no inference can be drawn regarding the physical conditions pertaining to any other glimpse. But if, for example, the visibility V is not fully known, the fact that earlier glimpses have failed to detect may lead to the presumption that V is less than might otherwise have been supposed, and hence that later changes of detection are less: the expression $(1 - g)^n$ is false.

This is, of course, a repetition of the general ideas set forth in Section 1, but in more concrete terms.

The method of procedure is clear. The first step is to carry out the calculations as described in the previous sections of this chapter, assuming fixed conditions (such as V, A, C). The second step is to average the results obtained for the probabilities (e.g., over the possible values of V, A, C, with appropriate weighting). Only the final result can reasonably be expected to furnish the probabilities that accord with the operational data. What is true of probabilities is also true of mean or expected values defined by them.

This will be illustrated by many practical examples in subsequent chapters, but three simple cases can be mentioned here. First, suppose that the lateral range curve (Section 4) involves a parameter λ referring to an unknown factor in the underlying physical conditions. Its equation is $p = p(x, \lambda)$. Once the distribution of frequencies with which the different values of λ occur in an operational situation has been estimated, the operational lateral range curve $p = p_{op}(x)$ (i.e., the one furnished by a histogram of the observed data) is found by averaging $p(x, \lambda)$ over the values of λ on the basis of this frequency. Thus it might be reasonable in some cases to assume that the values of λ are normally distributed about a known mean l with a known standard deviation σ. Accordingly,

$$p_{op}(x) = \frac{1}{\sigma\sqrt{2\pi}} \int_{-\infty}^{+\infty} p(x, \lambda) e^{-(\lambda - l)^2/2\sigma^2}\, d\lambda.$$

Thus if $p(x, \lambda)$ results from a definite range law of range $R = \lambda$, so that

$$p(x, \lambda) = 1, \text{ when } x < \lambda,$$

$$p(x, \lambda) = 0, \text{ when } x > \lambda,$$

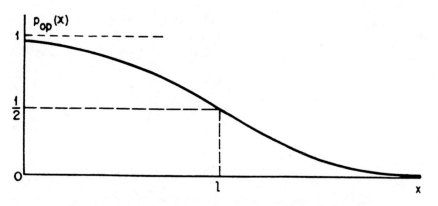

Fig. 3-14. Lateral range curve based on a normal distribution of definite ranges.

the equation becomes

$$P_{op}(x) = \frac{1}{\sigma\sqrt{2\pi}} \int_{x}^{+\infty} e^{-(\lambda-l)^2/2\sigma^2} \, d\lambda$$

$$= \frac{1}{2}\left(1 - \operatorname{erf} \frac{x-l}{\sigma\sqrt{2}}\right),$$

the graph of which is shown in Fig. 3-14. It is noted that when $x = 0$, $p_{op}(0)$ is slightly less than unity, whereas it should exactly equal unity. This is because the normal distribution of definite ranges allows a (slight) chance of negative ranges, a physical absurdity. It would have been more realistic to have assumed a skew non-negative distribution, e.g., *Pearson's Type III distribution* $k\lambda^{m-1}e^{-\beta\lambda}$, but this 1946 notion had to wait 23 years before being implemented (under its modern name of *gamma density*) in problems of the present class by Stone [3, 4] and Richardson and Belkin [2]. We return to this problem in Appendix C.

As a second example, consider the search for a fixed target by two parallel sweeps at distance S apart. If the underlying conditions are the same during the two sweeps, and if $p(x)$ is the lateral range probability, the chance of detection of a target between the paths and x miles from one of them is shown by the usual reasoning to be

$$P(x, S) = 1 - [1 - p(x)][1 - p(S - x)]$$

$$= p(x) + p(S - x) - p(x)p(S - x).$$

If $p(x) = p(x, \lambda)$, a weighted averaging process must be performed in order to get the operational probability $P_{op}(x, S)$ from $P(x, S, \lambda)$ given by the above equation. And of course if x is determined at random between 0 and S, a second averaging must be done to get $P_{op}(S)$, the operational probability of detecting the target given only to be somewhere between the sweeps and with a given distribution of physical conditions. The order in which these two averagings are done is immaterial. A corresponding treatment is given in the case of infinitely many parallel sweeps. It may be remarked that the operational effective visibility E_{op}, which is defined by the equation (see Section 7)

$$P_{op}(2E_{op}) = \int P(2E_{op}, \lambda) f(\lambda) \, d\lambda = \frac{1}{2},$$

is quite different from the average $\overline{E}$:

$$\overline{E} = \int E(\lambda) f(\lambda) \, d\lambda,$$

of the effective visibility defined under fixed conditions corresponding to a particular value of λ. Here $f(\lambda)$ is the assumed frequency with which the values of λ are taken to be distributed under the operational conditions in question.

As a third example, suppose that a radar set is chosen at random from a lot, only the fraction ε of which are in good adjustment, the remaining $1 - \varepsilon$ not in a condition to make any detections possible. The radar lateral range curve $p(x)$ for a radar set in good adjustment and, e.g., mounted on an aircraft, must be multiplied by ε to obtain the operational curve that will be obtained when many observations are made with the aid of many sets chosen in this way. When a set or similar observing instrumentality or setup is not giving the results that could be expected of it, it is often said to be working at an *efficiency* less than 100 percent. In the above case, a natural definition of efficiency is 100ε. In more complicated cases, the concept, while useful as a general one, may not be convenient to define in all precision.

As implied at the outset of this section, these operational uncertainties in the conditions, varying from operation to operation, lead to a violation of our assumption of independence—or, more precisely, show that *after* our derivations based upon it have been made, a subsequent process of averaging over certain parameters remaining in the result must be made. We may say that the lack of independence is of the nature of a *Lexis correlation*.

In conclusion, the following principle is laid down:

If the object of the calculation of probabilities, averages, and similar statistical detection quantities is to coordinate and explain the data of operations of the past, then the heterogeneity of conditions (dispersion of slowly varying parameters) is placed at the apex of the discussion, the influence of "subjective" probabilities and short-term fluctuations (the main subject of this chapter) usually playing a secondary role.

If on the other hand the object of the calculation is to obtain contemplated performance data for the design of search plans to be used in the future, and, as is generally the case, when the conditions (slowly varying parameters) are known, then the probabilities originating from subjective and rapidly fluctuating sources occupy the center of the stage; any study of the heterogeneity of conditions is made only in order to check the sensitivity of the search plan to accidental imperfections in the knowledge of the conditions.

All this will be made clear on the basis of examples in the succeeding chapters.

11. THE EFFECT OF INTEGRATION TIME

Throughout this chapter the act of detection has been treated as in itself an instantaneous event—however long the searcher had to await its occurrence. It is important in closing to note the effect of the opposite assumption, corresponding with the fact that many modern instruments of detection require an *integration time* during which the image presented to the observer grows to its maximum degree of detectability. Thus the traces produced on an electronic scope or the markings of a chemical recorder are formed progressively. Many minutes, up to an appreciable fraction of an hour, may be required for their full development. If the marks remained *totally* unrecognizable before the elapse of the full integration interval, the detection problem would be the simple one of isolated glimpses, studied in the earlier sections of this chapter. But the situation here is radically different, inasmuch as the image presented has some degree of recognizability very early in the integration period, which increases as the buildup of the image progresses.

In mathematical terms, the detection coefficient γ of Section 2 (Eqs. (3), (6)) changes with time, $\gamma = \gamma(t)$, as t goes from 0 to the end of the integration period T. Even under fixed external conditions, it will vary in a manner depending on the physical characteristics of the detection device and the psychophysical nature of the phenomenon of "recognition." Clearly $\gamma(t)$ can be given only as a rough approximation. Certain of its general features can be inferred from its definition. Thus we know that it increases smoothly from zero for $t = 0$ to an essential maximum at $t = T$, simply by definition of T. Since for small values of the exponent, one minus the exponential differs from the exponent by higher order terms, and since this is the integral of γ from 0 to an arbitrary time, $p(t)$ and its derivative both vanish for $t = 0$. Therefore the graph of $p(t)$ is tangent to the t-axis at $t = 0$. Further, since the integrand in the exponent is positive and increases to $\gamma(T)$, after which it remains constant, $p(t)$ ends by having an exponential behavior. Therefore, finally, the graph has a point of inflection. It is represented schematically in Fig. 3-15.

Simple explicit expressions for $p(t)$ are readily obtained by setting $\gamma(t) = ct^a$, where a is a positive constant. Thus with $a = 1$ the graph of $p(t)$ is an inverted piece of a Gauss curve; when $a = \frac{1}{2}$, an equally simple function. Obviously, the only utility of such expressions is their illustration of the sort of possibilities of behavior to expect—certainly not to take literally. Before any definite expression can be used in practice, a very thorough investigation of its degree of correspondence with reality must have been made.

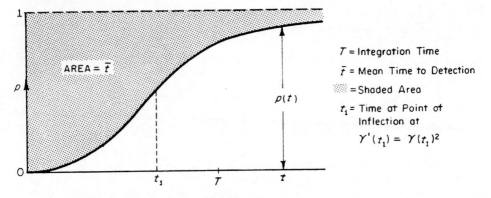

Fig. 3-15. The effect of integration time.

The mean time $\bar{t}$ to detection is found by the reasoning of Section 2 and integration by parts. Hence the area interpretation in Fig. 3-15.

$$\bar{t} = \int_0^\infty t\, dp(t) = -\int_0^\infty t\, d \exp\left[-\int_0^t \gamma(t)\, dt \right] = 0 + \int_0^\infty \exp\left[-\int_0^\infty \gamma(t)\, dt \right] dt.$$

t_1 satisfies $p''(t) = 0$, i.e., $\gamma'(t_1) = \gamma(t_1)^2$.

REFERENCES

1. Koopman, B. O. 1979. An operational critique of detection laws. *Operations Res.*, vol. 27, pp.115–133.
2. Richardson, H. R., and Belkin, B. 1972. Optimal search with uncertain sweep width. *Operations Res.*: 20, 764–784.
3. Stone, L. D. 1969. Optimal search using a sensor with uncertain sweep width. Report (AD 785288) of D. H. Wagner, Assts.
4. Stone, L. D. 1975. *Theory of optimal search.* New York: Academic Press, pp. 59–63.

Chapter 4

Target Localization

Search in its general conception as a part of a larger operation (cf. Section 8 of Chapter 1) starts with some degree of knowledge of the targets' possible positions and motions and ends (when successful) with much more precise and useful knowledge of these. In technical terms, a successful search replaces an a priori distribution by a more usable a posteriori one, by applying Bayesian reasoning to the various data obtained in the search. Since there is always motion and change, not only space but time enters among the terms of reference. This means mathematically that not only Bayesian updates of the a priori distributions will be made, but their evolution in time as *stochastic processes* must be treated. (These and other technical matters in the theory of probability are treated in detail in Appendix A, and more briefly in Section 2 below.) All these ideas have been introduced in general terms in Chapter 1 and have recurred in later ones. Here and in the next chapter they will be given precise expression, when motion is not the driving factor, and when it is, respectively.

As in any application of mathematics to actual events, a preliminary study breaks the large problem down into more or less self-contained parts. The latter are then simplified by setting aside (provisionally at least) what appear to be inessential features before the appropriate mathematical treatment is applied. All this may have to be repeated, with the progressive gain of experience and change in emphasis. (Here as in all hard problems in science—pure or applied—there is no general way to an answer. Various branches of technology, mathematics, and computer science may be powerful auxiliaries, but they cannot provide a mechanical substitute for rational thought.)

The first part of the general problem is to determine the a priori distribution of the target(s). Under a wide variety of conditions this has a simple solution: when the general conditions remain the same during long periods, it may be assumed that the a priori probabilities are independent of time. In this sense they represent what may be called *steady states*, which we shall consider in Section 1. Next in simplicity (and time order) is the situation in which more specific information concerning the target at a particular time is obtained, for example, from knowledge of when it left port, was observed to signal, or was detected by some system of sensors. Then Bayes's theorem will update the former probabilities, replacing them by a new distribution, valid at the time in question, and of a nature dependent upon the characteristics of the information-gathering system. We shall consider many of the possibilities in Sections 2 and 3, and in the case of interdependent sets of targets in 4. Localization by multiple sensors will be considered in Sections 5–8.

The distributions obtained as just described will in general evolve with the passage of time; i.e., will not represent a steady state. The law of evolution (the *transition probabilities*) will obviously depend on the nature of the case: whether the targets are fixed (e.g., sunken objects); moving at predictable speed and course (e.g., units in transit); in predictable speed but random course (cf. Chapter 2, Section 5); drifting with wind and tide (as a life raft); or are practicing evasive maneuvers and deceptive motion (as with hostile units on patrol). These various cases will be treated in Chapter 5.

When in important practical matters so much must be inferred from so little, certain general principles may lend their aid. In the present situation, some use may be made of the minimax reasoning of the theory of games, and certain distributions may be selected by reasoning based on the mathematical theory of information. An example of the former is given in Chapter 7, Section 8; the latter is touched on in Appendix A, Section 8.

We note again the precise distinction between "region" and "area" as defined in the introduction of Chapter 1.

1. TARGET DISTRIBUTIONS IN THE STEADY STATE

The simplest example is the case of the uniform distribution of targets, without systematic motion, in a large region $\mathcal{Q}$ of area A. This has been defined in detail in Chapter 2, Sections 4 and 5, and applied in Chapter 3, Sections 4–9. In the latter sections it served as the basis of the definition of *equivalence* of different laws of detection: their property of detecting the same mean or expected number of targets per unit time out of a uniform random distribution. This is also expressed by saying that such equivalent laws have the same *search rate*. It is hardly necessary to stress that the assumption of uniformity of the random distribution is essential in this definition; other distributions would in general give quite different results in the comparison of detecting systems.

If a particular target is uniformly distributed in the sense considered above, the probability of its being at any particular time t in any specified subregion $\mathcal{B}$ of $\mathcal{Q}$ of area B is (by definition) B/A: it has the probability density $1/A$. Let us suppose that there are many targets thus distributed over $\mathcal{Q}$, the total number not being known, but that their mean density N is known. As explained before, N is the expected number in a (small) area divided by the area (precisely: the limit of this quotient); it is positive but not usually an integer. Evidently the expected value of the (unknown) total number in $\mathcal{Q}$ is NA. Let us suppose that one of the targets is actually in the region $\mathcal{B}$; what is the (conditional) probability that some other target will be in a specified region $\mathcal{B}'$? Here $\mathcal{B}$ and $\mathcal{B}'$ may be quite separate, may share a portion of boundary, may overlap, or may be coincident. Furthermore, the above assumption that the first target "is in $\mathcal{B}$" is hypothetical: it does not necessarily imply that such and such a detecting device has in fact been set in operation and observed it there. Finally, we are idealizing the situation by assuming that the targets are mere points—having dimensions that can be ignored in comparison with those of the regions considered. (This is no less realistic than the assumption made in much of celestial mechanics—that the sun and planets are mere Newtonian particles.)

The answer to the above question may be derived from an assumption of *independence* of the targets: the conditional probability that the second target will be in $\mathcal{B}'$ is still B'/A—equal to the unconditional probability. This assumption is based on the notion that the targets in question are not moving in formation, are not coordinated in time, and in fact are acting as if each were unconscious of the other's presence (except, perhaps, just enough to avoid collision). It would, in particular, not apply if the total number of targets were small and known, or small and assigned different parts of $\mathcal{C}$ in which to remain, as in patrol. It is nevertheless a sufficiently close representation of the facts in a large number of situations to make its consequences important to consider. The opposite assumption, on the other hand, underlies Section 4.

From the above assumptions it follows mathematically that the targets obey a *Poisson law*: the probability that exactly s will be in the region $\mathcal{B}$ is

$$(1) \qquad P_s[\mathcal{B}] = \frac{u^s}{s!} e^{-u}, \quad u = NB = N \cdot \text{area of } \mathcal{B}.$$

This formula, often taken for granted as self-evident, is easily proved by deriving a recurrence formula, easy to solve explicitly. More details are given in Appendix A, Section 8(3) in the more general case in which the random distribution is not uniform, so that N and in consequence u, depend on position.

There is a second type of steady state in which the targets have a constant and independent spatial distribution over the region $\mathcal{C}$, but have a very purposeful motion, as when they are in transit through it. They enter, at a random time and place, through a part E of the boundary of $\mathcal{C}$ and leave through another part L, the expected number entering and leaving being equal and not changing with time. If their sole object is to make the *transit* from E to L and they have no reason to loiter in $\mathcal{C}$ or to move evasively, they will travel with fixed speed, changing course only to avoid geographical or meteorological obstructions, or political constraints, and since this is the shortest distance from E to L, it is an essentially predictable path, the precise times of passage being the only random factor left. If on the other hand the targets wish to make a prediction of their positions less easy for the searcher, but yet make their stay in $\mathcal{C}$ as brief as possible, they may spread their paths out in $\mathcal{C}$, possibly making evasive changes in course, and, if geography permits, may cross E and L at randomly chosen points. This means that a certain amount of extra time in $\mathcal{C}$ will be sacrificed to secure extra safety from detection.

Just what distributions can be inferred from these considerations will depend on the specific geographic and similar factors. The ideas will be illustrated by two simple cases, which have shown themselves of practical importance.

The first example of such randomized transit distributions is the case in which $\mathcal{R}$ can be approximated by a rectangular region with E and L as opposite sides, the targets being free to enter and leave at any point. The obvious paths are straight lines perpendicular to E and L and uniformly but randomly spaced throughout $\mathcal{R}$ —a uniform (and Poisson) distribution of targets in this region. The only difference between this and the former case becomes manifest in the evolution of a posteriori probabilities after a non-alerting detection. These considerations will be applied to barrier patrols in Chapter 8.

The second example is the case in which the geography leads to circular boundaries, as shown in Fig. 4-1. In (a) the targets enter and leave through the circular arcs, and may be assumed to move along radial lines at their cruising speed, but uniformly spaced at random. (This could represent leaving a port and passing into a broader expanse of water. L could be a shore or merely a geometrical division of the sea, beyond which a different type of progress may be demanded.) In (c) the port of exit is reduced to a point, while in (b) the two circles are the sole boundaries of $\mathcal{R}$, and we have a simplified picture of targets leaving an island. Note that in all three cases the roles of E and L can be interchanged, the targets now moving toward the center O instead of away from it.

In all these circular cases the target density N is inversely proportional to the radial distance $r = \overline{OP}$ to the target at P. To see this, we observe that if w is the target speed in its radial motion (this w is the magnitude of the target's vector velocity; it must not be confused with its use in Chapter 2 and later, as a relative velocity value), an element of area $r_0 \, dr_0 \, d\theta$ at $t = t_0$ will go into $r_1 \, dr_1 \, d\theta$ at $t = t_1$, where $r_1 = r_0 + w(t_1 - t_0)$. Therefore any target in the former at t_0 will be in the latter at t_1, and hence the expected number in the two elements is the same. Therefore if N_0 and N_1 are the densities at (r_0, θ) and (r_1, θ), we have $N_0 r_0 \, dr_0 \, d\theta = N_1 r_1 \, dr_1 \, d\theta$, and since $dr_0 \, d\theta = dr_1 \, d\theta$, we have $N_0 r_0 = N_1 r_1$, proving that $\underline{N}$ is

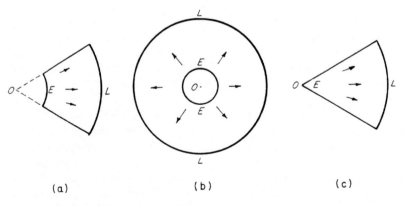

(a)   (b)   (c)

Fig. 4-1. Circular transit regions.

inversely proportional to r, as stated above. This can be written in the form $N = K/r$, where K is a constant, depending on the mean rate of entrance of targets into $\mathcal{C}$.

It is evident that such targets are more likely to be detected if a search is conducted in a region of greater density; in the circular case, in positions of small r. In fact, it appeals to common sense that the hardest conditions for detecting a target in $\mathcal{C}$—other things being equal—are those in which the target's distribution is uniform: $N = $ constant. This fact will be established for many laws of search in a later chapter. But granting that this is the case, and to give a simple example of the *minimax* reasoning of game theory, we may raise the question of whether the targets *can* cross the type of region of Fig. 4-1 in such a way as to produce a constant density N instead of the strongly variable $N = K/r$. Assuming that the conditions for a steady state are satisfied, so that the density and mean rate of flow through any circular arc are independent of time, the only way in which a constant density can be maintained in radial motion is to have the target speed w vary as a function of r. For if in the elements considered above, $N_0 r_0 \, dr_0 \, d\theta = N_1 r_1 \, dr_1 \, d\theta$, N_0 and N_1 are to be equal, we must have $r_0 \, dr_0 = r_1 \, dr_1$, or, dividing by dt, we have $r_0 w_0 = r_1 w_1$, so that the speeds are inversely proportional to r: $u = k/r$: very fast when r is small and slowing down with increasing r. This leads to the differential equation $dr/dt = k/r$ having the solution $r = \sqrt{r_0^2 + 2k(t - t_0)}$, where $r = r_0$ when $t = t_0$. Such a mode of motion is a strange one and unlikely to be adopted—even in cases in which the considerable variations of speed correspond to a practical operation.

The results of the last paragraph have application to target motion after detection by an *alerting* method of observation. Thus if a hostile submarine knows that at a certain time and position it is detected, it is natural for it to leave that spot as fast as possible in a random direction, and after a while to slow to more moderate cruising speeds. This tends to produce a somewhat more uniform distribution of possible positions than would otherwise occur, as we shall see in later sections. The extreme assumption that after a time t following detection of such a target at 0 the searcher can postulate that it has a uniform probability distribution $1/\pi u_0^2 t^2$ in the circle centered at 0 and of radius $u_0 t$, where u_0 is the maximum speed of the target, is frequently made. It is false unless the detection has alerted the target, as noted above, and even then, it assumes an extraordinary type of target maneuver. The problem of finding a more realistic assumption will be examined in the following chapter.

2. LOCALIZATION BY DETECTION: GENERAL PRINCIPLES

As we have explained in Section 6 of Chapter 1, and have noted in various subsequent places, when a target is detected by some less primitive method than seeing it and thus automatically knowing where it is, the knowledge of its position *even after detection* is not exact and must be expressed in terms of probabilities. We have explained that there are two points at which probability enters: the a priori probability distribution of the target (or targets), and the conditional probability that it will be detected, given the positions of target and searcher, as well as the attendant circumstances, such as the target's aspect, strength of any emissions relied on for its detection, condition of the medium, and many other factors. The first has been discussed in Section 1 on the basis of simple examples; the second has formed the subject of Chapter 3. We should add that there is a third point of entry of probabilities: In all cases in which it is not certain that the act of detection is by a purely passive observation in the sense of Section 5 of Chapter 1, we must consider the likelihood that the mechanism of detection could alert the target or otherwise change the physical conditions attendant upon the continuation of the search.

Bayes's formula gives in all cases of search by *passive observations* a complete answer to the localization question, after the results of an attempt at detection are known. While a detailed proof of the formula, combined with the explanation of exactly why it may fail to be applicable when *active observations* are involved, is given in Appendix A, Sections 2 and 3, a brief sketch of these matters may be useful at this point.

Let $f(X, Y)$ be the conditional probability that a target *given to be at X* will be detected by the searcher situated at point Y—by a passive observation. If $p(X)$ is the a priori probability density of the target, the probability that the target will be in the small region $d\mathfrak{M}$ at X of area dM *and* be detected is (to quantities of higher order) $p(X)f(X, Y) dM$. That it will be detected *somewhere* has the probability $P(Y)$ given by total probability as the integral

$$(2) \qquad\qquad P(Y) = \int \int p(X) f(X, Y) \, dM,$$

the integral being taken with respect to X over the whole region of ocean searched. The localization problem requires the *inverse*: the probability density $p'(X, Y)$—the a posteriori probability—given that it has been detected. The textbook proof of Bayes's formula consists in finding this probability by equating the two expressions for the compound probability that the target be in $d\mathfrak{M}$ *and* will be detected—i.e., equating the product found above with $P(Y)p'(X, Y)$. On canceling dM from the resulting equation and applying (2), we obtain Bayes's formula

$$(3) \qquad\qquad p'(X, Y) = p(X)f(X, Y) / \int \int p(X)f(X, Y) \, dM.$$

That this reasoning could break down when the detection involves active observations can be made crudely evident by the extreme case in which the mechanism of detection destroys the target so that it ceases to exist, or when detection ejects it entirely from the ocean surface. This may seem far-fetched, but as Appendix A explains, *the logical combination of the physical events* to which the laws of probability are applied may have to be reconstrued in many cases of events defined by incompatible conceptual trials; this fact has had a profound influence on modern theoretical physics. Its importance to search theory was first pointed out by Dobbie (ref. [2], Preface).

Returning to the case of passive observations, suppose that under the assumptions set forth above, the search *fails to detect* the target; what locational information does this fact give the searcher? The answer is found by applying (3) after replacing $f(X, Y)$ by the complementary probability, $\bar{f}(X, Y) = 1 - f(X, Y)$. The validity of this modification of (3) assumes that the target actually is in the part of the ocean searched ($\int\int p(X)\, dM = 1$) and is established exactly as before. It may be remarked that such a negative result may often give very important information as to the target's location.

The considerations above have their relevance to the repeated application of Bayes's formula, and the possibility of having to change the various functions involved in such successive updates.

3. FOUR EXAMPLES OF LOCALIZATION

In the last paragraph of Section 4, Chapter 3, one case of target localization was given on the basis of the lateral range curves. We shall give four further examples.

The first example applies the *definite range law*: all targets within range R of Y are detected; no others. Clearly $f(X, Y) = \chi(r)$, where $r = \overline{XY}$ and $\chi(r)$ is unity or zero according to whether r is less than or greater than R. The answer is given in (3): $p'(X, Y)$ is zero when r exceeds R, and equal to the original density $p(X)$ divided by its integral inside the circle centered at Y and of radius R when r is less than R. In the generalization, the law of *definite detection* or *clean sweep* (Chapter 3, Section 9), we depart from the use of the two-point detection probability $f(X, Y)$, and on denoting the region swept clean by $\mathcal{B}$, our detection probability is the *characteristic function* of this figure, $\chi_{\mathcal{B}}(X)$, equal to 1 when X is in it, to 0 otherwise. Again (3) (with the above replacement of f by $\chi_{\mathcal{B}}$) gives 0 when X is outside the region, and $p(X)$ divided by its integral over $\mathcal{B}$ within. All this has been seen in Chapter 3, Section 9, and so indeed has the resulting updated distribution after one or the other of these laws has *failed* to detect: one simply replaces the region swept clean (the circle or the more general figure $\mathcal{B}$) by its *complement*, the set of points not belonging to this figure. Thus (3) applies, but now with f replaced by $1 - \chi_{\mathcal{B}}(X)$.

Our second example is provided by the many cases in which the circumstances of the search justify the application of the general form of the law of random search (40'), derived in Section 6 of Chapter 3. The track density λ and sweep width W may depend on the position X: the former, when the amount of search varies from point to point; the latter, when the detectability (e.g., visibility) is different in different places. Thus the conditional probability of detecting a target given to be at X is $1 - e^{-W\lambda}$ and is in general different for different positions X. Here again, it is the negative result that raises the question of interest to the localization problem: given that a total length of track L has been followed by the searcher, distributed with the density λ, and that the target has not been detected, what is its updated probability distribution?

In this case the probability of failure $\bar{f} = 1 - f$ replaces f in (3), and $\bar{f} = e^{-W\lambda}$, thus giving the a posteriori distribution

$$(4) \qquad p'(X, Y) = \frac{p(X)e^{-W\lambda}}{\int\int p(X)e^{-W\lambda}\, dM_X}.$$

This formula will be applied to problems of sequential search in later chapters. It is essential to realize that the passive character of the observations is the sure basis of its validity.

A third example is the case in which the detection involves a "target fix." An aircraft before being forced to "land" at sea, is able to signal its location to shore stations, and the crew escapes in a life raft. Or a submarine, normally maintaining radio silence, at a certain moment signals to its home base, where direction-finding equipment may receive this signal and locate the submarine by simple geometrical constructions. In each of these and many similar cases, the localization is not perfectly accurate: the aircraft's message is subject to errors of navigation and the high-frequency direction-finding (HFDF) fix is liable to errors of reception in which the variability of atmospheric refraction may play a part. But in all such cases a bivariate normal law may be safely assumed as a useful approximation. Let this Gaussian probability density that a target, actually at X_0: (x_0, y_0), be reported at X: (x, y) be

$$(5) \qquad G(X - X_0) = G(x - x_0, y - y_0),$$

where G contains as parameters the principal variances and the direction of the principal axes. See Sections 6, 7, 8, below. The reasoning establishing (3) now gives for the a posteriori probability

$$(6) \qquad P_0(X) = \frac{p(X_0)G(X - X_0)}{\int\int p(X_0)G(X - X_0)\, dM_X}.$$

Of course this simplifies in the case of the circular normal distribution

$$(7) \qquad G(X - X_0) = \frac{1}{2\pi\sigma^2} e^{-r^2/2\sigma^2}, \quad r^2 = (x - x_0)^2 + (y - y_0)^2.$$

In these applications, (6) may very often be applied under the assumption of a uniform a priori distribution $p(X)$, which then drops out of the formula, the a posteriori probability density then being simply

$$(8) \qquad P_0(X) = G(X - X_0).$$

In Section 7 the important case of fitting these expressions to accord with many simultaneous observations of the same target will be considered. It arises for example in localization after detection by broad area surveillance systems. Practical methods are given in Section 8.

Our fourth example deals with the case in which the localizing datum is given by the response of any *array* of elementary detectors, each activated by target-produced radiation, and combining their individual receptions—both in amplitude and phase—into a single joint response, presented to the searcher. The target-produced radiation may be electromagnetic or acoustical, and, in either case, may have been generated by the target or have been a reflection or echo from the target of radiation created elsewhere. In the latter case the source of radiation may be at the searcher, as in conventional radar or acoustic echo-ranging, or it may come from another point, as in the so-called *bistatic* detection and in certain applications of laser—and in the oldest case of all: illumination by the sun or a lamp.

The effects of the arrays considered here are given geometrically by the classical formula for the intensity of power received (resulting by combination from the elements of the array) at different angles θ from the perpendicular bisector of the array. This bisector is a plane in the complete spatial picture, but often conveniently thought of in the plane containing both target and array, where it is a line. The useful convention is to write the formula for the ratio ρ of the power received at the angle θ to the maximum power. In the simplest case (considered here) the latter is the power received when $\theta = 0$. The formula is then

$$(9) \qquad \rho(\theta) = \left(\frac{\sin m\theta}{m\theta} \right)^2 \qquad \text{where } m = 2\pi\nu na/2c.$$

Here ν and c are the frequency and speed of the radiation, a the distance between array elements, and n their total number. In deriving this formula a set of physical assumptions is made and mathematical approximations are employed (explained in the derivation given in the acoustic case in Appendix D, where references to usual treatments are found).

When ρ is plotted in polar coordinates as a function of θ, and when its very small values corresponding with very large values of this angle are ignored, the figure obtained consists of a central lobe, tangent to the unit circle and to the two radial lines at $\theta = \pm \theta_0$, θ_0 being the smallest positive θ for which $\sin m\theta = 0$: $\theta_0 = \pi/m$. Then there are smaller side-lobes. Once graphed, we must realize that in space the figure of revolution generated by revolving this graph about the array axis may be important.

When this array presents a signal to the searcher, we consider the target localization problem and assume that only the principal lobe comes into play, that the array is horizontal, and that the problem is that of localization referred to the ocean surface. Of course there are many other important situations, but the one assumed is itself important enough to use as an illustration of the much more general reasoning.

For localization, three further quantitative factors are essential: the *signal strength* or power emitted or reflected by the target (at the frequency ν in question), the *transmission loss* or law of decay of this radiant power with range r from target to searcher, and the *efficacy* of the finally processed signal in telling the operator that a target-like message is present. For we must never forget that the logical basis of any answer that can be given to questions of the location of the target is its probability $f(X, Y)$ when at X of producing a signal detected by the observer at Y; the evaluation of this probability inevitably involves all these factors.

The three factors noted above are the subject of intensive and continuing research, any detailed or exhaustive account of which would go far beyond the scope of this book. Here we can show, on the basis of somewhat drastic simplifications, how the mathematical reasoning can give answers.

We shall denote the signal strength produced at the target by E_T and, assuming that the transmission loss depends only on the range r, denote by $f(r)$ the ratio E_0/E_T, where E_0 is the power of the signal displayed to the observer as the end product of the array, at optimum bearing $\theta = 0$. Finally, we shall assume that the probability of detection $f(X, Y)$ is a known function $\Delta(E)$ of the actual signal power E presented. (For simplicity we have absorbed the "array gain" into $f(r)$ and the "background noise" from external and internal sources into $\Delta(E)$. Finally, in many actual cases, more than one frequency ν comes into play. Moreover, questions of *recognition* enter; see Section 2 of Chapter 1.) The latter assumption has a useful geometrical consequence: the family of "level lines" $\Delta(E) = \text{const.}$ is the same as that of level lines $E = \text{const.}$ Furthermore from the aforementioned simplifying assumptions, together with the formula (9) for $\rho(\theta)$, these curves are given in polar coordinates as loci of

(10) $$E = E_0\rho(\theta) = E_T f(r)\rho(\theta) = \text{const.},$$

or, equivalently, as the loci of $f(r)\rho(\theta) = \text{const.}$

The law of transmission loss $f(r)$ will depend on the nature and condition of the medium, the depths of the target and array, and on other factors such as the frequency ν. There are, however, two situations in which a useful first approximation may be given: the case of unobstructed propagation in open space with the inverse square law $f(r) = \text{const}/r^2$ ("spherical spreading") and the situation in which the refractive effect of the medium so confines the rays in the vertical that they can only spread horizontally and the law of "cylindrical spreading" $f(r) = \text{const}/r$ is applicable. Introducing these expressions into the preceding equations for the level lines and applying (9), they become, in terms of the positive parametric constants A and B

(10′) $$r = A\frac{\sin m\theta}{m\theta} \quad \text{for spherical spreading;}$$

$$r = B\left(\frac{\sin m\theta}{m\theta}\right)^2 \quad \text{for cylindrical spreading.}$$

Fig. 4-2 shows the single lobe curves ($\rho = r$ when $A = B = 1$) for an angle θ_0 of $10°$, while the second formula (10′) is given for four values of B and, for ease of visualizing, a θ_0 of $50°$. [In fact, much smaller angles occur.]

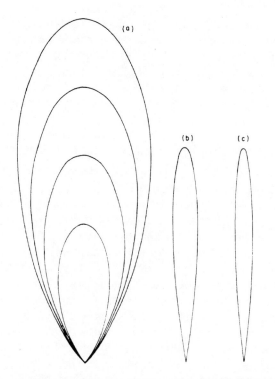

Fig. 4-2. Localization after detection by one array. (a) Curves of equal probability of location: cylindrical spreading and semilobe angle θ_0 of 50° (b) Spherical spreading ρ-curve (c) Cylindrical spreading ρ-curve; each with θ_0 of 10°.

These curves represent only the first step in localization: we know that the detection probability is constant on each curve. If we are detecting a target when a steady state has ruled, as described in Section 2, we may in most cases assume a uniform a priori distribution: the application of (3) then gives the distribution $p'(X, Y) = (\text{const.}) \times \Delta(E)$; therefore, we can say that the level curves shown in Fig. 4-2 are also the curves of constant probability density of target positions after the target's detection.

The next step in the localization requires more definite knowledge of the function $\Delta(E)$. A frequently made rough approximation is that it is a step function: zero for values of E less than a particular constant E_r (the "recognition differential"), unity for greater values. Then the target lies inside the lobe bounded by the curve $\Delta(E) = \Delta(E_r)$. A more refined assumption is that $\Delta(E)$ rises more or less rapidly from zero to unity as E moves through the value E_r. Then the sharp boundary of the earlier lobe is replaced by a somewhat diffused one. Finally, if not merely recognition but a more or less rough magnitude of E can be recorded, only parts of the lobe figure are indicated as probable positions of the target.

It is important, in regard to this example, to note that there is usually the capability of *directing the array* in order to search. This can be accomplished mechanically by turning it or its platform, or electrically by using delay lines, etc. in the circuitry, as noted in Appendix D. The rotation can be continuous or by closely spaced steps. All such cases come under the term *sector scan*. From this point of view, the array acquires the character of a *measuring instrument* as well as a detecting one. The chief quantity that it measures is the *angular bearing* ϕ of the target, when detected. The position 0 of the array being known, and the bearing measured (conventionally from true North in a clockwise direction, see Chapter 2), the target X would have its line of bearing $\overrightarrow{YX}$ determined. But of course, as in all measurements, this bearing is subject to error.

It is essential in target localization by an array to have a reliable estimate of the *law of error in bearing*. Figure 4-2 indicates that there are at least two situations. First, by the relatively small range or high signal strength, the target may be in the nearer part of the region traversed by the lobes, so that their straight stem-like portions rather than their more distant rounded parts come into play in estimating the target's position. This region we call the *zone of steady signals*, because throughout this zone the bearing error is essentially independent of range. This is made clear geometrically by Fig. 4-2 and is supported by considerable operational evidence, gathered under conditions of the sort described. Second, the target may not satisfy these conditions, and then it is in the region of the more distant rounded parts of the lobes. Here not only the geometry of the lobes, but the weakness of the signal, subjects its reception to an increased influence of the varying and least ascertainable condition of the target and the medium. This we call the *zone of unsteady signals*. We cannot assume the independence of bearing error on range in this zone, and there is operational evidence that a different law is more nearly correct.

In conclusion, it must be emphasized that there are many other types of arrays, exploiting circular or other curved placing, and other types of spacing and circuitry. But whatever their characteristics, their effect in search is always subject to the same probabilistic reasoning as has been illustrated in the simple examples just given.

4. THE CASE OF MANY TARGETS

In the present section we deal with the *many-target* localization problem. Search is conducted in the region $\mathcal{Q}$ for a certain type of target, but, in contrast to the assumption made in the previous examples, not for one particular target given to be in $\mathcal{Q}$, but for any of a set of targets, usually of unknown or only roughly known total number.

As in the first case treated in Section 1 above, we assume that the mean density of targets $N = N(X)$ is given (or can be inferred) as a function of position X on the surface $\mathcal{Q}$, but we do not necessarily assume that it is a constant. If one target has been found by a passive observation to be in subregion $\mathcal{B}$, as in Section 1 we raise the question of the probability that a second (different) target will be in another region $\mathscr{B}'$. The answer given to the same question in Section 1 was based on the assumption of *target independence*, i.e., that the event β of a target being in $\mathscr{B}$ and the event β' of another target being in $\mathscr{B}'$ are independent events, and that the conditional and the unconditional probabilities are equal: $P(\beta') = P(\beta'|\beta)$, etc. By virtue of the principle of compound probability (used earlier and analyzed in detail in the present notation in Appendix A) this is equivalent to

$$(11) \qquad P(\beta\beta') = P(\beta)P(\beta').$$

This target independence is part of the hypothesis leading to the Poisson distribution (1), with a position-dependent u and N, as proved in Appendix A.

Such target independence represents only a very special case, although a highly important one in search theory. It occurs when the targets are numerous and widely spaced and random in their mutual interaction. In more general situations, just what sort of target dependence must be assumed can only be determined by a thorough physical and tactical analysis of the case. Beyond setting forth some of the general concepts needed in the formulation and giving two practical examples, any comprehensive treatment would well exceed the scope of this book.

The conceptual framework involves the *joint* or *simultaneous probability densities*. For two targets it is defined as follows, $d\mathfrak{M}_X$ and $d\mathfrak{M}_Y$ being elementary regions at X and Y of areas dM_X and dM_Y,

$$(12) \qquad P_{1,2}(X, Y)\, dM_X\, dM_Y =$$

$$P\{\text{1st. target in } d\mathfrak{M}_X \text{ and second in } d\mathfrak{M}_Y\} = P(\beta\beta').$$

In terms of conditional probability densities, $p(X|Y)$ (the density of the first target, given the second at Y, etc.), we have

$$(13) \qquad P_{1,2}(X, Y) = p_1(X)p_2(Y|X) = p_2(Y)p_1(X|Y) = P_1(X)p_2(Y)h(X, Y).$$

The first two equations are by general compound probability; the last, by definition of the function $h(X, Y)$, which expresses the mutual dependence of the two targets. The expected value of its logarithm

$$(14) \qquad \bar{h} = \int\int P_{1,2}(X, Y) \log h(X, Y)\, dM_X\, dM_Y$$

is a recently much used information-theoretic expression for the *quantity of dependence* between the positions of the two targets. It is always nonnegative, and zero if and only if they are independent. See Appendix A, Section 8, for further details.

If we are interested only in the *numbers* of targets at various places without distinguishing them individually, we obtain the results by combinations according to the laws of probability. Thus the *expected number density* $N(X)$ is the sum of the individual probability densities: $N(X) = p_1(X) + p_2(X) + \cdots$. In general, no such simple expression of the simultaneous expected number densities $(N(X), N(Y))$ in terms of $P_{i,j}(X, Y)$ is possible. This is because the general case would involve the higher order simultaneous probability densities of all sets of k targets:

$$(15) \quad P_{i_1}, \ldots, {}_{ik}(X_1, \ldots, X_k) \, dM_1 \cdots dM_k = P\{i_1 \text{ in } d\mathfrak{M}_1, \ldots, i_k \text{ in } d\mathfrak{M}_k\}.$$

There is a great simplification when the targets can be regarded as *identical*—physically and tactically—so that the subscripts are dropped from the P-symbols. This occurs in antisubmarine warfare, as well as in many problems of molecular physics and chemistry. Methods of formulation and calculation are much further advanced in the latter subjects than in the former.

We conclude with two practical examples. The first involves *collision avoidance* between ensembles of targets. Surface units in large areas have no real problem except in tight formations under adverse conditions. But with submarines on patrol, or required to bar transit of other units, the problem may be very real. To avoid collision and other disasters of too close approach, they may be assigned specified regions in which to remain, separated by appreciable distances. Then there is a *negative* dependence in the sense that for very appreciable lengths $\overline{XY}$, $P(X|Y)$ is small in comparison with the unconditional densities at the same spot. More precisely, $h(X, Y)$ in (13) is very small.

The opposite case is that of submarines attracted by the same objective, as in *wolf-pack* tactics. Then $P(X|Y)$ is larger than $P(X)$ in the regions in question. More precisely, $h(X, Y)$ is much larger than its value (unity) in the case of independence.

5. LOCALIZATION BY MANY COOPERATING OBSERVERS: GENERAL CONSIDERATIONS

The results of the previous sections, and most particularly of the last example in Section 3, show that even after detection, the target's position may be uncertain. This can often prevent the effective performance of subsequent operations. As noted at the outset of this chapter, a successful detection can only be expected to narrow down the possible positions; other detections are often required to limit them enough for the purpose of the search.

Multiple search by means of increasingly precise sensors (Chapter 1, Section 4) is based on the sequential use of different detecting systems. Before one passes from a system of broad coverage at the expense of precision, however, to one in which the tradeoff between coverage and precision is the opposite, it is important to know how well several systems of the first type, acting cooperatively, can localize the target. In the rather special situation that the target is stationary and a single searcher is mobile and its detection system nonalerting, the searcher can evidently repeat its detection from various different positions, combining them (essentially, by the repeated use of (3)), and thus obtaining increasing precision. Or again, the searcher may be in a fixed installation and the targets of interest in some order of regular motion, as considered in Section 1; then there are successive relative positions, and the combination of detection data may, as before, narrow down the target's position. Such one-searcher cases formed the basis of most of Chapter 3.

Here we shall be concerned with *multiple observers* of the same sort acting in cooperation at a definite time, and which therefore may be regarded as fixed—whether permanently or not—and essentially, as nonalerting.

The remaining sections of this chapter will be devoted to the very important case of detection, localization, and tracking of a target (submarine) by several observers stationed at observation posts O_i that are fixed, at least for extended periods, and using steerable arrays, as in the fourth example of Section 3. The observers are in mutual communication and hence can cooperate in localizing the target. We assume further that in the regions of detectability of the target its a priori distribution is uniform. Hence if a single observer, e.g. at $Y = O_1$, makes a detection, the a posteriori density $p'(X, Y)$ is given by (3) but with the constant $p(X)$ canceled, so that $p'(X, Y)$ is proportional to $f(X, Y)$. With the approximate array formulas (9) and (10), the resulting level curves are given schematically by Fig. 4-2, as we saw before. But if, as in Section 6 below, two observers O_1 and O_2 detect the target at the same time, the a posteriori distribution is more complicated. It is still proportional to the corresponding detection probability, $f(X, O_1, O_2)$ [which—under the simplifying assumptions of "no coaching" of one observer by a successful one and of known fixed detectability conditions—is the product of the two independent probabilities, $f(X, O_1, O_2) = f(X, O_1)f(X, O_2)$], but the level curves of the latter are far more complicated than those of either factor, and much more sensitive to the assumptions.

For this reason approximations must be made. The oldest and crudest simply replaces probability by geometry: a definite detection law in which $f(X, Y)$ is zero outside the indefinite sector between two lines through Y, with its axis that of the directed array and semiangular opening equal to the bearing error and unity inside this sector. A "fix" by two observers places the target in their quadrilateral intersection, the "submarine probable area" (SPA). Not only is this approximation unnecessarily inaccurate, but, in the case of more than two observers, it can be ambiguous when they produce different SPAs and seriously misleading if several are superposed, since the inference could be drawn that the many observations provide little more accuracy than just enough to determine the SPA.

In consequence there is a recent trend to return to probability. The method described below is based on normal law approximations and the application of the method of least squares for localization and the appraisal of its reliability. The zone of steady signals, with bearing errors independent of range, is the case treated, but by methods easily extended to the zone of unsteady signals and the assumption that the error in distance from the central directed array axis is little dependent of range (see end of Section 3). The errors are assumed to be *conditionally independent* (given X).

6. CROSS-FIX LOCALIZATION BY TWO OBSERVATION POSTS

Figure 4-3 shows the underlying geometry for using the "flat earth" model in which a rectangular system of coordinates is established, although the axis of abscissa is

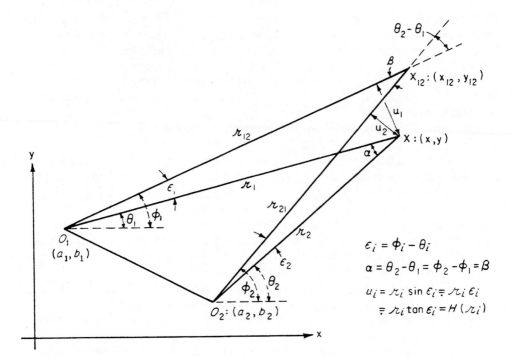

The equations shown in the figure:

$$\epsilon_i = \phi_i - \theta_i$$

$$\alpha = \theta_2 - \theta_1 = \phi_2 - \phi_1 = \beta$$

$$u_i = r_i \sin \epsilon_i \doteq r_i \epsilon_i$$

$$\doteq r_i \tan \epsilon_i = H(r_i)$$

Fig. 4-3. Fix by two observers.

directed to true north and the convention of positive sense of angular change thus orients the axis of ordinates eastward. For convenience we draw the figure in the more familiar position of analytic geometry, with horizontal abscissa and counterclockwise rotation to the ordinate axis. This amounts to a view from the inside of the earth, with an appropriate turn. The target is at $X: (x, y)$, the observers are at $O_i: (a_i, b_i)$, and the other quantities and relations are as shown.

Two assumptions are made in addition to those already mentioned of independent observations and uniform a priori distribution. The first is *the assumption of small errors*—common, indeed, to most of the theory of errors. The second is the Gaussian assumption of an unbiased normal distribution of errors of bearing with given standard deviations. By virtue of the first assumption,

$$H(r_i) = r_i \tan \epsilon_i \doteq r_i \epsilon_i \doteq r_i \sin \epsilon_i = u_i; \quad \epsilon_i = \phi_i - \theta_i.$$

Therefore if one of these, e.g., $H(r_i)$, is Gaussian, so are the others.

In the first treatment to be given we assume a common value σ for the standard deviation of the bearing error ϵ_i, so that the error in the normal distribution of the distance u_i from true position X to observed line of bearing has the standard deviation $r_i \sigma$. (As noted in remark 1 below, following Eq. (28), the method remains virtually unchanged if different σ_i are used for each O_i).

From our assumptions of the Gaussian distribution of bearing lines (the approximation to $f(X, O_i)$) and of their product in determining $p'(X, O_1, O_2)$, (see end of the preceding section), we obtain for the a posteriori probability that the target will be in the region for which the distances mentioned above lie in the intervals $(u_1, u_1 + du_1)$ and $(u_2, u_2 + du_2)$ a value proportional to the product of the two distributions of u_1 and u_2:

(16) $\qquad p'(X, O_1, O_2)$ prop. to $\dfrac{du_1\, du_2}{2\pi\sigma^2 r_1 r_2} \exp \dfrac{-1}{2\sigma^2}(u_1^2/r_1^2 + u_2^2/r_2^2).$

Now $du_1\, du_2$ is proportional to an area dM on the surface. Actually $dM = du_1\, du_2 \cos \beta = du_1\, du_2 \cos \alpha$. We may then write (16) in the more geometrical form

(17) $\qquad p'(X, O_1, O_2) = \dfrac{\sec \beta}{2\pi\sigma^2 r_i r_2} \exp \dfrac{-1}{2\sigma^2}(u_1^2/r_1^2 + u_2^2/r_2^2) \cdot dM.$

As it stands, (17) is not strictly Gaussian in the variable point $X: (x, y)$, since it is not of the form of the product of a constant times an exponential of a quadratic polynomial in these variables. It is at this point that the assumption of small errors comes again into play: We replace certain quantities involving (x, y) by approximations containing only the observed or known quantities and free from (x, y), or, when in the exponent, of degree no higher than the second in (u_1, u_2).

First we replace the true ranges r_1 and r_2 by the observed ranges to X_{12}, r_{12} and r_{21}. Second, we write in the exponential

(18) $\qquad u_i/r_i = \tan \varepsilon_i \doteq \sin \varepsilon_i = \sin(\phi_i - \theta_i)$

$\qquad\qquad = \sin \phi_i \cos \theta_i - \cos \phi_i \sin \phi_i$

$\qquad\qquad = [(x - a_i) \sin \phi_i - (y - b_i) \cos \phi_i]/r_i$

$\qquad\qquad \doteq [(x - a_i) \sin \phi_i - (y - b_i) \cos \phi_i]/r_{ij}.$

The result is the following approximate expression

(19) $\qquad p'(X, O_1, O_2) = \dfrac{K}{r_{12} r_{21}} \exp\left[\dfrac{-1}{2\sigma^2} F(x, y)\right] \cdot dM,$

where, as before, K is a normalizing factor to be determined later, and $F(x, y)$ is a quadratic polynomial in (x, y), with coefficients involving only known or measured quantities. Thus we have obtained the required Gaussian form; it remains to derive the geometrical and probabilistic information needed to complete the localization of the target.

First, the position of the fix point $X_{12}: (x_{12}, y_{12})$ is determined by solving the equations of the observed lines of bearing for (x_{12}, y_{12}), which are evidently

(20) $\qquad -(x_{12} - a_i) \sin \phi_i + (y_{12} - b_i) \cos \phi_i = 0, \quad i = 1, 2.$

Their determinant is easily reduced to $\sin(\phi_2 - \phi_1)$, which is not zero since then the observed lines of bearing would be parallel—a situation we are excluding. Hence (20) determines the coordinates of X_{12} by the elementary formulas. We will see that this position is the most likely one for the target.

Second, to examine the probabilities of the target's positions near X_{12}, we shall shift the coordinate axes to a parallel position, but with X_{12} as the new origin. This replaces x and y by $\bar{x} = x - x_{12}$ and $\bar{y} = y - y_{12}$. To express the $F(x, y)$ in (19) in terms of the new coordinates, we add the left-hand members of each equation (20), divided by r_{ij}, to the corresponding right-hand member in (18), obtaining

$$(21) \qquad u_i/r_i = \left[\bar{x} \sin \phi_i + \bar{y} \cos \phi_i \right]/r_{ij}.$$

Since $F(x, y)$ is the sum of the squares of these expressions, it is a quadratic form in $(\bar{x}, \bar{y})$ with known coefficients:

$$(22) \qquad F(x, y) = A\bar{x}^2 - 2B\bar{x}\bar{y} + C\bar{y}^2 = \bar{F}(\bar{x}, \bar{y});$$

$$A = \frac{\sin^2 \phi_1}{(r_{12})^2} + \frac{\sin^2 \phi_2}{(r_{21})^2};$$

$$B = \frac{\sin \phi_1 \cos \phi_1}{(r_{12})^2} + \frac{\sin \phi_2 \cos \phi_2}{(r_{21})^2};$$

$$C = \frac{\cos^2 \phi_1}{(r_{12})^2} + \frac{\cos^2 \phi_2}{(r_{21})^2}.$$

Since $\bar{F}(\bar{x}, \bar{y})$ was obtained as a sum of squares, it is a *positive definite* quadratic form, and its level lines, the loci of $\bar{F}(\bar{x}, \bar{y}) = \text{const.} > 0$, are ellipses. They are, by (19) and (22), also the level lines of the probability density. The solution of the localization problem will be completed when the principal axes and their common orientation are determined, a problem of elementary analytic geometry.

To find the orientation of the ellipses we rotate the axes of coordinates through an angle ψ, keeping the origin X_{12} fixed. Denoting the new coordinates of $(\bar{x}, \bar{y})$ by (ξ, η), we have the trigonometric relations

$$(23) \qquad \bar{x} = \xi \cos \psi - \eta \sin \psi, \quad \bar{y} = \xi \sin \psi + \eta \cos \psi.$$

Substituting these into (22), a new quadratic form $Q(\xi, \eta) = \bar{F}(\bar{x}, \bar{y})$ is obtained, the coefficients being linear in the original ones and containing sines and cosines of ψ. If B had been zero, the change of coordinates (23) would have been unnecessary. When $B \neq 0$, the coefficient of $\xi\eta$ in $Q(\xi, \eta)$ can be made to vanish by taking for ψ the smallest positive angle for which

$$(24) \qquad \text{ctn}(2\psi) = (C - A)/2B.$$

This accomplishes the desired reduction: $Q(\xi, \eta) = L\xi^2 + M\eta^2$, where L and M are positive and expressed through (22), (23), and (24) in terms of known quantities. Introducing $a = 1/\sqrt{L}$, $b = 1/\sqrt{M}$, we see that the level curves are the loci of

$\xi^2/a^2 + \eta^2/b^2 =$ const., and so they are all similar ellipses of axes proportional to a and b.

There is a simple and direct way of finding the elliptic axes without the lengthy substitutions implied in the last paragraph, based on the fact that the *roots of the characteristic equations* of the quadratic forms $\overline{F}(\overline{x}, \overline{y})$ and $Q(\xi, \eta)$ are the same. This equation for F is the determinant equation in λ:

$$\begin{vmatrix} A - \lambda & -B \\ -B & C - \lambda \end{vmatrix} = \lambda^2 - (A + C)\lambda + (AC - B^2) = 0$$

If λ_1 and λ_2 are the characteristic roots we obtain, using (22),

(25)
$$\lambda_1 + \lambda_2 = A + C = 1/(r_{12})^2 + 1/(r_{21})^2$$

$$\lambda_1\lambda_2 = AC - B^2 = \frac{\sin^2(\phi_2 - \phi_1)}{(r_{12}r_{21})^2}.$$

On the other hand, for $Q(\xi, \eta) = \xi^2/a^2 + \eta^2/b^2$, the characteristic roots are found immediately to be $1/a^2$ and $1/b^2$. Therefore a and b are inversely proportional to the square roots of the characteristic roots.

The semiaxes of the ellipse $Q(\xi, \eta) = k^2$ are ka and kb, and hence its area is $\pi k^2 ab = \pi k^2/\sqrt{\lambda_1\lambda_2}$. Therefore, its area is, finally,

(26)
$$(\text{area of } Q(\xi, \eta) \leqslant k^2) = \frac{\pi r_{12}r_{21}}{|\sin(\phi_2 - \phi_1)|} k^2.$$

Returning to the probability density of the target after the fix, expressing equation (19) after the substitution $F = Q$ assumes the standard form of the bivariate normal law in the coordinates (ξ, η), and this allows the value of the normalizing constant K to be supplied by inspection. The result is the probability density $p(\xi, \eta)$, which can be written in terms of the two principal standard deviations σ_1 and σ_2 as

(27)
$$p(\xi, \eta) = \frac{1}{2\pi\sigma_1\sigma_2} \exp\frac{-1}{2}\left(\frac{\xi^2}{\sigma_1^2} + \frac{\eta^2}{\sigma_2^2}\right);$$

$$\sigma_1 = \sigma a = \sigma/\sqrt{\lambda_1}, \quad \sigma_2 = \sigma b = \sigma/\sqrt{\lambda_2};$$

$$\sigma_1\sigma_2 = \sigma^2/\sqrt{\lambda_1\lambda_2} = \sigma^2 r_{12}r_{21}/|\sin(\phi_2 - \phi_1)|.$$

The maximum value of $p(\xi, \eta)$ occurs when $\xi = \eta = 0$, i.e., at the fix point X_{12}. It is $1/2\pi\sigma_1\sigma_2$, and this is the reciprocal of the area of the ellipse of semiaxes $\sigma_1\sqrt{2}, \sigma_2\sqrt{2}$. This area plays a role in the localization. First, we have the

Theorem. *The probability that the true position X of the target will be in the ellipse of semiaxes $\sigma_1\sqrt{2}, \sigma_2\sqrt{2}$ centered at the fix-point X_{12} is* $1 - 1/e = 0.632$.

This is proved by integrating $p(\xi, \eta)$ over the ellipse in question, e.g., by using as new variables of integration the polar variables (ρ, θ) obtained by setting $\xi = \sigma_1 \rho \cos \theta, \eta = \sigma_2 \rho \sin \theta$, and integrating over the region $\{0 \leqslant \theta \leqslant 2\pi, 0 \leqslant \rho \leqslant \sqrt{2}\,\}$.

In some questions it is necessary to find the actual shape of this and similar equiprobability density ellipses. One then solves the quadratic equation $\lambda^2 - (\lambda_1 + \lambda_2)\lambda + \lambda_1\lambda_2 = 0$, where the coefficients have the values given by (25). The result is readily reduced to the form

$$(28) \qquad \left.\begin{matrix} 2\lambda_1 \\ 2\lambda_2 \end{matrix}\right\} = \frac{1}{(r_{12})^2} + \frac{1}{(r_{21})^2} \pm \left[\frac{1}{(r_{12})^2} + \frac{1}{(r_{21})^2} + \frac{2\cos^2(\phi_2 - \phi_1)}{(r_{12}r_{21})^2}\right]^{1/2}.$$

With the location and dimensions of the probability ellipses given by (24) and (28) and the critical ellipse of the theorem determined, the one cross-fix localization problem is solved under the assumptions stated at the outset. Four remarks are appropriate in conclusion.

1. The results are immediately extended to the case in which the bearing errors at the two observation posts O_1 and O_2 are different, denoted, e.g., by σ' and σ''. Then $u_i/\sigma r_i$ in (16) and (17) are replaced by $u_1/\sigma' r_1, u_2/\sigma'' r_2$; the corresponding factors are taken into the denominators in (21), (22), and (23); thence they enter implicitly into the principal standard deviations σ_1 and σ_2.

2. In the zone of unsteady signals, the independence of bearing error on range cannot be assumed. The lobes of Section 3 indicate other laws of error, a rough approximation being that *the perpendicular distance to the observed line of bearing may be little dependent on range.* Some rough interpretations of certain operational data indicate that this is not an unreasonable assumption. If it is made, the mathematical developments are just as simple as with the assumption of constant angular error: they start with a formula corresponding to (16) but with the products σr_i (or $\sigma' r_1$ and $\sigma'' r_2$) replaced everywhere by σ (or σ' and σ'').

3. The critical ellipse of the theorem above, with axes $\sigma_1\sqrt{2}$ and $\sigma_2\sqrt{2}$, has an interpretation that will be established in Chapter 7: After the fix, let a further search be conducted in such a way that the law of definite detection or clean sweep applies, and let this be laid on progressively and optimally (see Chapter 3, Section 9). Then the area covered up to the moment of detection is a random variable, having an expected value $1 - 1/e$.

4. When the base line O_1O_2 is considerably smaller than the range to the target, the ellipses tend to be very long and thin. When the critical ellipse has a very long major axis, a strict interpretation of the theorem may be misleading, since the dimensions may be too great for the basic assumption of small errors to be correct. This is particularly emphasized when the distances are so great that the flat earth assumption becomes inadequate, and a projection of the elongated ellipses in the tangent plane is made on the spherical earth. Rather fantastic shapes resembling "bananas" have been obtained, which, needless to say, must be taken with a grain of salt.

We close with a schematic diagram showing how the localization area A of the critical ellipse depends on the position of the target in the case of two observation

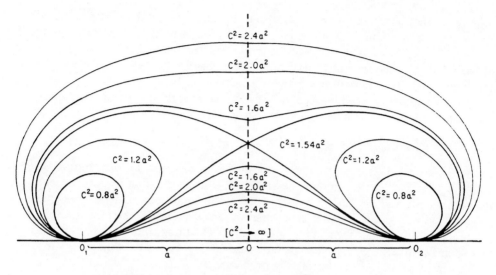

Fig. 4-4. Lines of constant accuracy of target fix.

posts O_1 and O_2. The x-axis is on the line O_1O_2 and the y-axis its perpendicular bisector. The "level lines" of constant A are given by the equation $r_1r_2/\sin(\theta_2 - \theta_1)$ $= C^2$, where $C^2 = A/2\pi\sigma^2$, a constant characterizing the level line in question. This equation, written in the Cartesian coordinates with the notation $2a = O_1O_2$, is easily found to be $(x^2 + y^2 - a^2)^2 + 4a^2y^2 = 2aC^2y$. Therefore we are dealing with the level lines of the function $f(x, y) = (x^2 + y^2 - a^2)^2/2ay + 2ay$, which, for positive y, are given by $f(x, y) = C^2$ and are symmetric in the x-axis. (For negative y, a^2 is replaced by $-a^2$.)

The critical points, points of inflection, maxima and minima, etc., are found as straightforward exercises in calculus. The results are shown in Fig. 4-4.

7. LOCALIZATION BY MANY OBSERVATION POSTS: GENERAL METHODS

The specific problem solved here is the extension of the one treated in the preceding section, but in the case of more than two observation posts. Let these be $O_i (i = 1, \ldots, n)$, at which the arrays are located, and which are searching a region $\mathcal{R}$ of ocean, assumed to be flat. The same assumptions are made as before, in particular, that the target, before the observation, has a uniform probability distribution over $\mathcal{R}$ and that this region is in the zone of steady signals. We continue to assume that the errors are small, individually obey the Gauss law, are free from systematic error, and are independent. The novel feature in the present case is that the observed lines of bearing will in general intersect in many points X_{ij}: 3 if $n = 3$; $n(n - 1)/2$ in general. In the earlier case there were two measured quantities ϕ_1 and ϕ_2 to determine the two unknown coordinates x and y of the target's position; the only uncertainties were in the errors in these measurements. These errors are produced by a complex combination of such largely unknown and uncontrollable factors as the state of the target and the detailed refractive structure of the medium at the time of observation. The errors are "small" only in comparison with distances to targets and between observers.

The n equations connecting the bearing errors ε_i with the target coordinates (x, y) and the measured values ϕ_i can be written as follows, where $i = 1, \ldots, n$:

(29) $(x - a_i) \sin \phi_i - (y - b_i) \cos \phi_i = r_i \sin \varepsilon_i; \quad r_i^2 = (x - a_i)^2 + (y - b_i)^2;$

for we have $(x - a_i)/r_i = \sin \theta_i$, etc. From the assumed Gaussian distribution of ε_i about zero with constant standard deviation, now to be denoted by s_i (in place of the earlier σ, σ', and σ''), and in consequence of the conditional independence (i.e., given (x, y)) of these n random errors, we may multiply their n individual probabilities to obtain their joint probability. Denoting this product of their Gaussian densities by $g(\cdot)$, instead of the former $f(\cdot)$, we have the following—to be multiplied by $d\varepsilon_1 \, d\varepsilon_2 \cdots d\varepsilon_n$ to get the probability:

(30) $g(\varepsilon_1, \ldots, \varepsilon_n | x, y) = \dfrac{(2\pi)^{-n/2}}{s_1 \cdots s_n} \exp \dfrac{-1}{2} \left[(\varepsilon_1/s_1)^2 + \cdots + (\varepsilon_n/s_n)^2 \right]$

From this point two steps remain to obtain the a posteriori density of the target. They essentially repeat our reasoning used earlier (Sections 3, 5, 6).

First, because of the uniformity of the target distribution over $\mathcal{C}$, the probability of its being in a region of elementary area $dM_X = dx \, dy$ at $X: (x, y)$ is $dx \, dy / A$. Thus the probability of the compound event—of its being in this region *and* of making n errors in the intervals ε_i, $\varepsilon_i + d\varepsilon_i$—is the product of $g(\varepsilon_1, \ldots, \varepsilon_n | x, y)/A$ times that of the $n + 2$ differentials $dx, \ldots, d\varepsilon_n$. But as usual, this compound event can have its probability expressed as the unconditional probability of having the errors in the above n intervals (the integral of the preceding product over $\mathcal{C}$ with respect to x, y), times the desired probability of target location—given these sets of bearings, which (Bayesian) probability density we now denote (without the previously used prime) $p(x, y | \varepsilon_1, \ldots, \varepsilon_n) = p(x, y | \varepsilon)$. Thus we have shown that the latter is proportional to the $g(\cdots)$ in (30), the coefficient of proportionality being essentially constant in virtue of the assumption of small errors.

Second, we calculate the expression in the exponential in (30) by replacing $\varepsilon_i = \sin \varepsilon_i$ by its value drawn from (29), obtaining for it the new expression

(31) $\displaystyle\sum_{i=1}^{n} (\varepsilon_i/s_i)^2 = \sum_{i=1}^{n} \left[(x - a_i) \sin \phi_i - (y - b_i) \cos \phi_i \right]^2 / (r_i s_i)^2$

$= F(x, y; \phi_1, \ldots, \phi_n) = F(x, y; \phi).$

Thus we have the *theoretically complete* solution of the localization problem, as based on our many assumptions:

(32) $p(x, y; \varepsilon) = K \exp \dfrac{-1}{2} F(x, y; \varepsilon),$

where the normalizing factor K is the reciprocal of the integral of the exponential with respect to (x, y) over the whole target region $\mathcal{R}$. It depends on ϕ_i but of course not on (x, y). It remains to put this solution into a practical form, by constructions and calculations that can actually be carried out.

Before completing the problem above, we shall once again look at the case mentioned at the end of Section 3, when the range or quietness of the target places it in the *zone of unsteady signals*. Accordingly, the assumption is made that the perpendicular distance $u_i = r_i \sin \varepsilon_i$ is measured with an error that is independent of range, the bearing error being roughly inversely proportional to range. To find the a posteriori localization probability we must solve (29) for the n variables u_i:

$$(33) \qquad u_i = (x - a_i) \sin \phi_i - (y_i - b_i) \cos \phi_i$$

and then, using s_i now to denote the standard deviation of the u_i variables, take the product of the n corresponding normal individual densities, obtaining

$$(34) \qquad p(x, y|u) = \frac{(2\pi)^{-n/2}}{s_1 \cdots s_n} \exp \frac{-1}{2} \sum_i (u_i/s_i)^2.$$

8. APPLICATION OF LEAST SQUARES TO LOCALIZATION

The theoretical solution of the localization problem was given in Section 7 as a probability distribution resulting from the observations. If it is to serve as a basis for action, however, (e.g., to approach the target in order to carry out a further operation), it must be put into a directly usable form. In the present situation, the *most probable position* of the target is required (more generally, the values of the variables x_i), and also a quantitative estimate of the *error* or *degree of doubt* that must be associated with this estimated position. In other words, from the infinitude of values contained in the target's probability distribution, we must distill out a small number of the most useful. This process has been carried out in the simpler case of Section 6, where the cross-fix point X_{12} of the two observed lines of bearing was submitted as the most probable position of the target, and the critical ellipse of probability $1 - 1/e$ was determined by its dimensions and orientation. The first task of this section is to extend that method to the case of n observation posts, showing in particular the relation of the critical ellipse for the combined system to those corresponding to the $n(n - 1)/2$ pairs, the ellipse for each pair being constructed as in Section 6. We shall be led to obtain the most probable target position as a *weighted mean* (or center of gravity) of n masses, which the method gives automatically. The second task is to show how accurately the target position is determined, again in terms of the dimensions and orientation of the ellipse of the system of observation posts. All the results are extended with little formal or logical change to the case of (34).

For the multiple fix problem, solved theoretically by the expression (32) for the probability distribution $p(x, y|\phi)$, we must find the most probable target position

X': (x', y')—the one that maximizes $p(x, y|\phi)$. Since K is, as stated before, independent of (x, y), this point is also the one at which $F(x, y; \phi)$ is a *minimum*. Applying (31) we obtain, as in the work leading to (22) in Section 6,

$$(35) \qquad F(x, y; \phi) = Ax^2 - 2Bxy + Cy^2 - 2A'x - 2B'y + C'$$

as the function to minimize. Since the *coefficients* contain (x, y), the minimization problem is not, as things stand, identical with minimizing a quadratic polynomial in x and y; as in the earlier case, approximations will be required to bring it into such a form.

It will be found convenient both for simplicity of the formulas and for their later manipulations to introduce the following arrays, which could be called n-vectors or single-row matrices. We write

$$(36) \qquad u = (u_i) = (\sin \phi_i / s_i r_i); \quad v = (v_i) = (\cos \phi_i / s_i r_i);$$

$$w = (w_i) = ((a_i \sin \phi_i - b_i' \cos \phi_i)/s_i r_i); \quad h = \left(\sqrt{a_i^2 + b_i^2} \, / s_i r_i\right).$$

Further, we use the scalar product notation, writing $u \cdot v = \sum\limits_{i=1}^{n} u_i v_i$, etc. Then a direct calculation of F by means of (31) gives

$$(37) \qquad \begin{array}{lll} A = u \cdot u, & B = u \cdot v, & C = v \cdot v, \\ A' = u \cdot w, & B' = -v \cdot w, & C' = h \cdot h. \end{array}$$

In seeking an approximate solution to our problem, instead of the actual minimizing point X', we shall calculate the coordinates of the point X_0: (x_0, y_0) at which the quadratic polynomial $F(x, y; \phi)$, regarded as having its *coefficients in* (37) *constant*, is minimum. The coordinates (which depend on r_i and hence on x and y) are the solution of the following linear equations, obtained by setting $\partial F/\partial x = \partial F/\partial y = 0$:

$$(38) \qquad \begin{array}{l} Ax_0 - By_0 = A'; \\ -Bx_0 + Cy_0 = B'. \end{array}$$

The Cramer solution is

$$(39) \qquad \left\{ \begin{array}{l} x_0 = D_x/D, \quad \text{where } D = \begin{vmatrix} A & -B \\ -B & C \end{vmatrix}, \\[3mm] y_0 = D_y/D, \quad D_x = \begin{vmatrix} A' & -B \\ B' & C \end{vmatrix}, \; D_y = \begin{vmatrix} A & A' \\ -B & B' \end{vmatrix}. \end{array} \right.$$

These determinants all have a common form, reducible by means of Lagrange's identity, as follows:

$$\Delta = \begin{vmatrix} p \cdot p' & p' \cdot q \\ p \cdot q' & q \cdot q' \end{vmatrix} = \sum_{i<j}^{1 \cdots n} \begin{vmatrix} p_i & p_j \\ q_i & q_j \end{vmatrix} \begin{vmatrix} p_i' & p_j' \\ q_i' & q_j' \end{vmatrix}.$$

This, together with its obvious extension to determinants of order greater than two, is shown by very easy methods in Appendix B.

In reducing D in (39), we write $p = p' = u$, $q = q' = v$ and thus obtain, after applying a trigonometric formula,

$$D = \sum_{i<j}^{n} \left[\frac{\sin(\phi_i - \phi_j)}{s_i r_i s_j r_j} \right]^2 .$$

This is the sum of the $n(n-1)/2$ determinants obtained in Section 6 for each pair of stations O_i, O_j, cf. (26).

To reduce D_x we take $p = w$, $p' = u$, $q = q' = v$ and obtain, after some obvious trigonometric and algebraic reductions,

$$D_x = \sum_{i<j} \left[\frac{\sin(\phi_i - \phi_j)}{s_i r_i s_j r_j} \right]^2 x_{ij},$$

where the point X_{ij}: (x_{ij}, y_{ij}) is the intersection of the i'th and j'th lines of observed bearings, obtained by solving for (x, y) the two equations contained in (29) with the subscripts i and $j > i$. Similarly D_y is reduced by setting $p = p' = u$, $q = w$, $q' = v$ in the above identity, which leads to

$$D_y = \sum_{i<j} \left[\frac{\sin(\phi_i - \phi_j)}{s_i r_i s_j r_j} \right]^2 y_{ij}.$$

Thus the coordinates of X_0 are expressed in terms of those of the $n(n-1)/2$ intersections of pairs of observed lines of bearing, after introducing these three determinants into (39). The resulting expressions still contain the unknown true ranges r_i. Our final approximation consists of replacing r_i by the *observed* range r_{ij} from O_i to X_{ij}, the intersection of the lines of observed bearings at O_i and O_j. This is precisely what was done in Section 6 (for $i = 1$ and $j = 2$). With this approximation we shall write

$$W_{ij} = \left[\frac{\sin(\phi_i - \phi_j)}{2\pi s_i s_j r_{ij} r_{ji}} \right]^2$$

and give the following expression for the coordinates of X_{00}, the approximation to X_0, which was in turn an approximation to X', the point of maximum likelihood of the target's position X:

(40) $$x_{00} = \left(\sum_{i<j} W_{ij} x_{ij} \right) / \sum_{i<j} W_{ij}, \quad y_{00} = \left(\sum_{i<j} W_{ij} y_{ij} \right) / \sum_{i<j} W_{ij}.$$

The last result can be described in the following mechanical terms. Imagine weights W_{ij} placed at the points X_{ij}, the "pairwise fixes." Then the best practical estimate of X is their center of gravity. Since, according to Section 6 (26), these weights W_{ij} are the squares of the reciprocals of the "localization areas," viz., those of the critical ellipses about the corresponding fix points, and since these represent a "measure of ineffectiveness" in the information given by the fix, we see that it is natural, in getting the best combined result, to take such a weighted (vector) average.

It remains to find the overall precision. For this purpose we introduce, as in Section 6, the coordinates $\bar{x} = x - x_0$, $\bar{y} = y - y_0$, which converts $F(x, y; \phi)$ to a quadratic form $\bar{F}(\bar{x}, \bar{y})$ plus a constant, which we can absorb into the normalizing constant, in (32). Then $p(x, y|\phi)$ is proportional to $\exp\dfrac{-1}{2}\bar{F}(\bar{x}, \bar{y})$, and $\bar{F}(\bar{x}, \bar{y})$ is diagonalized by a rotation of coordinate axes as in Section 6. The critical area is again $S = 2\pi\sigma_1\sigma_2 = 2\pi/\sqrt{\lambda_1\lambda_2} = 2\pi/\sqrt{D}$, but now the expansion previously given for D can be used to relate the overall precision to those of the pairwise fixes. The relations may be written in terms of

$$(41) \qquad W = \sum_{i<j} W_{ij}, \qquad W = 1/S^2, \qquad W_{ij} = 1/S_{ij}^2,$$

where S and S_{ij} are the areas of the critical ellipses. Thus the overall localization area S is the reciprocal square root of the sum of the reciprocal squares of the $n(n-1)/2$ pairwise fix localization areas S_{ij}. Explicit formulas for the semiaxes and orientations of the critical ellipse can be given as in Section 6.

Thus the problem of detection and localization by many arrays is solved. The results in usable form have been programmed in computers. The general ideas, when there are different types of long-range data for the localization, are extended by similar mathematical reasoning. Some indications are found in Appendix B.

9. AMBIGUITY OF TARGETS

No discussion of the long-range localization problem considered in Sections 5–8 would be complete without considering the effect of abandoning our constant assumption that there is only one target in the region of search $\mathcal{R}$. Under the conditions of chief interest, there is the possibility of two or three, and sometimes more, targets. Then a purely beam-training method of localization may run into ambiguities. Thus if there were three observation posts and two detectable targets, there would be two lines of observed bearings emanating from each, and these six lines could have a total of two triple intersections (at the targets) and three double intersections (spurious ones) *provided that there were no great bearing errors*. In this case an effective system of communications could weed out the spurious ones. If on the other hand the bearing errors were not far from the angles subtended by the targets at the observation posts, there might be nothing but double intersections, possibly 12 in number, and without additional information, a degree of confusion could be produced.

Actually there are a number of possible ways to obtain enough further evidence concerning the individuality of the targets. They often depend, however, on special circumstances or on rapidly developing equipment and sensors. Their discussion would exceed the limits set in the present book.

Chapter 5

Time Evolution of Target Positions

After a target is detected and localized, an interval of time inevitably passes before
any further operation upon it can be carried out, and if the time is appreciable and
the target is mobile, a wide spread of new positions often has to be considered. In
certain cases there is enough knowledge of the factors governing the target's
motion to enable the searcher to calculate its later position with fair certainty.
More often the knowledge of such factors is quantitatively or qualitatively insufficient for precise prediction but is ample for an estimate of the probabilities of
the future positions. An important case of the latter possibility is in following up a
contact with a target that demands immediate attention: A hostile submarine must
be attacked; survivors on a life raft must be saved before they perish. When this
followup is impossible before the lapse of an interval of time T, we have the
time-late factor in our operation. In other cases the situation calls only for
recording trends in the motion of the targets of interest, as in *wide-area surveillance*.
Many practical examples of these operations will be given in Chapter 8, together
with some references to the many and increasing works on these subjects.
Whatever their individual nature, they come under the operation called *prediction*.

1. ANALYSIS OF FACTORS

It is convenient to separate the factors that affect target motion into *deterministic*
and *random* ones. The former presuppose that the target's motion is governed by a
"simple" and known or observable law, so that if the initial position X_0 at $t = t_0$
and the values of any other parameters that enter in the law of motion are known,
the target's subsequent position X_t at $t > t_0$ can be calculated. All this naturally is
thought of as within the approximations tolerated by the practical operations. This
case will be briefly considered in the next two sections, to be followed by a more

important deterministic situation: the case in which the motion is deterministic in principle and by a known law, but where the law contains unknown parameters or the initial position is not accurately given. Then, when a reasonable assumption regarding the probability distribution of these unknown quantities can be deduced from what is given, a probability calculation gives a distribution of the later positions X_t. This approach, as will be shown in Chapter 8, has formed a useful guide in later search operations.

The *random factors* governing the target's motion are those that prevent the practically useful assumption that it obeys any law of the sort mentioned above. In other words, whatever "law" it obeys, so many parameters are involved that only general principles, such as the central limit theorem of probability or an assumption of maximum entropy, are available for deriving the target's probability distribution at a later epoch t. We must face the fact that the parameters necessary to determine the target's future positions may well be infinite—viz., correspond to unknown *functions*. This would be true in particular when the motion is subjected to the effects of wind and waves and unknown states of the medium. For practical operations, we are obliged to make more or less drastic simplifying assumptions, consciously replacing reality by a "model." One class of models is based on the *Markov* stochastic process, which has many varieties and has undergone extensive development. Basically it assumes that the probabilities of the possible states of the system considered (in case of search, the position X_t) are determined by some known law by the immediately preceding state, in a sense that is made precise in the particular case. The assumption would rule out the very important situations in which the probabilities of the future states require for their determination the whole past history of the system (Lexis series, phenomena of hysteresis and plasticity, many cases examined in economics, history, and sociology). In fact successful applications have been inspired by the study of time series and communication theory. Since the days of modern computers the Markov assumption, in its general form, has been the basis of many computer programs. Processes that in reality are not Markovian have recently been treated by the method underlying the *Kalman filter*. Briefly, after a study of the mechanism of the evolution of the system has revealed its undetermined parameters and led to acceptable "best estimates," the method replaces, at each epoch t, the data observed up to then by the best estimate of the preceding state, and then uses the latter as the basis of a Markov prediction. By thus eliminating inessential *fine structure*, practical simplicity is established. For a contemporary account of its more advanced phases, see [4].

In the present book the vast subject of prediction can be treated only in a few simple cases that have shown importance to the theory of search. There is a simple way to characterize the general nature of the problems that enter into the operational problems in military prediction. There are two time intervals: T, the time required for the searcher to take action once he has detected the target; and τ, the interval between tactical changes of the target's course or the time for various external randomizing effects on its position to take effect. When T is much *less* than τ, a deterministic basis for the prediction is appropriate. When T is much *greater* than τ, the random effects predominate and the methods mentioned in the previous paragraph have to be used. They will lead us to the diffusion equation, with or without drift, the effect of geographical boundaries, and many parts of the modern theory of kinetic probability. Our treatment will be in outline only, illustrated by a model that can be visualized (the swarm of randomly moving but noninterfering particles) and documented by references to the literature. For an explanation of many of the matters in the theory of probability and its basic techniques, Appendix A gives a summary outline.

There remains the question of the situation arising when T and τ are of the same order of size. This would occur when searcher and target are naval units in combat, as in a duel between submarines—but also in the case of a person trying to catch a butterfly! The variety of possibilities and entire dependence of these on the special nature of the case removes them from the scope of the present work.

2. EVOLUTION PRODUCED BY DETERMINISTIC MOTION: THE ONE-TO-ONE CORRESPONDENCE OF STATES

This is the situation first described in the preceding section in which the initial X_0 at t_0 determines the X_t at the later epoch t. It is the case long made familiar in the studies of deformable media, as in hydrodynamics. There the relationship $X_0 \rightarrow X_t$ is described as a "flow" (in two dimensions, in the present case). The functions describing it by giving the coordinates of the image X_t of X_0 are regular (in the conventional sense of this term in mathematical physics: single-valued and continuous through derivatives of sufficiently high order for the purposes of the calculus). Furthermore, except at points of singularity which enter the problem as sources or sinks or similarly easily identified physical peculiarities, the transformations have regular inverses. In the case of deterministic motion of targets, there may be a corresponding situation. Thus, targets may emerge from a restricted area such as a port; they may head for another port. These may usually be regarded as sources and sinks in their motion. Such positions are exceptional, and we may regard the motion, as in the case of fluid flow, as a one-to-one transformation of the plane into itself and apply the familiar mathematical theory of such transformations. See, e.g., Osgood [6] Chap. V for an elementary account.

In the flow of a material substance there is a relation expressing the conservation of matter or mass. Let dM_0 be the area of the elementary region $d\mathcal{M}_0$ at X_0, and dM_t the area of the region into which it goes—point by point—during the evolution of the system from the epoch t_0 to t (for the distinction between "region" and its "area" see introduction to Chapter 1). Evidently the matter in the former is the same as that in the latter. If ρ_0 is the initial density (mass per unit area) and ρ the final, then since their masses are $\rho_0 \, dM_0$ and $\rho \, dM_t$, and these must be equal, we have $\rho_0 \, dM_0 = \rho \, dM_t$. Dividing through by dM_0 and letting the two elementary regions shrink to their respective points, we obtain in the limit an equation involving $\lim(dM_t / dM_0) = J$. Now by a classical theorem of the calculus [6, Chap. XII], this limit J is the *Jacobian* determinant of the four first partial derivatives of the new coordinates of X_t with respect to the initial ones:

(1)
$$J = \frac{\partial(x, y)}{\partial(x_0, y_0)} = \begin{vmatrix} \partial x/\partial x_0 & \partial y/\partial x_0 \\ \partial x/\partial y_0 & \partial y/\partial y_0 \end{vmatrix}.$$

In this notation our equation takes on the form of the *equation of continuity* in the case that the equations of motion are known: $\rho J = \rho_0$.

An exactly similar equation of continuity holds in the case of a probability distribution, with the probability density $p = p(x, y, t)$ replacing $\rho = \rho(x, y, t)$. It is sometimes called the equation of "conservation of probability"; but its actual basis is in the relation of probability with logic. Consider the elementary parts that correspond point-by-point in the flow; if the target is in $d\mathfrak{M}_0$ when $t = t_0$, it will evidently be in $d\mathfrak{M}_t$ at the epoch t—and conversely. Now it is a fundamental principle of probability that if two events are so related that either one implies the other, their probabilities are equal (see Appendix A, Section 3). Their respective probabilities being $p(x_0, y_0, t_0) \, dM_0$ and $p(x, y, t) \, dM_t$, the same reasoning as before establishes the equation (dM = area of $d\mathfrak{M}$, etc.)

(2)
$$p(x, y, t)J(x, y, t) = p(x_0, y_0, t_0).$$

Here we have expressed the determinant J in (1) in terms of the variables without the 0 subscript, simply by expressing the latter in terms of the plain variables after the differentiations in (1), by using the inverse equations (which express the coordinates of the initial point in terms of those of the final point) and giving t_0 an arbitrarily chosen value, e.g., 0.

3. THE SWARM OF PARTICLES WITH A GIVEN VELOCITY FIELD

The relations developed in Section 2 apply to functions that embody the law of motion of the targets searched: they cannot be used for calculating future positions or probabilities of these until the functions are known. This raises the fundamental practical question: just what can a searcher realistically be supposed to know in typical cases? In Chapter 4, Section 1, we gave a simple set of examples, illustrated by Fig. 4-1, of targets moving radially away from (or toward) a central point, representing a harbor, beach-head objective, or a position from which they were attempting to escape from a followup of a detection that they believed to have been made of them. In these cases the known or inferred physical characteristics of the targets could give the searcher a good estimate of the targets' speed, while the radial character of their direction was gathered from general tactical considerations. This means that the *field of vector velocities* was known. There are many cases in which the targets' velocity field can be known inferentially and can, as was shown in the radial examples just cited, lead to knowledge of the probability density.

Let us then suppose that the rectangular components of the vector velocity are the known functions $u = u(x, y, t)$ and $v = (x, y, t)$. They are, of course, the partial derivatives with respect to t of the functions expressing the coordinates of the moving target, in the result of which differentiation the coordinates of the initial position X_0 are replaced by their values as functions of the final coordinates by use of the inverse equations, etc. But the important practical question is the converse: given the functions u and v, how can we obtain the equations of the target's motion?

The answer is given by the elementary theory of ordinary differential equations, in the present case of the second order. The process just described for finding u and v as partial derivatives of x and y (holding the initial coordinates fast) is called *differentiation along the path of motion* and is denoted by dx/dt and dy/dt. Thus we have the system of differential equations

(3) $$dx/dt = u(x, y, t), \qquad dy/dt = v(x, y, t).$$

Their solution yields x and y as functions of t and of the initial data x_0, y_0, and t_0 —in other words, the desired equations of target motion.

The formula for changing variables in partial differentiation shows that if $f = f(x, y, t)$ is any function, its derivative along the path is

(4) $$df/dt = \partial f/\partial t + u\, \partial f/\partial x + v\, \partial f/\partial y.$$

Applying this to (2) with $f = pJ$, we obtain a result that is readily put into the form of the *differential equation of continuity*

(5) $$\frac{\partial p}{\partial t} + \frac{\partial(pu)}{\partial x} + \frac{\partial(pv)}{\partial y} = 0$$

The reduction of $d(pJ)/dt = 0$ to the above form requires the formula $dJ/dt = J$ $(\partial u/\partial x + \partial v/\partial x)$, proved by the rules of determinant differentiation and their elementary properties.

The conventional proof of (5) [6, Chap. XII, Section 12] is based on a *flux diagram* of the sort shown in the plane in Fig. 5-1. To prepare for the more complicated cases of diffusive flow (targets' velocity affected by random) to be examined later, we shall outline the proof on the basis of the representation of a probability density $p(x, y, t)$ at t by a *swarm of noninterfering particles* (targets). Their expected number per unit area at (x, y) and time t is $N = N(x, y, t) = N_A p(x, y, t)$, where N_A is their total number in the whole region $\mathcal{R}$. This idea was introduced in Chapter 2, Section 4, and applied under special assumptions in later sections. Actually the situation shown in Fig. 4-1 can be interpreted as a picture of centrifugally moving swarms, etc. In the case to be considered here, all the particles in the neighborhood of each given point X have at t a common velocity vector **w**: (u, v).

Figure 5-1 gives the traditional construction of the flux of particles across the arc Γ in the sense of the normal vector **n**. The expected number that will, between t

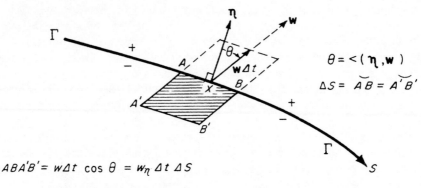

$$ABA'B' = w\Delta t \cos \theta = w_\eta \,\Delta t \,\Delta S$$

$$X : (x, y) \; ; \; \mathbf{A'A} = \mathbf{B'B} = \mathbf{w}\,\Delta t$$

Fig. 5-1. Flux through element of arc Δs.

and $t + \Delta t$, cross the elementary arc AB comes from the "parallelogram" $ABA'B'$, of area $w\,\Delta t\,\Delta s \cos \theta = w_n\,\Delta t\,\Delta s$; hence it is this area multiplied by the density. Thus the flux at X is $Nw_n = N_A p w_n$, and taking its line integral around the whole boundary Γ of any given region S, we obtain the net mean loss of particles from S (**n** being its exterior normal). On the other hand the expected rate of increase of particles in S is the time derivative of the expected number in it, that is, of the integral of N over S. Clearly the rate of increase in S plus the rate of exit across must be zero. The former rate may (by Leibniz's rule) be written as

$$(6) \qquad \frac{d}{dt} \iint_S N(x, y, t)\, dx\, dy = \iint_S \frac{\partial}{\partial t} N(x, y, t)\, dx\, dy,$$

while the line integral becomes a double integral by use of Green's theorem:

$$(7) \quad \int_\Gamma Nw_n\, ds = \int_\Gamma N(-v\, dx + u\, dy) = \iint_S \left[\partial(Nu)/\partial x + \partial(Nv)/\partial y \right] dM.$$

Therefore the vanishing sum of (6) and (7) coincides with an equation stating that the integral over S of N_A times the expression on the left in (5) is zero. Since this is true for all S and since the integrand may be supposed to be continuous, the usual reasoning shows that it vanishes identically—a second proof of (5). Later we shall apply this treatment to the case in which the target velocity vectors at a given place and time are not all the same, but are affected by randomizing conditions, only the expected value being predictable. Then the resulting equation, while possibly containing terms such as (5), will also have second-order partial derivatives with respect to x and y; it will be the *diffusion equation*, reducing to the heat equation in simpler cases.

The most important type of motion in search is the *steady* one, viz., when in (3) the velocity field is independent of the time: $u = u(x, y)$, $v = v(x, y)$. Then the density p or N that satisfies (5) may or may not depend on the time; in the latter case $\partial p/\partial t = 0$, and p is called a *stationary* distribution. It applies to situations that have persisted so long that a quasiequilibrium is reached, as implied in the cases examined in Chapter 2. Nonstationary cases are important in prediction of future positions of a target whose initial probable positions have been determined by a fix, as in Chapter 4, Sections 5–8. Practical implementation in both cases will be treated in Chapter 8.

Returning to the general case of (3) and (5) we note that the latter, by use of (4), may be put into the form (involving the divergence of **w**)

$$(8) \qquad \frac{dp}{dt} + p\left(\frac{\partial u}{\partial x} + \frac{\partial v}{\partial y} \right) = 0.$$

We recall that any nonconstant function $f = f(x, y, t)$ that remains constant along each path of motion defined by (3)—i.e., for which $df/dt = 0$—is called a *first integral* of (3). If p_1 and p_2 are two positive densities each satisfying (5), then it is easy to show by use of (8) that their quotient $f = p_2/p_1$ is a first integral. Conversely, if a nonnegative first integral f is known, from a density p a second one is pf. Since any function of first integrals is also evidently another one, an infinitude of densities can be found as $pG(f)$ where G is nonnegative (and a normalizing constant factor may be introduced to make it integrate to unity). This shows how far the velocity field is from determining densities.

To illustrate these general facts in a simple but important case, we return to the radial velocity field of Fig. 4-1, assuming that vector **w** is directed on OX, but that its magnitude, or the speed w, is unrestricted. In polar coordinates (r, θ) at O, we then have

$$(9) \qquad x = r \cos \theta, y = r \sin \theta; u = w \cos \theta, v = w \sin \theta.$$

Then a routine change of variables of differentiation shows that (5) becomes

$$(10) \qquad \frac{\partial p}{\partial t} + \frac{\partial (pw)}{\partial r} + \frac{pw}{r} = 0.$$

As a first application of (10), assume that p is a stationary distribution, $\partial p/\partial t = 0$. Then (10) becomes an ordinary differential equation in the function pw and independent variable r, but involving θ as a parameter. Its solution gives that pwr is independent of r, but it may depend on θ: $pwr = G(\theta)$. In the first case treated in Chapter 4, Section 1, we assumed that w is constant, and rotational symmetry $G(\theta) = $ constant, thus obtaining the formula giving p as a constant divided by r. The more general solution giving the density proportional to $G(\theta)/r$ may be used to describe a strategy of target exits or approaches that favors certain directions over others. The second cases treated sought a law of motion that maintained the distribution uniform. This requires in the stationary case that w be inversely proportional to r, as (10) shows; a mathematical truth, but requiring an operationally incredible implementation, as noted in Chapter 4.

Finally let us see what (10) shows regarding a time-dependent but spatially constant p over a growing circular region centered at 0. The importance of this question is evidenced by the fact that many follow-up search plans have come into use that assume such a density as possible. Suppose that inside a growing circle of radius $R = R(t)$, $p = 1/\pi R^2$, and outside $= 0$. Then (10) reduces to an ordinary differential equation, giving the general solution $W = r\ (d \log R/dt) + c(t)/r$, where $c(t)$ is an arbitrary function of t. Such a mode of motion is practically altogether unrealistic; searches based on it may be very far from optimal.

4. EVOLUTION UNDER CONSTANT UNKNOWN MOTION

In the cases considered above, the velocity field (at least in direction) was known, and the problem of predicting the future distribution of targets was tied to that of finding solutions of (5) restricted by special conditions reflecting the nature of the operation. It is largely an initial-value problem. We must now consider a further source of random: the case of a velocity field known only in form, and containing certain parameters, the values of which are needed to determine the motion completely. We suppose that we are able to find a plausible probability distribution for the latter. Such cases have occurred in Chapter 2 in Sections after 4, where the direction of the velocity vector, but not its magnitude, was unknown and could reasonably be assumed to be uniformly distributed through all angles.

Our first problem is based on the same assumption, but assumes further that initially (at $t = 0$) the target's position is not known precisely but that it has a circular normal distribution about the known initial point O and with the known standard deviation σ. This situation arises in a wide variety of cases, as when a submarine is initially detected by high-frequency direction finding (HFDF), always of limited accuracy, and can be presumed to be moving at the known speed w but in an arbitrary and unknown direction.

Figure 5-2 shows the construction of the distribution $p(x, y, t) = p(X, t)$ that evolves after t hours from the initial one

$$(11) \qquad p(X, 0) = f(r) = \frac{1}{2\pi\sigma^2} e^{-r^2/2\sigma^2}.$$

Consider first the case of a target whose vector velocity w makes a given angle γ with the direction from O to the contemplated position [γ is measured as usual

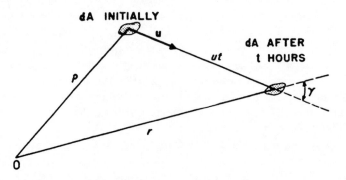

Fig. 5-2. Entry of target into dA.

from vector **r** (from O to reference point in $d\mathcal{C}$) to vector **w**]. This target will be in dA if and only if it had initially been in a region congruent to dA and situated wt miles away in the direction of the reversed vector $-\mathbf{w}$, as shown in Fig. 5-2. The probability of this event is

$$\frac{1}{2\pi\sigma^2} e^{-\rho^2/2\sigma^2} \, dA = \frac{1}{2\pi\sigma^2} e^{-(r^2 + w^2t^2 - 2rwt\cos\gamma)/2\sigma^2} \, dA.$$

Now the probability that **w** will make an angle with **r** between γ and $\gamma + d\gamma$ is $d\gamma/2\pi$. The probability of both these events is the product of these two probabilities, and to obtain the required total probability $f(r, t) \, dA$ this product is added (integrated) over all possible initial positions of dA, i.e., over all values of γ from 0 to 2π:

$$f(r, t) = \frac{1}{2\pi\sigma^2} \cdot \frac{1}{2\pi} \int_0^{2\pi} e^{-(r^2 + w^2t^2 - 2rwt\cos\gamma)/2\sigma^2} \, d\gamma$$

$$= \frac{1}{2\pi\sigma^2} e^{-(r^2 + w^2t^2)/2\sigma^2} \cdot \frac{1}{2\pi} \int_0^{2\pi} e^{2rwt\cos\gamma/2\sigma^2} \, d\gamma.$$

Now we have

$$\frac{1}{2\pi} \int_0^{2\pi} e^{rwt\cos\gamma/\sigma^2} \, d\gamma = \frac{1}{2\pi} \int_0^{2\pi} e^{-rwt\cos\gamma/\sigma^2} \, d\gamma$$

$$= \frac{1}{2\pi} \int_0^{2\pi} e^{i(irwt)\cos\gamma/\sigma^2} \, d\gamma$$

$$= J_0\left\{i\left(\frac{rwt}{\sigma^2}\right)\right\} = I_0\left(\frac{rwt}{\sigma^2}\right),$$

where $i = \sqrt{-1}$ and J_0 denotes the ordinary Bessel function of zeroth order, I_0 its value for pure imaginary values of the argument [8, Chap. XVII]. Thus the equation

$$(12) \qquad p(X, t) = f(r, t) = \frac{1}{2\pi\sigma^2} e^{-(r^2 + w^2t^2)/2\sigma^2} I_0\left(\frac{rwt}{\sigma^2}\right).$$

The graph of $f(r, t)$ for different values of t is shown in Fig. 5-3 as a function of r. The graph of $p(X, t)$ is the surface of revolution generated by revolving the corresponding curve of Fig. 5-3 around the vertical axis. It is seen how the probability spreads outward with time, so that the target is most likely to be in an expanding *ring* about O.

An application of the asymptotic approximation

$$(13) \qquad I_0(z) \sim e^{-z}/\sqrt{2\pi z}$$

for large z shows that

$$(14) \qquad f(r, t) \sim \frac{1}{2\pi\sqrt{rwt}} \cdot \frac{1}{\sigma\sqrt{2\pi}} e^{-\frac{(r - wt)^2}{2\sigma^2}},$$

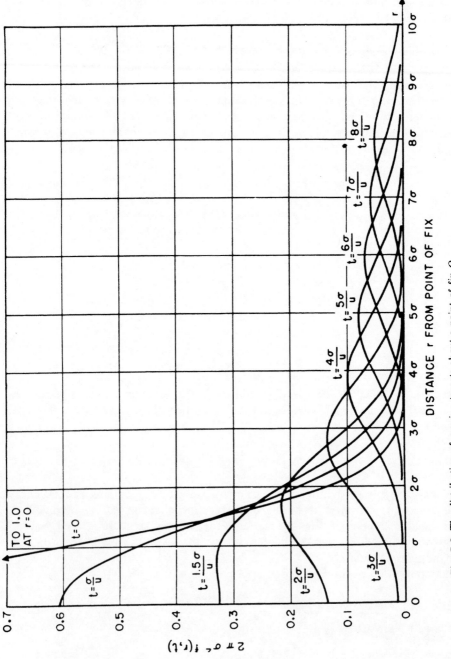

Fig. 5-3. The distribution of moving targets about a point of fix O.

and thus its cross section by a generating vertical plane is proportional to a one-variate normal distribution of mean wt and standard deviation σ. The coefficient is an (approximate) normalizing factor, since the integral of $f(r, t)\,dA = f(r, t)r\,dr\,d\theta$ over the whole plane must be unity.

The distribution (12) was introduced into antisubmarine warfare in 1943 by the late G. E. Kimball. At about the same time it was applied to bullet-hole distributions on aircraft returning to England after combat missions, and has become known as the *Carlton distribution*, after the author of those investigations.

A further problem of evolution under constant unknown motion is important: the generalization of the one just treated to the case that the velocity vector **w**, instead of having its length (speed w) known, is to be thought of as having been chosen once and for all from a normal distribution on the velocity plane of (u, v). The principal standard deviations and axes are supposed known. As for the mean $(\bar{u}, \bar{v}) = (Eu, Ev)$, only its distance from the origin is known, while its direction $\gamma = \tan^{-1}(v/u)$ is uniformly distributed as before.

The first step in the solution is to express the density after t hours as that of the sum of the two normally distributed vectors, $\overrightarrow{OX}$ and (ut, vy), in terms of the postulated values of $(\bar{u}, \bar{v})$. By a standard theorem, this is a normal distribution, easily expressed in terms of the known or postulated data; (see Appendix A). After expressing this result in terms of the length of $(\bar{u}, \bar{v})$ and angle γ, it is averaged over the latter, by dividing its integral over the interval $(0 \leqslant \gamma \leqslant 2\pi)$ by 2π. Results very similar to (12) are obtained.

The chief value of these and similar refinements is to test the sensitivity of the predictions to the imperfect estimates of the parameters, etc. We reemphasize that all the results obtained thus far assume that the prosecution time T is *much less* than the time τ between the target's changes of velocities.

5. TARGET DISTRIBUTIONS EVOLVING BY RANDOM COURSE CHANGES

The remainder of the present chapter will be based on the assumption that the prosecution time T is *much longer* than the average time τ between changes in the target's motion. A greater scale of geographic distances is implied. The basic assumption regarding the target's motions is their randomness—their unpredictability by the searcher. This may be caused by such external actions as wind, waves, and currents on a life raft, or by human confusion, as the disorientation of a lost person wandering in the wilderness. It may also be due to a deliberate strategy on the part of a hostile target which, aware that it is exposed to occasional detection, hopes to degrade the predictive value to its enemy of such occasional localizations. In the latter case the target may combine the random zigzagging with a mean progress toward a particular geographical objective.

Mathematically, the evolution of the target's distribution is usually well described by a *parabolic partial differential equation* of the second order. In simple cases this may be the *heat equation*; in more complicated situations, the *diffusion equation*, with or without *drift*. These equations have recently been much applied to *stochastic processes* governing a wide variety of physical phenomena, such as Brownian motion, diffusion of electrons in metals and semiconductors, "drunkard's walk," Wiener processes, and many others. In addition to the phenomena at the molecular and electronic level, these equations are entering into various branches of operational research. A few more details and references to the conventional texts will be given in Appendix A.

In order to show how the present questions of target motions can be brought under these equations and methods, we return to our model of the swarm of noninterfering particles, but without the assumption that the velocity of a particle at a given time t is determined by its position (x, y). In principle, we have now to deal with a probability distribution in a "space" of the four variables (x, y, u, v). This corresponds to the *phase space* in the Hamiltonian theory of systems of two degrees of freedom. The basic function is $\mathfrak{N}(x, y, u, v, t)$, where its product $\mathfrak{N}\, dx\, dy\, du\, dv$ is the expected or mean number of particles in the elementary 4-volume in question: at the epoch t being in the element of area $dx\, dy$ at (x, y), and having a velocity vector $\mathbf{w}$ in the element $du\, dv$ at (u, v). This function corresponds to Boltzmann's "number density" of gas molecules in his theory of irreversible flow (here, in two dimensions). In fact, the analogy between that theory and our swarm of particles is useful in some respects, but could be misleading in others. The reason is that molecular *encounters* play a basic part in the kinetic theory of gases, whereas they never occur in our model of the swarm of particles, where their motions are internally determined or are driven by external and not mutual forces.

This function $\mathfrak{N}$ of its five variables contains all the statistical information concerning our swarm of particles at t—deferring for the moment their time-correlation. Thus, integrating over all velocities,

$$(15) \qquad \int\int \mathfrak{N}(x, y, t, u, v)\, du\, dv = N(x, y, t);$$

$$(16) \qquad \int\int \mathbf{w}\mathfrak{N}(x, y, t, u, v)\, du\, dv = N(x, y, t)\, \mathbf{c}\,(x, y, t),$$

where $\mathbf{c}$ is the expected or mean velocity of a particle given to be at (x, y) at the epoch t. It is a conditional expected value, and the formula becomes an evident consequence of the laws of probability if we divide out the common constant factor (total number of particles), thus replacing N and $\mathfrak{N}$ by probability densities (the former by p, etc.). This vector $\mathbf{c}$ represents the "deterministic" part of the motion, corresponding to the "mass motion" of a molecular medium. The difference $\mathbf{w}' = \mathbf{w} - \mathbf{c}$ is the purely chaotic part, comparable to the thermal agitation of the molecules of a gas. Furthermore, (15) gives positional density of targets, precisely as it was defined in the previous sections. Finally, the quotient $\mathfrak{N}(x, y, u, v, t)/N(x, y, t)$ is the conditional distribution of the vector velocities of those particles that are at (x, y) at the time t.

With our assumption that τ is much less than T, a fairly wide range of *relaxation times* between them exists. Let Δt be such a time interval; during it, many changes in the motion of the target can occur, but no marked changes in the geography of the search takes place. If one of our particles is, at epoch t, at point X_t, it will at later epoch $t + \Delta t$ be at point $X_{t+\Delta t}$. We say that this particle has made a *vector advance* $\mathbf{g}(\Delta t) = \overrightarrow{X_t X_{t+\Delta t}}$ and has advanced a distance $g(\Delta t)$. Owing to the fact that during Δt the particle will normally have had many changes in its motion, there is no simple relation between $g(\Delta t)$ and $w \Delta t$, where w was its speed at epoch t. In fact, as we shall see, to obtain consistent results, we must suppose that $g(\Delta t)$ is of the order of $\sqrt{\Delta t}$, and thus the quotient $g(\Delta t)/\Delta t$ is of increasingly large order as Δt moves toward its lower range of permissible values—in contrast to the fact that if Δt were allowed to fall below the relaxation range and actually approach zero, the quotient would approach w. These simple facts have led to such fanciful statements as that "a Brownean particle has no velocity (or an infinite one)"; this has nothing to do with the physical facts, but is merely an artifact of a mathematical approximation applied beyond its range of validity.

As in Section 3, we apply the law of conservation of the particles of our swarm, first calculating the expected net number crossing an arc of a curve Γ during the time interval $(t, t + \Delta t)$ in an arbitrarily chosen "positive" direction, then equating this to the expected increase in any region bounded by Γ. For obvious reasons, Fig. 5-2 has to be replaced by Fig. 5-4—based on the *advance class* $\mathbf{g}(\Delta t)$—rather than the *velocity class* $\mathbf{w}$.

The figure is drawn to so small a scale that curves are indistinguishable from straight lines and all functions of position and time may be replaced by their linear Taylor approximations. Moreover, as an essential part of the "relaxation time" property of Δt, we assume that the expected number of particles at the different points in and near the parallelogram $ABA'B'$ that have a given value of their advance vector varies only slightly from point to point.

The particles of the advance class $\mathbf{g}$ that cross the small arc $\overset{\frown}{AB}$ on Γ of length Δs must come, during Δt, from the "parallelogram" constructed as shown in the

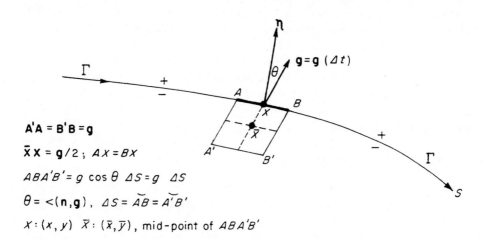

$$A'A = B'B = \mathbf{g}$$
$$\bar{x}x = g/2\,; \quad Ax = Bx$$
$$ABA'B' = g \cos\theta\ \Delta S = g\ \Delta S$$
$$\theta = \sphericalangle(\mathbf{n},\mathbf{g}), \quad \Delta S = \overset{\frown}{AB} = \overset{\frown}{A'B'}$$
$$x:(x,y) \quad \bar{x}:(\bar{x},\bar{y}),\ \text{mid-point of } ABA'B'$$

Fig. 5-4. Flux through element Δs during relaxation time Δt.

figure: they will cross "positively" if **g** makes an acute angle θ with the positive normal **n**, negatively if θ is obtuse. The expected number crossing $\widehat{AB}$ is therefore the expected number at epoch t in the parallelogram: the integral of $N(X, t)$ over it. An elementary exercise in calculus shows that the integral of a linear function over a region having a center of symmetry is equal to the value of the integrand at this point, times the area of the region. Since $\bar{X}$ is the center of symmetry of $ABA'B'$, and since we are approximating to N linearly by its Taylor expansion about X, our integral is

$$\left\{ N(X, t) + (\bar{x} - x)N_x(X, t) + (\bar{y} - y)N_y(X, t) \right\} area(ABA'B').$$

The area is $g \cos \theta \, \Delta s$ when θ is acute, and its negative when obtuse. Hence, if this expression is substituted for the area in the above, we shall have the correct sign: positive when the crossing is from the negative to the positive side of Γ, negative in the contrary case. Further, we may suppose the x and y coordinate axes are in the direction of **n** and of the positively directed Γ. Then $N_x = N_n$ and $N_y = N_s$: the normal and tangential derivatives of N. Finally,

$$\bar{x} - x = \frac{g}{2}\cos \theta, \qquad \bar{y} - y = \frac{g}{2}\sin \theta.$$

Putting these results together, and dividing by Δs to get the expected flux per unit arc across Γ at X from t to $t + \Delta t$ of the advance class **g**:

(17) $F(X, t, \mathbf{g}) = N(X, t)g \cos \theta$

$$-\frac{1}{2}N_n(X, t)g^2 \cos^2 \theta - \frac{1}{2}N_s(X, t)g^2 \cos \theta \sin \theta.$$

To find the net (algebraic) expected flux, we must sum $F(X, t, \mathbf{g})$ over all possible advance vectors **g** with their appropriate weighting factors. It is at this point that the special assumptions relevant to the various applications must be stated explicitly. What principles govern the erratic motions of the targets in such a way as to produce the various possible advance vectors **g**? If only natural or humanly uncontrollable factors produce the result, we may reasonably assume that $\mathbf{c} = 0$ and that **g** is uniformly distributed over positions and directions and with its length g independent of directions. Then θ is uniformly distributed, and to find the net expected flux, we simply integrate the F in (17) over the interval $(0 \leqslant \theta \leqslant 2\pi)$ and divide by 2π. We easily see that the first and third terms on the right in (17) lead to zero, whereas the second term leads to $-N_n(X, t)g^2/4$. To complete the result we must introduce some reasonable weighting factor, viz., probability distribution for g, and thus convert its square to $\overline{g^2}$: the *mean square advance*. Thus the flux density outward from our region is $-N_n(X, T)\overline{g^2}/4$. Reversing the sign to obtain the flux into it, and applying Green's theorem, we obtain for the rate of expected inflow

(18) $$\int_\Gamma \frac{\overline{g^2}}{4} \frac{\partial N}{\partial n} \, ds = \iint_\mathcal{B} \frac{\overline{g^2}}{4} \nabla^2 N \, dM.$$

During Δt the expected increase in number of particles in $\mathcal{B}$ is Δt times the integral of N over the region; this being equal to the above double integral (and this for all regions $\mathcal{B}$), the usual reasoning establishes the equality of the integrands. The resulting differential equation, written in terms of p, is

(19)
$$\frac{\partial p}{\partial t} = \frac{\sigma^2}{2}\nabla^2 p, \qquad \sigma^2 = \overline{g^2}/2\,\Delta t.$$

The striking feature of this formula—which coincides with the heat equation in a homogeneous and isotropic medium, or the diffusion equation without drift under similar conditions—is that we have kept Δt finite: as long as it remains in the interval $\tau \ll \Delta t \ll T$, i.e., is of the order of magnitude of relaxation times in the system, σ will be essentially independent of Δt.

The solution of (19) having complete symmetry about a given point $X_0 \; X_0$: (x_0, y_0) is well known: the Gaussian function

(20)
$$G(\overline{XX_0}, t) = \frac{1}{2\pi t\sigma^2}e^{-r^2/2t\sigma^2}; \quad r = \overline{XX_0}.$$

It is also known that this is the transition probability controlling the evolution of any given initial distribution $p_0(x_0, y_0)$ by the equation

(21)
$$p(x, y, t) = \int\int p_0(x_0, y_0)G(x - x_0, y - y_0, t)\,dx_0\,dy_0.$$

Thus it plays the role of the *Green's function* in the present "parabolic" case.

We conclude this section by outlining the necessary modifications in our very simple assumptions regarding the distribution of the vector advance g. Various possibilities arising in the operations involving search may make more flexibility necessary.

In the most general case in treating (17), the weighting function of the g at (X, t) will depend on this point and epoch and will not have angular symmetry. It is therefore a function $L(X, t, g, \phi)$, where ϕ is the angle from the positive x-axis to g: (g, ϕ) are the polar coordinates of this vector. If ψ is the corresponding angle to n, clearly $\theta = \phi - \psi$. We must then multiply (17) by the element $Lg\,dg\,d\phi$ and integrate over all "velocity space" (g, ϕ) to get the desired flux across Γ at (X, t). First we note that the linear factor in (17) is $N_n \cos\theta + N_s \sin\theta$, and this is the directional derivative of N in the direction of g. It can be written as $N_x \cos\phi + N_y \sin\phi$. Thus our integrand becomes

$$FLg\,dg\,d\phi = NLg\,\cos(\phi - \psi)g\,dg\,d\phi$$
$$- \frac{1}{2}Lg^2(N_x \cos\phi + N_y \sin\phi)\cos(\phi - \psi)g\,dg\,d\phi.$$

Expanding and integrating over $0 < g < \infty$ and $-\pi < \phi < \pi$, we are led to the following five integrals, having obvious interpretations as means (denoted by bars) of x- and y-components of g and their powers and products:

$$\int\int L \cdot g\cos\phi \cdot g\,dg\,d\phi = \bar{g}_x, \qquad \int L \cdot g\sin\phi \cdot g\,dg\,d\phi = \bar{g}_y$$

$$\int\int L \cdot (g\cos\phi)^2 \cdot g\,dg\,d\phi = \overline{g_x^2}, \qquad \int\int L \cdot (g\sin\phi)^2 \cdot g\,dg\,d\phi = \overline{g_y^2}$$

$$\int\int L \cdot g\cos\phi \cdot g\sin\phi \cdot g\,dg\,d\phi = \overline{g_x g_y}.$$

Now for reasons already stated $\overline{g_x} = \overline{g_y} = 0$. Hence only the second line on the left survives in the integrand and, if we write

$$\overline{g_x^2} = \Delta t\, \sigma_x^2 \qquad \overline{g_x g_y} = \Delta t\, \rho\, \sigma_x \sigma_y, \qquad \overline{g_y^2} = \Delta t\, \sigma_y^2,$$

we obtain the final result for the flux (ρ = correlation of g_x and g_y):

$$-\frac{\Delta t}{2}\left[\sigma_x^2 N_x \cos\psi + \rho\,\sigma_x\sigma_y(N_x \sin\psi + N_y \cos\psi) + \sigma_y^2 N_y \sin\psi\right].$$

To get the total mean influx of particles into the region $\mathcal{B}$ bounded by Γ, we must multiply the above, with its sign reversed, by ds and take the line integral in the clockwise direction shown in Fig. 5-4. Equivalently, and in more direct connection with Green's theorem, we leave the negative sign unchanged, but integrate in the counterclockwise sense ("positive" with respect to the bounded region $\mathcal{B}$). Using the elementary geometry relations for the angles with the normal: $\cos\psi = -\,dy/ds$, $\sin\psi = dx/ds$, the integral becomes $(\Delta t/2)\int_\Gamma P\,dx + Q\,dy$, where

(22) $$P = -\left(\rho\,\sigma_x\sigma_y N_x + \sigma_y^2 N_y\right), \qquad Q = \sigma_x^2 N_x + \rho\,\sigma_x\sigma_y N_y.$$

The remainder of the derivation transforms the contour integral by Green's theorem into the surface integral of $\partial Q/\partial x - \partial P/\partial y$ over $\mathcal{B}$, and then equates it to the corresponding integral of $\partial N/\partial t$. Thus we obtain the following generalization of (19), written in terms of $p = p(x, y, t)$:

(23) $$\frac{\partial p}{\partial t} = \frac{1}{2}\frac{\partial}{\partial x}\left(\sigma_x^2\frac{\partial p}{\partial x} + \rho\,\sigma_x\sigma_y\frac{\partial p}{\partial y}\right) + \frac{1}{2}\frac{\partial}{\partial y}\left(\rho\,\sigma_x\sigma_y\frac{\partial p}{\partial x} + \sigma_y^2\frac{\partial p}{\partial y}\right).$$

When the coefficients are constant, this is reduced to the form (19) by a linear change of coordinates; whence it appears that it has the following elementary solution (Green's function):

$$p(x, y, t) = \frac{1}{2\pi t\,\sigma_x\sigma_y\sqrt{1 - \rho^2}}\exp\frac{-1}{2t(1 - \rho^2)}\left[\frac{x^2}{\sigma_x^2} - \frac{2\rho xy}{\sigma_x\sigma_y} + \frac{y^2}{\sigma_y^2}\right].$$

This is normalized, but centered at (0, 0). To get it at a general central point (x_0, y_0) replace x and y by $x - x_0$ and $y - y_0$ throughout.

6. RANDOMLY PERTURBED PURPOSEFUL MOTION: DIFFUSION WITH DRIFT

As stated in the first paragraph of the preceding section, the targets whose statistics have been represented by our swarm of particles may be combining their random course changes with their purpose of reaching a geographical objective. The case of the evasively moving submarine in transit is an obvious case in point, but so is the life raft buffeted by wind and waves and either drifting in a fairly strong current or attempting to gain shore. Whatever the cause, such cases cannot be treated by setting the mean velocity **c**, defined in (16), equal to zero: **c** will have to be taken into account in the flux calculation across Γ of Figs. 5-1 and 5-4.

During the relaxation time Δt, the particle that started at X_t will move to $X_{t+\Delta t}$. But now the vector displacement is the sum of two vectors, its mean motion and its random advance with respect to the class of particles in its neighborhood all moving with the same mean velocity **c**. Consequently

$$(24) \qquad \overrightarrow{X_t X}_{t+\Delta t} = \mathbf{c}\,\Delta t + \mathbf{g}(\Delta t).$$

In calculating the resultant flux we may simply sum the value obtained by the construction of Fig. 5-1 with that corresponding with Fig. 5-4. The final result of the reasoning of the sort used often before, based on the conservation of particles, is to obtain a differential equation like (23), but with $\partial p/\partial t$ replaced by the left-hand member of (10), u and v being the components of **c**:

$$(25) \quad \frac{\partial p}{\partial t} + \frac{\partial(pu)}{\partial x} + \frac{\partial(pv)}{\partial u}$$

$$= \frac{1}{2}\frac{\partial}{\partial x}\left(\sigma_x^2\frac{\partial p}{\partial x} + \rho\,\sigma_x\sigma_y\frac{\partial p}{\partial y}\right) + \frac{1}{2}\frac{\partial}{\partial y}\left(\rho\,\sigma_x\sigma_y\frac{\partial p}{\partial x} + \sigma_y^2\frac{\partial p}{\partial y}\right).$$

7. SOME APPLICATIONS AND PRACTICAL COMMENTS

There are two essentially different situations under which the target motions described in the Sections 5 and 6 can take place: distributions representing a *stationary state*, characterized by the fact that $\partial p/\partial t = 0$; and those representing a *transient condition*, when at a general fixed point, p changes with time. This distinction is identical with the one made in Section 3. As in the earlier case, steady states can occur only when the coefficients of the differential equation are independent of time: motion governed by *steady* conditions. Transients can occur under more general ones, but they are usually studied in the steady case, or when the coefficients are very simple in their dependence on time, e.g., are periodic, as in diurnal variation, when solutions of the same periodicity may be sought. (Similar distinctions are made in most practical applications of stochastic processes. The case of coefficients showing diurnal periodicity because of variations of demands on airports has led to a useful periodic solution to the waiting line problem. See Koopman [5].) Stationary states are important when there are many targets (better described by N than by p), and the situation has remained unchanged over a long period of time. Transients are important in the *prediction problem*: to estimate the target's later positions after a previous observation—or some other evidence—has localized it. Other things being equal, whether the motion is stationary or transient depends on the initial conditions, the function $p(x, y, 0)$.

In addition to the differential equations and the initial conditions, the evolution of target positions depends on the *boundary conditions*. As in the study of the flow of heat in a material plane, and in fact in all studies of stochastic diffusion equations, three types of boundaries are important: *emitting boundaries*, out of which particles (or heat) can flow, e.g., from which submarines set forth; *absorbing boundaries*, at which particles disappear (or heat leaves through a better conductor), e.g., a geographical objective where our targets land; and finally, the *reflecting boundaries*, which are not reflective in the precise optical sense, but are impassable to our targets, either for geographical or political reasons. For thermal flow, they are insulators. They influence the solution of the equation [e.g., of (19)] through the fact that the flux normal to the boundary must vanish (e.g., in (18) $\partial N/\partial n = 0$).

It is a result of the general theory of diffusion equations of the type that we have been studying that the equation, the initial conditions, and the full boundary conditions determine the solution $p(x, y, t)$ or $N(x, y, t)$. Therefore—granted the assumptions that led to these data—any method of calculating the solution, whether by explicit mathematical formulas, by performable indefinitely improving limiting processes, or by the use of modern computers programmed to the same assumptions, we are bound to get the same results, to the degree of approximation that it may be expedient to introduce. Correctly applied, all these are but superficially different approaches to the same result. If we emphasize this truism, it is because we have met so many misconceptions concerning the relative validity of results of the many approaches that have been taken to these very difficult and important problems. The difference is essentially one of practicality. (One criterion may be cost-effectiveness. During the development of the atomic bomb, *time* spent was the appropriate coin, and the neutron diffusion equations were solved crudely by Monte Carlo simulation. In more normal times it is money that may count. The author [5] has calculated the cost of solving an airport capacity problem to be $40 by computer-aided analysis and $25,000 by Monte Carlo simulation.)

Before any attack can be made on the problem of finding useful solutions, the coefficients in the differential equation must be determined effectively. In (25), the components u and v of the mean velocity $\mathbf{c}$ can usually be found from tactical or other general estimates; moreover, when they can be found at all, they usually have simple forms, either constants (uniform translation of our swarm) or corresponding to the types of radial motions examined in Section 3. A time-dependent change of independent variables then reduces (25) to the type of (23): an exercise in relative motion. As for the coefficients of the second-order terms, the situation is more complicated: Their values may vary strongly near boundaries. Furthermore, they may show the effect of high mean velocity of the target, since it is easier for the target to make sidewise evasive maneuvers than to make random variations of forward speed.

We shall consider only one simple example of the physical reasoning in finding these coefficients, the equation (19) in which $\sigma^2 = \overline{g^2}/2\,\Delta t$ is to be estimated and is assumed to be constant. To have a concrete picture of the reasoning, we shall use the classical example of the Pearson–Rayleigh problem of *random flights*. (For references and a solution, see, e.g., Watson [7] p. 419 (1962 ed.). An easier solution is obtained by the use of the Dirac delta function and Fourier transformations, by theorems noted in Appendix A.) A point moves in a plane in a connected succession of straight line segments of lengths h_i, each chosen in a random direction (uniformly distributed in angle). The problem is to find the probability distribution at the end of n such "flights." While the general solution involves Bessel functions, all that is needed for our purposes is the mean square distance $\overline{R^2}$ from the starting point. Taking the latter at the origin, the problem is to find the mean over each of the n angles θ_i of the quantity

$$R^2 = \left(\sum_{i=1}^{n} h_i \cos \theta_i \right)^2 + \left(\sum_{i=1}^{n} h_i \sin \theta_i \right)^2$$

$$= \sum_{i=1}^{n} h_i^2 + 2 \sum_{i<j} h_i h_j \cos(\theta_i - \theta_j).$$

Integrating this with respect to each θ_i from 0 to 2π and dividing by 2π we obtain $\overline{R^2} = \sum_{i=1}^{n} h_i^2$. When the flights are all the same length h, this is $\overline{R^2} = nh^2$. In practical cases, if h is the arithmetic mean of the n lengths that do not differ from it much, then the last formula applies when corrected by adding the much smaller sum of the squares of the residuals.

Suppose that there are enough flights during Δt to make the circular normal density a satisfactory approximation. Then (20) applies with t replaced by Δt, and the expected value of $\overline{R^2}$ is $2\sigma^2 \Delta t$, so that $h^2 n = 2\sigma^2 \Delta t$ and $2\sigma^2 = h^2(n/\Delta t)$, the latter factor being the number of flights or *changes of course* per unit interval of time (of the order of the relaxation time).

If a surface craft is moving at 12 knots and changing its course every 15 minutes, so that $h = 12/4 = 3$ and $n = 4 \Delta t$, then $h^2(n/\Delta t) = 9 \times 4 = 36$, and hence $\sigma^2 = 18$. Then (20), with this value of σ^2, measuring time in hours and distances in nautical miles will give the evolution on the ocean surface—assuming no nearby boundaries, no mean velocity, and a target at (0, 0) when $t = 0$. After 24 hours, the "critical ellipse" in which it has the probability $1 - 1/e = 0.632$ of being positioned is the circle of radius $\sigma\sqrt{2t} = 29.4$ miles and area 2,720 square nautical miles.

Standard analytic methods of solution of our diffusion equations in connection with their practical applications have formed an extensive subject in the literature for over a century, and particularly in recent times. We can barely outline some of the simpler and most used methods here, relying on references for further cases and details.

Stationary states under steady conditions do not involve t, and the diffusion equation is then an *elliptic* type of partial differential equation in the variables x and y. In most cases it is the *Laplace* equation, or is easily reducible to it. This is perhaps the most thoroughly understood second-order partial differential equation —governing conformal mapping, logarithmic potential, steady flow of heat and electricity in homogeneous plates, as well as the irrotational flow of frictionless liquids in the plane. Courant and Hilbert [1] treat it and its applications and generalizations in many places in Vols. I and II.

Transient states under steady conditions are most frequently treated by eliminating the time variable by a *Laplace transformation*. One multiplies through by e^{-st} and integrates with respect to t from 0 to $+\infty$. This reduces the equation to the elliptic type in x and y, containing the initial values, and s as a parameter. Having solved the resulting equation for the Laplace transform of p one gets back to the latter either by the use of tables of such transforms (if lucky!) or by use of the standard inversion formula. Calculation by contour integration and approximations, use of the method of steepest descent, etc., may be necessary. See Courant and Hilbert [1], Vol. II, p. 535; Doetsh [2], pp. 349 and 383; Feller [3], Vol. II, Chap. X, Sections 5 and 6.

Another classical method in the nonstationary case is to build up solutions as sums, finite or infinite, or as integrals of known simple solutions. In (19) the simple solution is given in (20), and the general one built up in this manner is (21). In this example we have assumed that there are no boundaries, but the method is general and will now be illustrated when simple boundaries are present.

When it is possible to approximate to the boundaries by means of a few straight lines, Kelvin's *method of images* may provide the key. We shall use (19) as the illustration. First, suppose that the target is confined to motion in the half-plane to the right of a vertical line L that acts as a reflecting boundary. The solution p must have the property of having its derivative normal to L vanishing. Suppose that we reflect this function in L, i.e., extend it to the other side of L so as to have at each point X' on the left of L the value the original function had at the symmetrically opposite point X. Clearly the extended function is a smooth solution of (19). Thus, in a sense, the boundary L has been replaced by the property of symmetry in it. Of course this implies that the equation itself has this symmetry. And so our final result is that, if O' is the symmetric image of O and if r' is the distance from O' to X, our symmetric elementary probability is $G(r, t) + G(r', t)$. Similarly for the application of (21).

When there are two straight boundaries and the target is confined to the angular space formed by them (when they intersect), we must not only base our function derived from (20) on O and its image O' in one of the lines, but also on the image of this pair, O and O', in the other line, and the resulting set of four points must be reflected in the first line, and so on. In brief, our set of images must be *invariant under reflection* in each of the lines. Such a set can be finite if and only if the angle is an integral submultiple of $360°$, e.g., $60°$; then it is easy to see that the invariant set consists of 12 points (which may take special positions and reduce to 6, etc.). The elementary probability is then the sum of as many functions (20), each centered in the respective points and divided by their number.

A fairly important case in searching submarines is the one involving their passage through a channel, which we will approximate by a pair of parallel straight reflecting boundaries. The method of images applied to (20) requires us to sum that function over a set of points going into the same set under reflection in each of the two boundaries. Evidently they will lie along the common perpendicular to the boundaries. Starting with a single point O in the strip (that models the channel), we find a sequence of points by successive reflections, and then, by taking the x-axis along the central channel axis and the y-axis through the invariant set, the two-way infinite sum is easy to simplify to a well-known form expressible in terms of the *Jacobi elliptic theta functions*. Since these are tabulated and have known properties, the result is numerically useful. These functions are treated in Whittaker and

Watson [8], Chap. XXI. They are applied to the heat flow analogue of our problem by Doetsh [2], Chap. 16, Section 1. Feller [3] gives applications of this method to stochastic diffusion processes in Vol. II, pp. 330, 331, and 594. These results in the form stated apply to the case of no mean motion, but when the particles of our swarm have a constant mean motion c along the channel, the problem is reduced to the case of no mean motion in a reference plane moving along the channel with the constant speed c.

Many cases of irregular boundaries and variable coefficients, etc., cannot be treated by closed analytical formulas. For this and other reasons modern computers have increasingly been used, the region of target travel being divided into small rectangles and laws of transition between them applied. The hesitation in accepting the numerical results of such methods is because a test of their reliability is so difficult. The sensitivity of their output to both kinds of input—*numerical* and, most important, *structural*—is so rarely tested. (Has the machine been programmed to do a realistic thing?) One method seems fairly obvious, namely, to apply the computer method to a problem such as the one described above, which can be solved analytically, and then to compare the results. To our knowledge this particular comparison has not been made in the case of erratic motion along a channel.

8. THE TRACKING PROBLEM

The transient states of motion have been stated as applying to the *prediction* problem: from one localization to estimate later positions. The *tracking* problem, on the other hand, is concerned with prediction after a *sequence* of more or less approximate target localizations have been made. In one important case *the target is visible only intermittently*. The results of the various detections then have to be combined, possibly applying least squares, and usually giving progressively less weight to the earlier observations. For the latter purpose an exponential decay law is sometimes used, as in gun prediction devices.

The subject of tracking is as important as it is vast. To go further into this subject, however, beyond recalling the notions of Kalman filters outlined in Section 1 and their relation to the tracking problem, would lead beyond the scope of this book.

REFERENCES

1. Courant, R., and Hilbert, D. 1966 *Methods of Mathematical physics.* Vol. II. New York: Interscience Press.
2. Doetsh, G. 1943. *Laplace transformations* (in German). New York: Dover.
3. Feller, W. 1966. *Probability.* Vol. II. New York: Wiley.
4. Gelb, A. 1974. *Applied optimum estimation.* Cambridge, Mass.: The M.I.T. Press.
5. Koopman, B. O. 1972. Air terminal queues under time dependent conditions. *Operations Res.* 20: 1079–1114.
6. Osgood, W. F. 1925. *Advanced calculus.* New York: Macmillan.
7. Watson, G. E. 1962. *Bessel functions*, 2nd ed. Cambridge: Cambridge University Press.
8. Whittaker, E. T., and Watson, G. N. 1943. *Modern analysis.* Cambridge: Cambridge University Press.

Chapter 6

The Optimum Distribution of Searching Effort

The present subject is deeply rooted in common experience. We may be looking for an object, and although we do not know where it is, we can reason out the chances of its being in various possible places. With a limited time to find it, where shall we look first and how long shall we look in each place? On having looked unsuccessfully during a first period, and granting that we might have failed to see it even if it were at a place where we have looked, to what extent can we eliminate certain places, and change our further looking? Again, we are expecting a friend arriving by train at a station, but there are two different exits not close together. If we decide that he is twice as likely to come out through gate no. 1 than gate no. 2, how should we divide our time watching them? If he is hard to recognize and we have a few friends to help us, how should they be distributed between the two gates? The list of such questions occurring in the ordinary lives of individuals or organizations could be multiplied indefinitely, but they have not traditionally been put into a quantitative form.

The author had the task during World War II of designing defensive screens for surface formations crossing submarine-infested waters. Using a barely sufficient number of screening units (see below, Chapter 9), he was led to a precise mathematical formulation and solution of the type of problem mentioned above. Indeed, both rough operational statistics and a priori reasoning indicated a greater proportion of attempted screen penetrations taking place at the two forward flanks than from due ahead. Could this fact be utilized to improve the placing of the all too few screening units? Other situations were given a similar formulation and solution, such as the followup of a target fix, where its inaccuracy or the time-late in its prosecution led to a probability distribution that could be used for optimizing the latter operation (see below, Chapter 8).

After these early results were obtained and applied [7, 9], the subject of optimized search has had a very considerable development. Thus, Dobbie [2] introduced the expected length of time to detection rather than the probability of detection within a given time, as a measure of effectiveness of a search. The exponential law of random search (Chapter 3, Section 6) has been replaced by more general expressions by de Guenin [4] and used by Stone [13] and others. Many generalizations are summed up by Stone [13]; a survey of the contributions up to 1968 is given by Dobbie [3]. Most important, in our view, is the great expansion of applications of these ideas to many other fields than the military, as suggested by the examples in Chapter 1, Section 1.

In all cases of optimal search, two categories of concepts are fundamental: the a priori distribution of targets (when essentially fixed, as discussed in Chapter 4; when moving, as in Chapter 5) and the effectiveness or ability to detect by a certain amount of search when the target's position is (hypothetically) given (Chapter 3). In the present type of question, the "amount of search," thought of as *localized* and often as *divisible*, has to be defined. The preconditions for its rational formulation will now be examined.

As always, it is important to maintain the precise distinction between "region" and "area" defined in the introduction of Chapter 1.

1. THE DENSITY OF SEARCHING EFFORT

In long-range surveillance systems, as discussed (e.g., in Chapter 4—the fourth example in Section 3, and Sections 6, 7, and 8), there are a small and fixed number of observation posts, they are constantly "looking," and their most favorable placement evidently depends on solving a problem of optimal search. This description does not belong, however, to the present category of problem, in which the searching endeavor is more localized, flexible, and repeatable and corresponds rather to the types of detection considered in Chapter 3.

An essential concept is the *density* $\phi(X)$ *of searching effort* at the point X of the region $\mathcal{R}$ in which a search is made. Its definition has to be based on an assumption of *scales of size*: we must assume as physically meaningful "small" dimensions, of the order of detection ranges, lengths of track near a target, and all such distances describing *details* of the searching process. We must also recognize the meaning of "large" dimensions, extending geographically so far that the a priori probabilities of the target's distribution and the amount of searching done may differ markedly at positions separated by such distances. And, finally, we must assume that there is a rather broad band of "intermediate" scales, much larger than the "small" and much smaller than the "large."

These assumptions were implied in the second derivation of the law of random search in Section 6 of Chapter 3. They are repeated in the case of scales of *time* intervals in Chapter 5, Section 5, where the intermediate intervals Δt are called "relaxation times," and connections with similar concepts in molecular theory are mentioned (see the remark in the paragraph following formula (16) there).

If, then, $\Delta\mathcal{R}$ is a region of intermediate dimensions, the probability density $p(X)$ may—by the definition of its size—be treated as constant. We can think of complete processes of search of the sort described in Chapter 3 taking place entirely within this region. In all actual cases the "amount" of search in $\Delta \mathcal{C}$ can be the mean interval of time $\overline{\Delta t}$ or distance $\overline{\Delta L}$ traveled (uniformly) while in this region. Denote it by $\Delta \Phi$. If ΔA is is the area of $\Delta \mathcal{C}$, the ratio $\Delta \Phi / \Delta A$ describes the "effort per unit area"—yet it would be meaningless to talk about its "limit" as $\Delta \mathcal{C}$ shrinks down to a point X, since for small dimensions of this region $\Delta \Phi$ *ceases to be defined.* On the other hand, the above ratio has the property of having practically the same value for all of a large class of regions $\Delta \mathcal{C}$ containing a fixed point X, namely, those of intermediate ("relaxation") size. This fact is what allows us to define the "quasidensity" as the common value of such ratios corresponding to X; and the value being tothis extent determined by X, we can use the function notation and denote it by $\phi(X)$. Its definition, we repeat, is predicated on the existence of the three scales of sizes postulated at the outset.

These considerations lead to the conclusion that if the intermediate sized $\Delta \mathcal{C}$ is searched by $\Delta \Phi$—all other things being equal—*the conditional probability of detecting a target, given to be at X, is determined by the ratio* $\Delta \Phi / \Delta A = \phi(X)$. This means that we have included, in the effect on the target at X, searching at other points X' only insofar as they are within $\Delta \mathcal{C}$. This is our assumption of *local effectiveness* of the search, the *local density* or intensity of which is the $\phi(X)$ defined above. It allows us to write the conditional detection probability as a function of two elements, the point X in $\mathcal{C}$ and density $\phi = \phi(X)$:

(1) $P(\text{detection using } \phi(X) | \text{target given at } X) = D(X, \phi)$.

Of course the success of the search may well depend on other factors besides X and ϕ, such as the condition of searcher, target, and their common environment, but these are usually, but not always, secondary effects. They are noted below and discussed in detail in Appendix C.

The examples that occupied much of Chapter 3 will be referred to below. When $\Delta \mathcal{C}$ is approximately rectangular and is searched by parallel sweeps of common spacing S throughout this region, the definite range law of range $W/2$ gives for the probability of detection of a target (randomly placed) in $\Delta \mathcal{C}$ the function of total track length L (graphed as the broken line, the upper curve in Fig. 3-12 of Chapter 3) and given by the expression $\min\{WL/\Delta A, 1\}$. Since $L/\Delta A = 1/S$, and this can be used as the measure of search density, we set $\phi = 1/S$, so that

(2) $D(X, \phi) = \min\{W\phi, 1\}$.

If on the other hand the inverse cube law, (10) of Section 2, is assumed in the search above, equation (45) gives

(3) $$D(X, \phi) = \text{erf}\left(\frac{\sqrt{\pi}}{2} \frac{W}{S}\right) = \text{erf}\left(\frac{\sqrt{\pi}}{2} W\phi\right).$$

It is shown in the lowest curves in the same Fig. 3-12. Finally, if $\Delta \mathcal{C}$ is searched by an irregular track of length L and density $\lambda = L/\Delta A$, equation (40) applies, or more generally, (40′), and we have, with the corresponding definition $\phi = \lambda = L/\Delta A$, (a modification of the usage in the third expression in (40′)):

$$(4) \qquad\qquad D(X, \phi) = 1 - e^{-W\phi}.$$

Its graph is the intermediate curve in Fig. 3-12. As in (40′), the W and ϕ may have to be regarded as varying with position X—although only over large scales of ranges. They may also depend on the time t, when it increases by more than the "relaxation time" under the conditions considered.

2. SINGLE-TRY SEARCHES AND THEIR OPTIMIZATION

In the historically earliest problems of optimized search, the commitment to a definite allocation of escorts in the screen was made once and for all—the penetrating unit takes one chance in crossing it—and the probabilities corresponded to those of a *single try* in gambling. Similarly, in prosecuting a *point of fix* (see Chapter 4, Sections 6–9), of an evanescent target, a total available effort Φ is laid on optimally, according to the judgment that if it fails, a hostile target would have escaped, or in a life-saving operation, undetected victims would have perished before the search could be repeated.

Such cases may be described as *single-try searches*, and the natural quantity to optimize is the probability that the target will be detected, given the total available effort Φ. The mathematical formulation of the problem is obviously as follows: to find the distribution of effort (the "allocation" $\phi(x)$ of Φ) which maximizes

$$(5) \qquad\qquad P[\phi] = \int \int p(X) D[X, \phi(X)] \, dM_X,$$

subject to the two conditions

$$(6) \qquad\qquad \int \int \phi(X) \, dM_X = \Phi; \quad \phi(X) \geqslant 0.$$

Here, as throughout, integration without symbol for the domain is over the whole region $\mathcal{Q}$, and dM_X (or dM) the element of area in the latter. The second condition in (6) is a *unilateral* constraint, and, as has been known to the calculus of variations since the last century, only *restricted* variations of $\phi(X)$ can be taken in applying the Eulerian formal derivations used since the eighteenth century. Evidently the formulation of our problem, (5), (6), includes the case that the target is in one of two different regions ($\mathcal{Q} = \mathcal{Q}_1 + \mathcal{Q}_2$), uniformly distributed over each, with respective probabilities p_1 and p_1 (densities p_1/A_1 and p_2/A_2). Similarly for n different regions.

Finally, in addition to the constraints (6), there may be others. For example, there may be a danger $\Psi[\phi]$ to the searcher when he spends the time required to search with the intensity $\phi(X)$ at X. This may be due to the presence of mine fields or of purely physical factors, or it may involve detection by an enemy (whose search may or may not satisfy the conditions of Section 1). In other cases, as when the amount of effort is measured by length of time, the earliness of detection may be of paramount importance, the subject of Chapter 7.

In such cases it may sometimes be possible to give such quantities the form of an integral of a function $\psi(X, \phi(X))$; but in more cases it depends so strongly on the whole tactical situation and its mathematical formulation as to be beyond the scope of what is attempted in the present work.

Except in cases in which the details of our search become known and used as such by the enemy, we may usually regard the searches as mediated by *passive observations*. The single-try situation is so fast that, while the target can lay its general plans on the assumption that we are able to search, it cannot react appreciably during the time involved. See the discussion on the penetrator of the screen, mentioned at the outset.

Problems of optimization of single-try searches will be considered in the present chapter, and progressive searches will occupy us in Chapter 7.

3. THE DIVISIBILITY OF SEARCHING EFFORT IN SINGLE-TRY SEARCHES AND THE EXPONENTIAL LAW

The concept of search density $\phi(X)$ as set forth above automatically implies that $\phi(X)$ can be separated into parts, e.g., $\phi_1(X)$ and $\phi_2(X)$: $\phi(X) = \phi_1(X) + \phi_2(X)$. This is an immediate consequence or the additivity of expected values; since it is proportional to the expected time or length of path searched in the region $\Delta\mathcal{C}$ of intermediate size. This property implies, of course, that there is no physical interference between the two processes of search in question—that, in other words, they represent *compatible* trials: otherwise, as explained in Appendix A, the additivity property would be inapplicable.

In a single-try search there is no opportunity for *revision* by the searcher. Whether the part represented by $\phi_1(X)$ succeeds or fails, the search is still committed to search by the amount $\phi_2(X)$. This is an essential part of the definition of "single try"—both theoretically and in practice.

Although the search can be subdivided in the above sense, it does not follow that, in the detection law defined in Section 2, $D(X, \phi)$ will be the *same function* for all the three parts. Thus in search by parallel sweeps, either with the definite range law (2) or the inverse cube law (3), the form of these detection functions is valid only on the assumption that the sweeps are *equally spaced*. If we pick out arbitrarily one set of sweeps in the rectangular $\Delta\mathcal{C}$ and take ϕ_1 as their total length divided by its area and define ϕ_2 in the same way with the remaining sweeps, we certainly have $\phi = \phi_1 + \phi_2$—not only as a numerical relation, but operationally: one searcher could be assigned the first set of paths, the other the second. But in general $D(X, \phi_1)$ and $D(X, \phi_2)$ are not given by the same formula (2), or (3), that gave $D(X, \phi)$ correctly for the combined search. This would require that each of the two subsets of sweeps should be equally spaced and that either one bisect the bands bounded by the other's paths.

When we come to the study of iterated and progressive searches in Chapter 7 we shall be confronted with a similar possibility. Thus if we are using such formulas as

(2) or (3) at all stages of the continued search, we should require at stage $n + 1$ at least twice the available amount of search as in stage n. This is a practical absurdity and contradicts the assumption of subdivisibility, upon which assumption the majority of treatments of progressive searches appear to have been based. See, e.g., the references [3] and [13].

Evidently it is important to know when a proposed detection function $D(X, z)$ retains its form as a function whether $z = \phi$, ϕ_1, or ϕ_2—these being three *performable* searches. The issue raised is one of physics and probability, as well as of mathematics.

We know of one case in which this property will be true: the exponential law of random search—provided that the searches involved are passive and that their various parts act as independent trials. This fact is an immediate consequence of the laws of probability, applied to the function in question. The following theorem contains in substance a converse of the above statement.

Theorem 1.   *If* (i) *the probability of detecting a target at X is determined by X and the value of $z = \phi(X)$, and if* (ii) *the search involves only passive observations, and if, finally* (iii) *the amount of search is (practically) indefinitely subdivisible, then $D(X, z)$ is the exponential law* (4): $D(X, z) = 1 - \exp\{-W(X)z\}$.

The proof is essentially the second one in Section 6 of Chapter 3. In order to prepare for generalizations, we repeat it in outline in the broader framework of search density varying over "long" distances, and of the various factors in the search different at different times (separated by more than the "relaxation" time).

Denoting by a bar the complementary probability, so that $\overline{D}(X, z)$ is that of nondetection, etc., we have by the general principle of compound probability —which is applicable since (ii) guarantees the compatibility of trials—

$$(7) \qquad \overline{D}(X, z_1 + z_2) = \overline{D}(X, z_1) \cdot \overline{D}(X, z_2, z_1), \qquad z_1 \geqslant 0, \quad z_2 \geqslant 0,$$

where $\overline{D}(X, z_2, z_1)$ is the doubly conditional probability of no detection with z_2, *given* that the target is at X and that the z_1 search fails to detect. The essential step in the proof is to show that

$$(8) \qquad \overline{D}(X, z_2, z_1) = \overline{D}(X, z_2),$$

in other words, that the two failures are the outcome of *independent* trials. This turns on the question: what *logical* impact can the knowledge of the z_1 failure have on the estimation of the probability of a z_2 failure? It certainly cannot cast doubt on the presence of the target at X, since that is postulated in the conditional nature of the detection probability. It cannot change the estimate of the effectiveness of the method of search or the detectability of the target, in virtue of item (i) in the hypothesis. The only remaining possibility is that the datum that the z_1 search fails makes no rational difference in the value of the probability of a z_2 failure. This establishes (8). (At the end of Section 3 of Appendix A, a purely formal definition of "independence" is contrasted with the conception used in the above reasoning, and it is pointed out that its application in such cases would give rise to difficulties of principle.)

From (7) and (8) we have the equation which, on leaving out the symbol X for the moment, becomes

$$(9) \qquad \overline{D}(z_1 + z_2) = \overline{D}(z_1)\overline{D}(z_2), \qquad z_1 \geqslant 0, \quad z_2 \geqslant 0.$$

If for some $z_0 > 0$, $\overline{D}(z_0) = 0$, it would follow that $\overline{D}(z) = 0$ for all $z > 0$. This is an immediate consequence of (9) for all $z > z_0$ as we can see by taking $z_1 = z_0$ and $z_2 = z - z_0$. If on the other hand z is positive but less than z_0, we can find an integer n so large that $z_0/n < z$; whereupon an n-fold application of (9) gives $\overline{D}(z_0/n)^n = \overline{D}(z_0) = 0$, so that $\overline{D}(z_0/n) = 0$. Repeating the former reasoning with z_0 replaced by z_0/n leads to $\overline{D}(z) = 0$: proving our original statement. Since this situation would imply that it is 100% probable to detect the target however small an amount of searching is done in its general proximity, it corresponds to the definite range or detection law, of Chapter 3, Sections 2 and 9.

In all other cases we can take logarithms in (9). If $L(z) = \log \overline{D}(z)$, we have $L(z_1 + z_2) = L(z_1) + L(z_2)$ for all nonnegative values. This is about the simplest and best known of functional equations; its only continuous solution: $L(z) = $ const. times z, which we shall write as $L(z) = -Wz$ where $-W = L(1)$—a constant with regard to z, but of course involving X. This solution is established first for $z = n/m$ by appropriate repeated applications of the functional equation; it is then extended to general values of z by continuity. (If u and v are any two positive incommensurable numbers we show in the same way that $L(ru) = rL(u)$ and $L(rv) = rL(v)$ for all rational r. It follows that unless $vL(u) = uL(v)$ the function $L(z)$ is discontinuous everywhere—a physical absurdity.) From this result the conclusion (4) of our theorem follows. That W is not negative is a consequence of the fact that otherwise (4) would give a negative probability—an absurdity.

Equation (4) shows that $D(X, z)$ increases as W increases. Thus this quantity represents what may be called an *index of detectability*. This was evident when, in Chapter 3, Section 6, it appeared as the sweep width. Now we do not require any such restrictive assumptions as were then made. Nevertheless, it is convenient to continue to use the term "sweep width" in this more general interpretation. The excluded case $\overline{D} = 0$ corresponds to $W = +\infty$.

Corollary. *If* (i) *in the hypothesis is changed by requiring that the detection probability of the target requires for its determination k further parameters* $(y) = (y_1, \ldots, y_k)$ *in addition to X, the conclusion remains valid, except that in* (4) $W = W(X, y, z)$.

Its implications are given in Appendix C; see also Koopman [10].

The proof is an evident modification of the one just given. The mathematical consequences of this generalization will be examined in Appendix C. It will be shown that in the formulation of the optimization problem (5), (6), one may be led to a "partial detection function" in the form of a Laplace–Stieljès transform of some probability distribution of a definable process—which, however, seems difficult to find in practice. Hence it is not considered in the body of the present work.

Dobbie [2] was the first to point out the consequences of removing (ii) from the hypotheses: Even under highly simplified conditions in other respects, (4) will in general be invalid—even with inclusion of parameters (y). Moreover, he showed that the generalization of (4) introduced by de Guenin [4], that $D(z)$ be a "regular" detection function (i.e., that its graph be increasing, concave downward, and pass through the origin with a positive slope) would in general be invalid without (ii). Finally, when (ii) is denied, and under general practical situations, D has to be regarded as a *functional* of $\phi(X)$ rather than as a function, since it will depend on its whole *spread* of values over large parts of the region, rather than just that in the intermediate region containing the target. Basically, the result of eliminating (ii) is to introduce incompatibility of trials and hence remove the basis of the simple probability relations such as (7); see Appendix A, and Chapter 7, Section 11.

Item (iii) in the hypothesis is rather unrealistic, since there is apt to be a *least* positive amount of search that can be meaningfully made in $\Delta\mathcal{C}$. If its value is h, (9) shows by recurrence that $\overline{D}(nh) = \overline{D}(h)^n$. Setting $W = -\log \overline{D}(h)$ we obtain $D(nh) = 1 - e^{-Wn}$, which is (4) with ϕ measured in units of h; cf. Chapter 3, Section 2.

4. ALTERNATIVE REGIONS OF SEARCH

We shall consider examples of optimal search under the conditions of Section 2. In most cases the motions of searcher relative to the target are irregular, whatever the plan of the searcher may be (cf. Fig. 10-4). Accordingly, the law of random search is the only reasonable approximation to $D(X, \phi)$. In a few cases, with stationary targets and possibilities of very accurate navigation, detection probabilities corresponding with greater regularity, such as the use of parallel sweeps, may be more appropriate. These will be considered later.

Let A_1 and A_2 be two parts of the ocean (either separate or having a common boundary). The target to be found is either in A_1 or in A_2, with the respective probabilities p_1 and p_2 of so being, so that relations

$$p_1 + p_2 = 1, \qquad p_1 > 0, \quad p_2 > 0$$

hold; the target being stationary, p_1 and p_2 do not change with time. Let the target be uniformly distributed in whichever of A_1 or A_2 it lies. Finally, let the total length of track of the observer (or observers) be L. How must L be distributed between A_1 and A_2 if the chance of detection is to be greatest? In other words, if $L = L_1 + L_2$, L_1 being the length of the observer's track in A_1, L_2 that in A_2, what relation must exist between L_1 and L_2 for the optimum search? If W is the search width, the probability p of detection is given by

$$(10) \qquad p = p_1(1 - e^{-WL_1/A_1}) + p_2(1 - e^{-WL_2/A_2}),$$

which corresponds in the present simple case to (5).

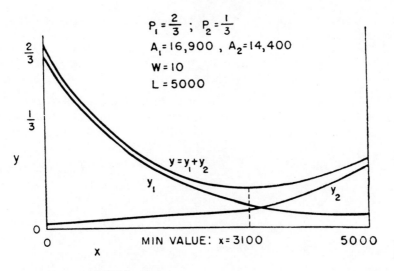

Fig. 6-1. Minimizing the sum.

Mathematically, the problem is to find the values of L_1 and L_2 which maximize equation (10), subject to the conditions

(11) $$L_1 + L_2 = L, \qquad L_1 \geqslant 0, \quad L_2 \geqslant 0.$$

It is convenient to proceed graphically. Setting

$$L_1 = x, \qquad L_2 = L - x,$$
$$y_1 = p_1 e^{-Wx/A_1}, \qquad y_2 = p_2 e^{-W(L-x)/A_2},$$

we have

$$p = 1 - (y_1 + y_2),$$

so that, for the optimum search, x must be determined so as to *maximize p*, i.e., to *minimize*

$$y = y_1 + y_2,$$

subject to the restriction that $0 \leqslant x \leqslant L$. Figure 6-1 shows the graph of y against x in a typical case; the ordinate is obtained by adding the ordinates of the graphs of y_1 and y_2, also shown in the figure; the latter are simple exponential curves. It is seen, either by differentiation or by an obvious graphical argument, that for y to have a minimum at a point x in the interval $(0, L)$ it is necessary and sufficient that the inclinations (absolute values of the slopes) of the tangents to the y_1 and the y_2 curves be equal and opposite (they are always opposite in the present case). Now the inclination of the y_1 is always down and that of the y_2 always up. The former inclination decreases with increasing x from its maximum at $x = 0$; the latter increases to its maximum at $x = L$. Thus there are three mutually exclusive possibilities.

Case 1. The inclination of y_1 at $x = 0$ is less than (or at most equal to) that of y_2 at this point, i.e.,

(12)
$$\frac{p_1}{A_1} \leqslant \frac{p_2}{A_2} e^{-WL/A_2}.$$

Then the inclination of y_1 will continue to be still less than that of y_2 throughout the interval. No internal minimum of y exists, but since y_2 increases faster than y_1 decreases as x moves from 0 to L, *the minimum occurs at $x = 0$ (i.e., $L_1 = 0$).*

Case 2. The inclination of y_2 at $x = L$ is less than (or equal to) that of y_1 at this point, i.e.,

(13)
$$\frac{p_2}{A_2} \leqslant \frac{p_1}{A_1} e^{-WL/A_1}.$$

Then, by a similar argument, *the minimum occurs at $x = L$.*

Case 3. Neither one of the above cases occurs:

(14)
$$\frac{p_1}{A_1} > \frac{p_2}{A_2} e^{-WL/A_2} \quad \text{and} \quad \frac{p_2}{A_2} > \frac{p_1}{A_1} e^{-WL/A_1}$$

Then the inclination of y_1 at $x = 0$ is greater than that of y_2 at this point, but this advantage is steadily diminished as x increases, and is reversed when $x = L$, at which point the inclination of y_2 exceeds that of y_1. Hence *there is just one point $x = x_0$ in the interval $(0, L)$ which makes y a minimum.* This value of X is found by solving the equation $dy/dx = 0$. A convenient form of the answer will be given below.

In order to grasp the meaning of the situation more easily, the following terms are introduced:

(15)
$$\rho_1 = p_1/A_1, \qquad \rho_2 = p_2/A_2$$
$$\phi_1 = WL_1/A_1, \qquad \phi_2 = WL_2/A_2$$
$$A = A_1 + A_2, \qquad \Phi = WL.$$

On account of the uniformity of the distribution of the target in whichever region it is, the probability that it will lie in a subregion of unit area within A_1 is the product of the probability p_1 that it will be in A_1 by the probability that (in this case) it will be in said subregion, $1/A_1$: Thus the probability in question is $p_1/A_1 = \rho_1$. Hence ρ_1 is the *probability density* for the first region; ρ_2 has the corresponding meaning for A_2. Furthermore, the length of observer's path L_1 in A_1 is a measure of the searching effort devoted to A_1. But WL_1 is an equally good measure: it is the area swept (some of it multiply) in A_1. Thus the expression $WL_1/A_1 = \phi_1$ is the density of *searching effort* in the first region, and ϕ_2 is that in the second; Φ is the total available searching effort, and we have

(16)
$$A_1\phi_1 + A_2\phi_2 = \Phi, \qquad \phi_1 \geqslant 0, \quad \phi_2 \geqslant 0.$$

[This slightly modified usage from that of earlier sections is more convenient in the present case.]

In the third case, corresponding with equation (14), the solution of $dy/dx = 0$ for x gives a result that can be simplified by first replacing x and $L - x$ by L_1 and L_2, and then replacing ratios by the quantities introduced in equation (15). The following equations result from this process; they answer the question concerning the optimum distribution of searching effort in the present case.

$$(17) \qquad \phi_1 = \log \rho_1 - \frac{1}{A}(A_1 \log \rho_1 + A_2 \log \rho_2) + \frac{\Phi}{A}$$

$$\phi_2 = \log \rho_2 - \frac{1}{A}(A_1 \log \rho_1 + A_2 \log \rho_2) + \frac{\Phi}{A}.$$

On the basis of equations (12), (13), and (14), expressed in the terms of equations (15) and (17), everything may be summed up as follows:

When the target's probability density ρ_1 in the first region is not only less than its density in the second, but is so much less that it remains less when the second is multiplied by the factor $e^{-\Phi/A_2}$ (< 1), i.e.,

$$(18) \qquad \rho_1 \leqslant \rho_2 e^{-\Phi/A_2},$$

then no searching whatsoever should be done in the first region, A_1, *and the whole effort should be devoted to searching the second,* A_2. Similarly, if

$$(19) \qquad \rho_2 \leqslant \rho_1 e^{-\Phi/A_1},$$

no searching should be done in A_2. When, on the other hand,

$$(20) \qquad \rho_1 > \rho_2 e^{-\Phi/A_2} \quad \text{and} \quad \rho_2 > \rho_1 e^{-\Phi/A_1},$$

the searching effort should be distributed in accordance with equation (17). If k denotes the exponential of the common value added to $\log \rho_1$ or to $\log \rho_2$ in (17), these equations become

$$(21) \qquad \phi_1 = \log k\rho_1, \qquad \phi_1 = \log k\rho_2.$$

Thus *the optimum densities of searching effort* [in case of equation (20)] *equal the logarithms of quantities proportional to the respective probability densities.*

It is interesting to compare the results for different amounts of available effort, mathematically, as Φ is progressively increased. To have a definite case, suppose that $\rho_1 > \rho_2$ and $A_1 < A_2$. When Φ is very small, equation (19) holds: all searching must be done in A_1, none in A_2. When Φ increases sufficiently, (20) becomes valid, and remains so for all further increase in Φ. Then the searching has to be distributed between A_1 and A_2 according to the logarithmic law enunciated in equations (17) or (21). This leads to a curious conclusion as Φ becomes extremely large. For equation (17) shows that

$$\lim_{\Phi \to \infty} \frac{\phi_1}{\phi_2} = 1.$$

Thus for very large Φ, ϕ_1 is about equal to ϕ_2, i.e., $WL_1/A_1 = WL_2/A_2$, which means in the present case where $A_1 < A_2$ that $L_1 < L_2$. The first region, which for very small Φ should take up all the searching effort, should for very large Φ actually have a shorter length of observer's track than the second region, a phenomenon of *reversal for large* Φ.

Suppose that after completing the optimum search with the expenditure of the total effort $\Phi = WL$, with no resulting detection, a further amount of effort $\Phi' = WL'$ becomes available. What is the optimum manner of expending this additional effort?

Assume that in the first part of the search, the third case was presented, so that Φ was distributed in accordance with equation (17). Since, as we are assuming, the target is not detected, the situation at the end of the search is similar to that at the beginning, except that the probabilities p_1 and p_2 have to be replaced by different values p_1' and p_2', the values of which are computed by means of Bayes's theorem. In this application, the a priori probabilities of A_1 and A_2 containing the target are p_1 and p_2, the a posteriori probabilities are p_1' and p_2'. The "productive probabilities" (those of not finding the target in A_1 or in A_2 when the Φ search is done as assumed in (17)) are the values that accrue to the quantities e^{-WL_1/A_1} and e^{-WL_2/A_2} when L_1 and L_2 are given by (17) in conjunction with (15). Thus the first productive probability is, by definition, the chance that if the target is actually in A_1 the searching effort $\phi_1 = WL_1/A_1$ devoted to this region shall fail to reveal it. By the formula of random search, this is e^{-WL_1/A_1}, and similarly for the second region. Hence by Bayes's formula:

$$p_1' = \frac{\rho_i e^{-\phi_i}}{A_1 \rho_1 e^{-\phi_1} + A_2 \rho_2 e^{-\phi_2}}, \qquad i = 1 \text{ or } 2,$$

or, using equations analogous to (15),

$$\rho_i' = \frac{\rho_i e^{-\phi_i}}{A_1 \rho_1 e^{-\phi_1} + A_2 \rho_2 e^{-\phi_2}}, \qquad i = 1 \text{ or } 2.$$

To find the optimum distribution of Φ', observe first that on account of (17), the relation $\rho_1 e^{-\phi_1} = \rho_2 e^{-\phi_2}$ holds; hence we are in the presence of the third case [the primed analogue of (20)]. Hence ϕ_1' and ϕ_2' are given by equations like (17) (with appropriate primes). An obvious algebraic simplification, using the original (17), shows that

$$\phi_1' = \phi_2' = \frac{\Phi'}{A}.$$

Now the total density of searching effort devoted to the ith region ($i = 1$ or 2) is simply $\phi_i + \phi_i'$. This reduces with the aid of (17) to

$$\log \rho_i - \frac{1}{A}(A_1 \log \rho_1 + A_2 \log \rho_2) + \frac{\Phi + \Phi'}{A}.$$

But this is exactly what (17) would have given if we had known in advance that the total amount of searching effort would be $\Phi + \Phi'$ rather than Φ. It leads to the next theorem.

Theorem 2. *Under the conditions set forth above, a well-planned search cannot be improved by a redistribution of search made at an intermediate stage of the operation in an attempt to make use of the fact that up to that time the target had not yet been observed.*

Of course as soon as the target *is* observed, an improvement can be made: Discontinue the search.

This theorem has been proved here only in the case where equation (20) is valid. Other cases are treated in a similar manner, with similar results.

In the case of equation (20), formula (17) gives only the magnitude of effort to be devoted to A_1 and to A_2; it does not tell how the search should be conducted *in time*. This actually makes the search a progressive one (Section 3), but it grows so simply out of the case just treated that it may serve as an introduction to that subject. The target is now supposed at rest. Suppose that at the end of t hours the amount of search effort is $\Phi(t) = ct$, where $\Phi = \Phi(T) = cT$, T being the total time available and c a constant of proportionality. Then in order to find the target as soon as possible, we must proceed as follows: Whatever the value of t (> 0), the search effort ct must be used so as to maximize the chance of detection up to that time, in accordance with the formulas developed above. Thus, if $\rho_1 > \rho_2$, we must make $\phi_1 = ct/A_1$, $\phi_2 = 0$, as t goes from zero to $A_2 (\log \rho_2 - \log \rho_1)/C$, i.e., when (20) comes into effect. From then on, ϕ_1 and ϕ_2 must be taken from equation (17) in which Φ is replaced by ct.

An obvious extension of the problem treated in this section is to the case of n regions $A_1, \ldots, A_n$.

When $n = 3$ a graphical method, apparently first used by Gibbs [6] in 1878, can make the situation clear. It makes use of the fact that the sum of the three perpendicular distances, ϕ_1, ϕ_2, and ϕ_3, from a point U inside an equilateral triangle equals twice its area divided by the length of a side—i.e., is constant. Taking units so that this is Φ, we see that every U in or on its sides represents an allocation of effort. The surface standing at the distance of y above this triangle, the graph of

$$(22) \qquad\qquad y = y(U) = \sum_i p_i e^{-Wx_i/A_i},$$

represents the probability of *failure* to detect with the allocation represented by U. Since all the second partial derivatives with respect to the x_i are nonnegative but are not all zero, it follows easily that the surface is strictly concave upward ($y(U)$ is a strictly *convex* function). Being always positive, it has a positive minimum—the optimum allocation. If this occurs inside the triangle, three equations such as (17) are valid for this point. If it occurs on a side, no search is to be made in the region A_i corresponding to that side, the other two being searched as in (17). Finally, if the

minimum falls at a vertex, all searching must be confined to the region corresponding to the opposite side.

If there are $n > 3$ different regions, the construction loses its visual usefulness,
although it continues to be valid as a basis for an analytic discussion. Thus if $n = 4$,
the triangle is replaced by a regular tetrahedron, the sum of the distances of a point
U on it to the four sides being 3 times its volume divided by the area of a bounding
face. For larger n, U is a point on a regular $(n - 1)$-dimensional solid bounded by n
congruent regular $(n - 2)$-dimensional faces, and the sum of the n distances x_i of U
from these faces is $(n - 1)$ times the $(n - 1)$-volume divided by the $(n - 2)$-volume
of a bounding face: again a constant. The second partial derivatives of the
corresponding sum (22) (with n terms) are $\geqslant 0$ and never all $= 0$. Hence y is
convex and has a unique minimum in the solid or on its boundary (faces, edges,
vertexes, etc.) giving, by equations such as (17), the optimum allocation of search.
The first directional derivatives of y at the boundaries will determine the case.

In most practical cases, the crudeness of the data warrants rough numerical
approximations, appropriate to mechanical computation.

An obvious extension of all these results is to the case in which the detectabili-
ties, measured by the sweep widths W, are different in different regions. The same
methods and formulas are applied, but with each term Wx_i/A_i in (22) and in all
previous formulas replaced by $W_i x_i / A_i$.

Before going further, certain somewhat different methods of approach involving
Lagrange multipliers will be given, also going back to J. W. Gibbs.

5. THE LAGRANGE MULTIPLIER WITH UNILATERAL CONDITIONS

The problems of maximizing sums such as that in (10) under the constraints of the
sort in (11) with inequalities are all of a type long familiar to classical calculus of
variations and apparently first applied by J. W. Gibbs [6 particularly p. 66, formula
(22)], his method being based on the following simple fact:

*If $f_1(x_1), \ldots, f_n(x_n)$ are n continuously differentiable functions of $x_1, \ldots, x_n$ for
nonnegative values, and if their sum $y = f_1(x_1) + \cdots + f_n(x_n)$, considered for all
nonnegative values of the x_i adding up to a given constant c, has a maximum at
$x_i = x_i^0$, then there exists a constant λ having the following "discriminating"
property for the derivatives:*

$$(23) \qquad If\ x_1^0 > 0\ then\ f_i'(x_i^0) = \lambda; \quad if\ x_i^0 = 0\ then\ f_i'(x_i^0) \leqslant \lambda.$$

To prove this, suppose that a particular $x_j^0 > 0$. Replace the optimizing set of
values $(x_i^0, \ldots, x_n^0)$ by an altered set in which "a piece of x_j^0" (i.e., $\Delta x > 0$, so small
that what remains, $x_j^0 - \Delta x > 0$) is "given" to x_k^0: the new set is the same except
that x_j^0 and x_k^0 are replaced by $x_j^0 - \Delta x$ and $x_k^0 + \Delta x$. The resulting set satisfies the
same constraints as before, but cannot, when substituted in $f_i(x_i)$, give a greater
sum. Since the two sums differ only in the values of the altered terms, we must

have, for all $\Delta x > 0$ and sufficiently small,

$$f_j(x_j^0 - \Delta x) + f_k(x_k^0 + \Delta x) \leqslant f_j(x_j^0) + f_k(x_k^0),$$

from which we obtain

$$\frac{f_k(x_k^0 + \Delta x) - f_k(x_k^0)}{\Delta x} \leqslant \frac{f_j(x_j^0 - \Delta x) - f_j(x_j^0)}{-\Delta x}.$$

Letting $\Delta x_j \to 0$ through positive values, this proves that $f_k'(x_k^0) \leqslant f_j'(x_j^0)$.

In the case that $x_k^0 > 0$ also, the above result, with the subscripts interchanged, shows that $f_j'(x_j^0) = f_k'(x_k^0)$. This means that the set of *positive* values of the maximizing x_i^0 gives a set of *equal* values for the derivatives $f_i'(x_i^0)$. By *defining* λ as their common value, and applying the above inequality to the zero values of x_i^0, (23) is proved. (For the original authorship of this theorem (often rediscovered since Gibbs's day), the present author is indebted to a personal communication from Dr. J. L. Danskin.) This discriminating constant λ is, of course, the Lagrange multiplier. It is a function of the given constant c.

In the application to the maximization of the detection probability with the detection functions $D_i(\phi_i)$, such as occurred in the last section with $D_i(\phi_i) = 1 - \exp(-W_i\phi_i/A_i)$, or with such other cases as in (2) and (3) of Section 1, the Gibbs theorem, (with $\phi_i = x_i$, $c = \Phi$, $f_i(x_i) = p_i D_i(\phi_i)$) leads to the existence of a λ such that (after optimization), $\phi_i > 0$ implies $p_i D_i'(\phi_i) = \lambda$, while $\phi_i = 0$ implies $p_i D_i'(0) \leqslant \lambda$. Note that since (2) defines a function having a *discontinuous* derivative (when $\phi_i = L_i$ is so large that $L_i\phi_i = A_i$), the result above can be applied under the qualification that this value is never reached (viz., with quite small available ϕ).

With the general law of random search, we obtain once more

$$(24) \qquad \phi_i > 0 \quad \text{implies } p_i \frac{W_i}{A_i} e^{-W_i\phi_i/A_i} = \lambda, \quad \text{hence } p_i W_i/A_i > \lambda.$$

$$\phi_i = 0 \quad \text{implies} \quad p_i W_i/A_i \leqslant \lambda.$$

Solving for ϕ_i, the first set gives

$$(25) \qquad \phi_i = \frac{A_i}{W_i} \log \lambda \left[\frac{p_i W_i}{A_i \lambda} \right] = \frac{A_i}{W_i} \left[\log \frac{p_i W_i}{A_i} - \log \lambda \right].$$

By summing over this set and using the equation $\Phi = \Sigma \phi_i$, an equation that can be solved for $\log \lambda$ is obtained, so that the ϕ_i can be expressed in terms of Φ and known quantities. Since the number of terms in the equation to be solved for $\log \lambda$ varies with different values of Φ, the following practical numerical procedure may be used.

Suppose the regions to be searched are so indexed that

$$(26) \qquad p_1 W_1/A_1 \geqslant p_2 W_2/A_2 \geqslant \cdots \geqslant p_n W_n/A_n.$$

Since when $\Phi \neq 0$, (24) shows that λ is not greater than all the terms in (26), it must be less than the first one. If it is greater than the second, then only the first is searched. If it is between the second and third, only A_1 and A_2 are searched, the allocation being according to (25). But then $\Phi = \phi_1 + \phi_2$ must be calculated to see whether it is exceeded—or if, when $\Phi > \phi_1 + \phi_2$, it is large enough to search A_3 and possibly others. What we do is to set λ equal to each term in (26) in succession, and for each choice calculate the ϕ_i from (25), each of which increases as λ decreases, and then the partial sums

$$(27) \qquad \phi_1 \leqslant \phi_1 + \phi_2 \leqslant \phi_1 + \phi_2 + \phi_3 \leqslant \cdots \leqslant \phi_1 + \cdots + \phi_n.$$

We next compare the given value of total effort Φ with these. If it is greater than all of them, all n regions are searched according to the allocation (25), the value of λ being easily obtained by summing all n of the latter and solving the resulting equation. Finally, if Φ is less than the kth sum but not less that the $(k + 1)$st, search only the first k regions, allocating according to (25) and calculating $\log \lambda$ by summing only the first k terms in this equation.

It is an easy exercise in the application of Bayes's theorem to show that if after applying the first installment of effort Φ optimally, a second installment Φ' became available and were applied optimally to the updated probabilities, its allocation would be such as to make $\Phi + \Phi'$ allocated optimally to the original a priori probabilities.

In the relatively unusual cases in which the immobility of the target and the accuracy of the navigation—as well as the exactness of the knowledge concerning the factors affecting the probability of its detection and the probabilities p_i—warrant using a law other than the exponential one above, explicit solutions of the result of applying the Lagrange multiplier method cannot in general be obtained, and modern computers must usually be used.

6. THE CASE OF CONTINUOUSLY DISTRIBUTED TARGETS

We turn now to the general case. The probability density $p(X)$ is continuously varying over most of the target region $\mathcal{R}$. More exactly, it is "piecewise smooth," i.e., continuously differentiable or made up of a finite number of such functions, in regions bounded by smooth curves, at which each piece may have a finite or an infinite jump—but of course integrating to unity over $\mathcal{R}$. The probabilities occurring in practice are all of this nature—at least to sufficiently high approximation.

Furthermore, the state of affairs described in detail in Sections 2 and 3 (single try, passive, localized and subdivisible searches, etc.) shall be assumed, so that all three items in the hypothesis of Theorem 1 are valid, leading to its conclusion, the exponential detection function $D(X, z)$ given by (4) with the coefficient of detectability or sweep width $W = W(X)$, thus allowing for a given dependence on local conditions.

In the rectangular coordinates $X: (x, y)$, $dM_X = dM = dx\, dy$, the equations (5) and (6) of the general search optimization problem become, respectively,

$$(28) \qquad P[\phi] = \int \int p(x, y)\left[1 - e^{-W(x,y)\phi(x,y)}\right] dx\, dy;$$

$$(29) \qquad \int \int \phi(x, y)\, dx\, dy = \Phi; \qquad \phi(x, y) \geqslant 0.$$

The most direct solution of this unilateral problem in the calculus of variations is by the application of the following obvious extension of Gibbs's method used in the preceding section. It will be applied on the assumption that the function $F(X, \phi)$ has in its variables the same order of continuous differentiability, etc. ("smoothness") as have $p(X)$ and $W(X)$:

$$(30) \qquad F(X, \phi) = p(X)(1 - e^{-W(X)\phi})$$

certainly has this smoothness. By this method we shall obtain a necessary condition that $\phi = \phi^0(X)$ satisfy the optimization problem (28) and (29) when $\phi^0(X)$ is assumed to have the same degree of smoothness as $p(x, y)$. By a "nonspecialized" point is meant one not lying on a possible (lower dimensional) locus of non-smoothness (discontinuity, etc.). The result of *Gibbs's method* is as follows

Corresponding to each $\Phi > 0$, there exists a unique constant λ having the following "discriminatory" properties for each nonspecialized point X (writing F_ϕ for $\partial F/\partial \phi$): when $\phi = \phi^0(X)$ maximizes $\int \int F(X, \phi) \, dx \, dy$ under (29):

    (i) *If $\phi^0(X) > 0$ then $F_\phi(X, \phi^0(X)) = \lambda$.*

    (ii) *If $\phi^0(X) = 0$ then $F_\phi(X, 0) \leqslant \lambda$.*

The proof applies the same idea as in the previous case: "take from the haves and give to the have-nots"; only now the amount transferred must be taken from an appropriately chosen neighborhood of X.

Suppose that $\phi^0(X) > 0$ at a nonspecialized point X. By continuity there will be a neighborhood $\mathfrak{N}$ (of positive area) about X, throughout which ϕ^0 is greater than some positive constant (e.g., $\phi^0(X)/2$). Let ψ be a smooth function that is positive in $\mathfrak{N}$, zero outside, and always less than ϕ^0 (the existence of such a function is easy to indicate graphically). Then $s\psi$ will have the same property for all $0 < s < 1$, and the difference $\phi^0 - s\psi$ will be nonnegative. If, then, X' is any other nonspecialized point, let $\mathfrak{N}'$ and ψ' be obtained from $\mathfrak{N}$ and ψ by translating them to X' (i.e., by a rigid parallel motion of the neighborhood and graph). Evidently the modified function $\phi^0 - s\psi + s\psi'$ satisfies (29) and gives an integral of $F(X, \phi)$ not greater than that given by the original ϕ^0—by the maximizing property of the latter. Since the two integrals differ only on the subregion of $\mathcal{Q}$ composed of $\mathfrak{N}$ and $\mathfrak{N}'$ (which we may assume small enough to be nonoverlapping), we obtain the inequality

$$\iint_{\mathfrak{N}} \left[F(X, \phi^0) - F(X, \phi^0 - s\psi) \right] dM \;\geqslant\; \iint_{\mathfrak{N}'} \left[F(X, \phi^0 + s\psi') - F(X, \phi^0) \right] dM$$

for all s in the interval mentioned above. Dividing this through by s and then letting $s \to 0$ through positive values (and applying the uniformity reasoning allowing the taking of limits inside the integral sign, as in the proof of Leibnitz's rule), we obtain

$$\iint_{\mathfrak{N}} F_\phi(X, \phi^0)\psi \, dM \;\leqslant\; \iint_{\mathfrak{N}'} F_\phi(X', \phi^0)\psi' \, dM'.$$

We now apply the first law of the mean for integrals, obtaining

$$F_\phi(\overline{X}, \phi^0(\overline{X})) \iint_{\mathfrak{N}} \psi \, dM \leqslant F_\phi(\overline{X}', \phi^0(\overline{X}')) \iint_{\mathfrak{N}'} \psi' \, dM'$$

where dashes refer to points in $\mathfrak{N}$ and $\mathfrak{N}'$. By the congruent construction of the integrands and regions of integration, the two integrals are equal. Being positive, they can be canceled without changing the inequality. Then, letting $\mathfrak{N}$ shrink up to X—so that $\mathfrak{N}'$ does to X'—we obtain, by the continuity at the two points,

$$F_\phi(X, \phi^0(X)) \leqslant F_\phi(X', \phi^0(X')).$$

In the case that $\phi^0(X') > 0$ also, the result above applies with X and X' interchanged, thus converting the inequality into an equation. We now *define* the constant λ as the common value of the quantity above at all those nonspecialized points X at which $\phi^0(X) > 0$. In view of the only type of singularities allowed, we can extend the same definition to such points also. On solving the resulting equation for $\phi^0(X)$, we obtain the desired conclusion, as stated above.

Applying this to (30), we obtain the following result, which we state with the zero superscripts dropped, as we shall do for simplicity from now on:

Theorem 3.   *If $\phi(X)$ is to be the optimal distribution of the given Φ under the conditions assumed above, a positive constant λ must exist such that when $\phi(X)$ is positive*

$$\phi(X) = \frac{1}{W(X)} \log \frac{p(X)}{\lambda} W(X).$$

This may also be written in the form

$$(31) \qquad \phi(X) = \max\left\{ \frac{1}{W(X)} \log \frac{p(X)}{\lambda} W(X), 0 \right\}.$$

Since the first expression in the braces is > 0 or $\leqslant 0$ according to whether $p(X)W(X) > \lambda$ or $< \lambda$, we are led to the decomposition of $\mathcal{C}$ into two parts: $\mathcal{L}(\lambda)$ on which the $> \lambda$ holds, and its complement $\overline{\mathcal{L}}(\lambda)$ for the $< \lambda$, together with the corresponding integrals:

$$(32) \qquad \mathcal{L}(\lambda) = \{X \colon p(X)W(X) > \lambda\}; \qquad \overline{\mathcal{L}}(\lambda) = \{X \colon p(X)W(X) \leqslant \lambda\}$$

$$L(\lambda) = \iint_{\mathcal{L}(\lambda)} \frac{dx \, dy}{W(x, y)}; \qquad \Pi(\lambda) = \iint_{\mathcal{L}(\lambda)} p(x, y) \, dx \, dy.$$

Then (31) becomes

$$(33) \qquad \phi(X) = \frac{1}{W(X)} \cdot \log \frac{p(X)W(X)}{\lambda} \quad \text{on } \mathcal{L}(\lambda); \qquad = 0 \text{ on } \overline{\mathcal{L}}(\lambda).$$

To find the relation between λ and Φ, integrate (33) and apply (29), obtaining in terms of X: (x, y)

(34) $$\Phi = \iint\limits_{\mathfrak{L}(\lambda)} \left\{ \log[\, p(x, y) W(x, y)] - \log \lambda \right\} \frac{dx\, dy}{W(x, y)}.$$

This relation can be described in terms of the following mechanical model. Consider the surface having, in the coordinates (x, y, z), the equation $z = \log[p(x, y) W(x, y)]$. Suppose that the *solid* under this surface (which may extend upward indefinitely in some places and downward indefinitely in others) is made of a material substance whose density is $1/W(x, y)$. It will be constant along each vertical line but will in general vary from line to line. Next, pass the horizontal plane $z =$ constant $= \log \lambda$ through the solid; it will cut a piece of matter, above the plane but under the surface, determined by the inequalities

$$\log \lambda \leqslant z \leqslant \log[\, p(x, y) W(x, y)].$$

Evidently its *mass* is the integral in (34). It should be intuitively evident that this mass decreases continuously as λ increases, and fairly clear that it approaches zero as λ increases without limit and that it becomes infinite as $\lambda \to 0$, so that $\log \lambda \to -\infty$. These facts are established analytically by a routine study of inequalities. (Details are given in Koopman [9], in which a geometric simplification, in terms of volumes and areas, is given; this was suggested to the author in 1946 by G. E. Kimball.) It follows that for just one height of the plane—viz., for just one value of λ—the mass of the solid equals Φ.

Having found these expressions, we have but to substitute the values in (33) and (34) into (28) to obtain, after obvious reductions and the use of (32), the following expression for the probability of detecting the target when the search is optimal:

(35) $$P_{\text{opt}}[\Phi] = \Pi(\lambda) - \lambda L(\lambda)$$

where λ must be determined by (34) as before.

We recall that the exponential detection function may contain variables in addition to those of position, according to the lemma of Theorem 1 (Section 3), which is shown in Appendix C to lead to an integral equation, etc., but so far has not led to practical applications.

7. APPLICATION TO NORMAL DISTRIBUTIONS WITH CONSTANT W

As we have seen in the last two Chapters, there are many circumstances in which the distribution of the target can be reasonably well approximated by a normal distribution, circular in the simplest cases, elliptical in more general ones. Thus, in searching for a target at a "point of fix" or for a life-raft or other accidentally immobilized vehicle that had given out its position just before the accident, we have to deal with inaccurate information, disturbed by factors that usually justify the Gaussian estimate. Under these conditions, changes in geographical positions near the point of fix are small enough to warrant the assumption that W is a constant.

After a possible change of coordinate axes, we may always assume the following form of the distribution:

$$(36) \qquad p(x, y) = \frac{1}{2\pi\sigma_1\sigma_2} \exp\frac{-1}{2}(x^2/\sigma_1^2 + y^2/\sigma_2^2).$$

Equation (33) gives a result that may be written as

$$(37) \qquad 2W\phi(x, y) = 2\log(W/2\pi\sigma_1\sigma_2\lambda) - (x^2/\sigma_1^2 + y^2/\sigma_2^2).$$

Since $\phi(x, y) \geqslant 0$, λ must be so small that the first term on the right is positive: we shall denote it by ρ^2, (37) becoming

$$(38) \qquad 2W\phi(x, y) = \rho^2 - (x^2/\sigma_1^2 + y^2/\sigma_2^2), \quad \rho^2 = 2\log(W/2\pi\sigma_1\sigma_2\lambda),$$

which shows that (x, y) must lie inside or on the ellipse, centered at the origin and of semi-axes $\rho\sigma_1$ and $\rho\sigma_2$; its area is $\pi\rho^2\sigma_1\sigma_2$. It also shows that within this ellipse, the graph of $\phi(x, y)$ is a paraboloid, concave downward, and cut by the xy-plane in this ellipse. No searching is done outside it: the graph reduces to the plane.

It remains to express λ in terms of Φ and the other given quantities. As in the derivation of (34), we integrate $\phi(x, y)$ over $\mathcal{C}$; but since it is zero outside the ellipse, this means an integration over the latter. Applying this process to (38), the left member becomes $2W\Phi$, while the first term on the right yields the constant times the elliptic area, $\pi\rho^4\sigma_1\sigma_2$. The integration of the quadratic expression over the ellipse is simplified by the change of variables of integration to polar coordinates (r, θ) by setting

$$(39) \qquad x = \rho\sigma_1 r \cos\theta, \qquad y = \rho\sigma_2 r \sin\theta, \qquad dx\, dy = \rho^2\sigma_1\sigma_2 r\, dr\, d\theta$$

and then integrating over the unit circle $(r \leqslant 1)$.

This integration yields $-\frac{1}{2}\rho^4\pi\sigma_1\sigma_2$. Thus the integral of the right side of (38) reduces to $\frac{1}{2}\rho^4\pi\sigma_1\sigma_2$, and the equation corresponding to (34) is

$$(40) \qquad 2W\Phi = \frac{1}{2}\rho^4\pi\sigma_1\sigma_2; \qquad \text{hence } \rho^2 = 2\sqrt{W\Phi/\pi\sigma_1\sigma_2} \,.$$

Inserting this value in (38) gives the density of search over the ellipse:

$$(41) \qquad \phi(x, y) = \sqrt{\Phi/(W\pi\sigma_1\sigma_2)} - \frac{1}{2W}(x^2/\sigma_1^2 + y^2/\sigma_2^2).$$

To find the probability that this distribution of searching will in fact find the target, we apply formula (35). $M(\lambda) = \pi\rho^2\sigma_1\sigma_2$, the elliptic area. To calculate $\Pi(\lambda)$, we integrate the Gaussian expression (36) over the ellipse, again applying (39). The result is $\Pi(\lambda) = 1 - e^{-\rho^2/2}$. Using (38) to express λ in terms of ρ and substituting all these values into (35), we obtain

(42) $$P_{opt}(\Phi) = 1 - \left[1 + \rho^2/2\right]e^{-\rho^2/2}$$

$$= 1 - \left[1 + \sqrt{\frac{W\Phi}{\pi\sigma_1\sigma_2}}\right]\exp\left(-\sqrt{\frac{W\Phi}{\pi\sigma_1\sigma_2}}\right),$$

the second form being derived from the first by use of (40).

For completeness, we give λ in terms of known quantities, by eliminating from the second equations in (38) and (40):

(43) $$\lambda = \frac{W}{2\pi\sigma_1\sigma_2}\exp\left[-(W\Phi/\pi\sigma_1\sigma_2)^{1/2}\right].$$

The most common applications are based on the assumption that the normal distribution is circular, so that $\sigma_1 = \sigma_2 = \sigma$, the paraboloidal graph of the search density is a surface of revolution, and the search is confined to a circle.

To consider a concrete case, let $\sigma = 100$ miles (which means that there is half a chance that the target is in a circle of 118-mile radius, and $1 - 1/e = 0.632$ within 141.4 miles. Assume that the target is motionless and detectable on the surface by aircraft having a $W = 5$ mile sweep width. Finally, let there be available five 130-knot aircraft, each for just five hours. Measuring Φ by total length of track available, we have $\Phi = L = 3{,}250$ miles. With these values (40) gives for the radius of the circle searched, $\rho\sigma = 121$ miles. Within this circle, the density of searching effort, measured by track length per unit area (in the 1946 edition of *Search and Screening*, Φ and ϕ were what are here denoted by $W\Phi$ and $W\phi$) is, at the distance r from the center of the circle,

$$\phi = \frac{(121)^2 - r^2}{100{,}000},$$

while no searching is done outside this circle. With this expenditure of effort, the probability of detection is barely 0.17, which is considerably less than the probability that the target actually will be in the region searched. This is of course because of the considerable chance of missing it. After all, the total area swept without overlapping is $W\Phi = 16{,}250$ square miles as compared with the area $\pi(121)^2$ of over 46,000 square miles. Barely more than a third of the area could be "swept clean," and in a region in which the target has little more than half a chance of being located.

This example illustrates another practical result of the study of search optimization. Obviously we could not have our five aircraft flying in such a way that they more than very roughly reproduce the density of coverage given by the preceding formula. In fact, their probability of detection will fall short of even the above modest maximum possible result. This can have a very strong bearing on these decisions: whether to increase the searching effort considerably or, if that is impossible, whether to do it at all, and, if this decision is made, how much worse off are we than if we had made the above rather inadequate search. Finally, the possibility of other ways of narrowing down the target position may be underlined. Such questions, which will arise again in our optimization of screens, are notoriously difficult to answer by actual trials at sea. Therefore any light that such theoretical analyses as the above can shed on them must be doubly welcome.

Before leaving the present subject, it must be emphasized that in long-range surveillance systems, as we have seen in Chapter 4, normal distributions often occur which are very far from circular, requiring the more general treatment given earlier in this section.

8. THE CONSISTENT ADDITIVE OPTIMALITY OF ITERATIVE SEARCHES

The property of "consistent optimality" considered here focuses on the following practical question: The searcher is given a quantity Φ of searching effort to detect a fixed target, by methods involving passive observations only. In spite of optimizing the allocation ϕ on the basis of Φ, he fails to detect the target. Then he is told to search again, by means of a new installment of effort Φ'. Naturally he replaces the original target probability density $p(X)$ by the Bayesian updated density $p'(X)$, given the first failure; then he optimizes his distribution ϕ' of Φ' on the basis of $p'(X)$. Has he any logical right to believe that if he had been given in advance the total available effort $\Phi + \Phi'$ to optimize, he would have made a better distribution —and hence had a greater chance of success (as viewed from the start)?

It is easy to see, on the basis of the discussion in Section 3 as applied to search by parallel sweeps, using for example (2) or (3), that in general the searcher would have done better if he had been able to dispose of the total effort $\Phi + \Phi'$ optimally in a single block rather than in separate installments. This is connected with the fact that $D(X, \phi_1 + \phi_2)$ is in such cases usually *greater* than $D(X, \phi_1, \phi_2)$, contrary to the hypothesis of Theorem 1 in that section. On the other hand, according to Theorem 2, this quantitative disparity fades out as the effort is applied in smaller and smaller pieces—vanishing in the limiting case of the continuous subdivisibility upon which iterative and progressive searches are based. Under these conditions the conclusion of Theorem 1 applies: our detection function is the exponent law of random search. Then the following theorem gives the answer:

Theorem 4.   *On the general assumption of a fixed target searched by passive observations, together with the special assumption of the exponential detection law* (4), *the optimal distribution of the sum* $\Phi + \Phi'$ *is the sum* $\phi + \phi'$ *of the partial optimal distributions,* ϕ *based on* Φ *and the a priori* $p(X)$, *and* ϕ' *based on* Φ' *and the a posteriori* $p'(X)$, *given failure of the former to detect.*

This generalizes Theorem 2, established in the case of the distribution of search between two regions, and stated at the end of Section 5 for n regions, for which the proof was described as an immediate extension of the former.

In Section 6, (33) and (34) give the optimal distribution of the first search and then, after replacing Φ, ϕ, p, λ, $\mathcal{L}(\lambda)$ by the corresponding letters with accents, that of the second. This leaves us with the task of expressing p' in terms of the other quantities. Finally, using the same formulas with Φ replaced by $\Phi + \Phi'$, etc., but with the original p, we can write the optimal distribution of this lumped sum. The conclusion that this is $\phi + \phi'$ will then become obvious.

To find p' by means of Bayes's theorem, we note that (35) gives the probability $P = P_{\mathrm{opt}}[\phi]$ of success on the first search and hence that of failure $\bar{P} = 1 - P$, which is

$$(44) \qquad \bar{P} = \bar{\Pi}(\lambda) + \lambda L(\lambda)$$

where $\bar{\Pi}(\lambda)$ is the probability that the target was actually outside the region $\mathcal{L}(\lambda)$ searched, while $\lambda L(\lambda)$ is that of missing it even when searched in the right place. Then Bayes's theorem gives

$$(45) \qquad p'(X) = \frac{p(X)e^{-W(X)\phi(X)}}{\bar{P}}$$

and this has two expressions, in accordance with the two for ϕ in (33):

$$(46) \qquad p'(X) = \frac{\lambda}{W(X)\bar{P}} \quad \text{for } X \text{ on } \mathcal{L}(\lambda); \qquad p'(X) = \frac{p(X)}{\bar{P}} \text{ on } \bar{\mathcal{L}}(\lambda).$$

We must examine λ' and $\mathcal{L}'(\lambda)$. On $\mathcal{L}(\lambda)$ the value of $p'(X)$ is a constant greater than its values on $\bar{\mathcal{L}}(\lambda)$, since on the latter region, by its definition (32) $p'(X) \leqslant \lambda / W(X)$, and our statement follows from (46) on dividing by $\bar{P}$. Hence the second search covers $\mathcal{L}(\lambda)$ and, unless $p(X)$ is zero outside it, it covers a further region, appropriately denoted by $\Delta\mathcal{L} = \mathcal{L}'(\lambda') - \mathcal{L}(\lambda)$. Furthermore, (46) shows that $\mathcal{L}'(\lambda') = \mathcal{L}(\lambda'\bar{P})$: this is because the condition $p'(X)W(X) > \lambda'$, which defines $\mathcal{L}'(\lambda')$, is equivalent to $p(X)W(X) \geqslant \lambda'\bar{P}$, since the smallest values of $p'(X)W(X)$ occur on $\Delta\mathcal{L}$ (or on the boundary of $\mathcal{L}(\lambda)$ if $\Delta\mathcal{L}$ does not exist). There $p'(X)$ is given by the second expression in (46).

Applying (33) to the primed quantities, but replacing $\mathcal{L}'(\lambda')$ by $\mathcal{L}(\lambda'\bar{P})$, we obtain for the optimum allocation with the second search

$$(47) \qquad W(X)\phi'(X) = \log(\lambda/\lambda'\bar{P}) \qquad \text{for } X \text{ on } \mathcal{L}(\lambda)$$

$$= \log(p(X)W(X)/\lambda'\bar{P}) \qquad \text{for } X \text{ on } \Delta\mathcal{L}$$

$$= 0 \qquad \text{for } X \text{ on } \bar{\mathcal{L}}(\lambda'\bar{P}).$$

Substituting these in the equation corresponding to (34) we obtain, using (46) again,

$$(48) \qquad \Phi' = \iint\limits_{\mathcal{L}(\lambda)} \log(\lambda/\lambda'\bar{P})\frac{dx\,dy}{W} + \iint\limits_{\Delta\mathcal{L}} \log\left[p(X)W(X)/\lambda'\bar{P} \right]\frac{dx\,dy}{W}.$$

We can now calculate $\phi + \phi'$, using (33) and (47), and find, after the simplest reductions,

$$(49) \qquad \phi(X) + \phi'(X) = \frac{1}{W(X)} \log \frac{p(X)W(X)}{\lambda'\overline{P}} \qquad \text{for } X \text{ on } \mathcal{L}(\lambda'\overline{P}),$$

$$= 0 \qquad \text{on the complementary set } \overline{\mathcal{L}}(\lambda'\overline{\mathcal{P}}).$$

Similarly, for $\Phi + \Phi'$, (34) and (48) lead to

$$(50) \qquad \Phi + \Phi' = \iint_{\mathcal{L}(\lambda'\overline{P}) = \mathcal{L}'(\lambda')} \log\left[p(X)W(X)/\lambda'\overline{P} \right] \cdot \frac{dx\,dy}{W}.$$

Now these are exactly the same equations as would have been obtained by the optimization of $\Phi + \Phi'$. Indeed (50), as we have seen in Section 6, *determines* the λ-quantity—in this case $\lambda'\overline{P}$—in terms of the total available $\Phi + \Phi'$, and then (49) gives its optimal distribution. This concludes the proof of the theorem.

The property thus established has a vital bearing on sequences of repeated searches and on continuously progressive ones, as will be seen in Chapter 7.

A theorem that has received wide currency is that the only type of search that has the property of consistent additive optimality is the one based on the exponential law (4) of random search. Stated thus, the theorem is incorrect, as the simple counterexample of the definite detection law shows. We saw in Chapter 3, Section 9, that it had this property. In order to be correct, the hypothesis would have to be increased: e.g., by the assumption that the search could be so localized that a detection function of the sort examined in Section 3 above exists. The definite detection law would thereby be excluded.

9. OPTIMUM SCANNING

It must not be supposed that the cases treated in the preceding sections exhaust the subject of optimal distribution of searching effort, even in very simple cases of practical importance. The optimal method of *scanning* is given as an example of a rather different situation.

Returning to the framework of ideas and notation of Chapter 3, suppose that the observer and target are on straight courses at fixed speeds, so that relative to the observer the target is moving in a straight line at the speed of w knots, its lateral range being x miles (see Chapter 3, Fig. 3-5). It is convenient here to regard the target as moving down the line parallel to the axis of ordinates cutting the axis of abscissas at the point of abscissa $x > 0$. Its position at the epoch t is at the point of coordinates (x, y), where x remains constant and $y = -wt$ (the negative sign, because of his downward motion; y decreases as t increases). The observer remains at the origin.

Instead of taking the instantaneous probability of detection $\gamma_t\,dt$ for granted, as we largely did in Chapter 3, we here propose to inquire into it more deeply, and in particular to examine the effect of varying the method of directing the line of sight (or the radar or sonar beam) from position to position over the field of view. We propose, in other words, to examine the effect of different scanning procedures upon γ_t and through it, upon the search width W. And we will say that *the scanning method is optimum if it renders W a maximum.*

For any method of detection (visual, radar, sonar, etc.), there exists a quantity ℓ defined as follows: Let the relative positions of the target and observer remain virtually unchanged during a short interval of time dt, during which the observer directs his axis of vision (or the radar or sonar beam axis) straight at the target. Assuming no previous detection, the probability of detection during dt is $\ell\, dt$, which can be called the instantaneous line-of-sight detection probability. We shall assume that ℓ depends only on range, $\ell = \ell(r)$. We shall assume furthermore that the probability of detection during dt is insignificantly changed by a slight change in the position of the target out of the line of sight, e.g., by an angle less than ε radians, but that it falls virtually to zero at greater angles. The reader will appreciate that this assumption is not unrealistic in the important case of a target close to the threshold of visibility, or with narrow radar or sonar lobes; cf. Fig. 4-2 of Chapter 4, Section 3.

For any method of scanning, there exists a function $f(z)$ (where z is an angle in radians measured from the positive axis of ordinates in the clockwise sense), defined as follows: $f(z)\, dz$ is the length of time out of a complete scanning cycle during which the axis of vision is between the angles z and $z + dz$. If the total time of one scanning cycle is T, obviously

(51) $$\int_0^{2\pi} f(z)\, dz = T; \quad \text{also} \quad f(z) \geqslant 0.$$

It is now possible to obtain γ_t, the instantaneous detection probability density resulting both from the instrument of detection and its use (method of scan). Let the angle ζ (from the positive axis of ordinates to the target, Figure 3-7 of Chapter 3) and the range r remain practically constant during one scanning cycle (slow relative motion or fast scan). Then at each cycle the length of time during which the target is within the angle ε of the visual axis is

$$\int_{\zeta-\varepsilon}^{\zeta+\varepsilon} f(\zeta)\, d\zeta = 2\varepsilon f(\zeta) \text{ to terms of higher order in } \varepsilon.$$

Hence the probability of detection is

$$g = 2\varepsilon f(\zeta)\ell(r).$$

This is the one-glimpse probability of detection. Indeed, the idea of scanning automatically commits us to the notion of detection by discrete glimpses rather than by continuous looking. In view of our assumption of a scanning that is fast with respect to the relative motions, however, it is a legitimate approximation to pass to the latter viewpoint, and to convert g into γ_t by division by T. (Compare with the similar reasoning in Section 2, Chapter 3, equation (7) in particular.) This we shall write

(52) $$\gamma_t = \gamma(r, \zeta) = \frac{2\varepsilon}{T} f(\zeta)\ell(r).$$

It is to be noted that whereas in the greater part of Chapter 3, $\gamma_t = \gamma(r)$, a function of range alone, the very nature of the present considerations focuses attention upon a γ_t that depends both on target range and *bearing*. Nevertheless, the relevant reasoning and formulas of Section 4 of Chapter 3 are applicable, and we have as the expression for the search width

(53) $$W = \int_{-\infty}^{\infty} \left[1 - \exp\left(-\frac{2\varepsilon}{Tw} \int_{-\infty}^{\infty} f(\zeta)\ell(r) \, dy \right) \right] dx.$$

The mathematical nature of the problem is now clear. The quantities w, ε, $\ell(r)$ are fixed by the conditions, whereas T and $f(\zeta)$ are at our disposal, subject only to the conditions (51) and that T must be small in comparison with the time required for an appreciable change in *relative* position of target and observer. And *we have to find that function $f(\zeta)$ which makes W a maximum.*

By an easy argument of symmetry, the optimum $f(\zeta)$ is symmetrical about the axis of ordinates: $f(-\zeta) = f(\zeta)$. Assuming this, the integrand in (53) becomes an "even" function of x, so that W is twice the integral from 0 to ∞. Similarly, the integral in (51) can be replaced by twice its value from 0 to π. Writing for convenience

$$\phi(\zeta) = \frac{2}{T} f(\zeta), \qquad \Lambda(r) = \frac{\varepsilon}{w} \ell(r),$$

(51) and (53) are further simplified, and our problem is reduced to the following: find that function $\phi(\zeta)$, $0 \le \zeta \le \pi$, which, among all functions satisfying

(54) $$\int_0^{\pi} \phi(\zeta) \, d\zeta = 1, \qquad \phi(\zeta) \ge 0,$$

makes the expression

(55) $$\frac{W}{2} = \int_0^{\infty} \left[1 - \exp\left(-\int_{-\infty}^{\infty} \phi(\zeta)\Lambda(r) \, dy \right) \right] dx$$

a maximum. This is again a unilateral problem in the calculus of variations, not to be solved simply by equating certain variations to zero.

Introducing polar coordinates (r, ζ), (55) becomes

(56) $$\frac{W}{2} = \int_0^{\infty} \left[1 - \exp\left(-x \int_0^{\pi} \phi(\zeta)\Lambda(x \csc \zeta) \csc^2 \zeta \, d\zeta \right) \right] dx.$$

The integral with respect to x will increase when its (nonnegative) integrand increases, and such an increase will take place when the integral in the exponent, i.e.,

$$U = \int_0^{\pi} \phi(\zeta)\Lambda(x \csc \zeta) \csc^2 \zeta \, d\zeta,$$

is increased. The evident difficulty is that U involves x as well as $\phi(\zeta)$. If we fixed the value of x we could try to find the function $\phi(\zeta)$ maximizing U subject to (54). But the resulting $\phi(\zeta)$ could be expected to be one function for one value of x, and a different one for another x, and consequently useless as far as maximizing $W/2$ is concerned. The remarkable fact is that in a broad class of cases, including all those important in practice, this turns out not to be the case. Indeed we have the theorem:

If $\ell(r) = \ell_1(r)/r^2$, where $\ell_1(r)$ decreases with increasing r, the optimum scan consists in fixing the line of sight directly along the axis of abscissas, dividing the time equally between right and left. When most of the relative motion is due to the observer (e.g., a searching aircraft), this means that all scanning should be done abeam.

To prove this theorem, we note that $\Lambda(r) = \Lambda_1(r)/r^2$, where $\Lambda_1(r)$ decreases as r increases. Hence

$$U = \frac{1}{x^2} \int_0^\pi \phi(\zeta)\Lambda_1(x \csc \zeta) \, d\zeta,$$

and our problem is to choose $\phi(\zeta)$ subject to (54) which maximizes this integral. As ζ goes from 0 to π, $x \csc \zeta$ decreases from $+\infty$ to a minimum of x at $\zeta = \pi/2$, and then increases to $+\infty$ again. Hence Λ_1 has its *maximum* when $\zeta = \pi/2$, and this is true for any $x > 0$. The graph of $\Lambda_1 (x \csc \zeta)$ against ζ is shown in Fig. 6-2, which also shows that of $\phi(\zeta)$ [with shading under it; the shaded area must be unity by virtue of (54)].

Geometrically, the problem is to deform the $\phi(\zeta)$ curve (always maintaining it above the ζ axis and bounding unit area) so that the area under the product ordinate curve $\phi(\zeta)\Lambda_1(x \csc \zeta)$ shall be a maximum. Obviously, the more the $\phi(\zeta)$ is peaked about the mid-point $\zeta = \pi/2$, the larger the area under the product curve. In other words, the more of the time the axis of vision is directed at the angle

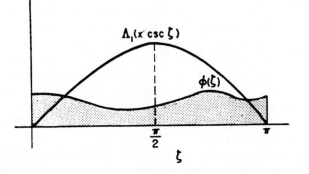

Fig. 6-2. Graphical representation of the scanning problem.

$\zeta = \pi/2$, the greater will be the value of the search width W. This proves the theorem above.

The case $\ell(r) = \ell_1(r)/r^2$, $\ell_1(r)$ decreasing with increasing r, occurs when $\ell(r)$ is an inverse nth power with n greater than 2—in particular with the inverse cube power law, but also when there is an exponential attenuation factor multiplying an inverse square or higher power. In fact, it occurs in the majority of cases studied in the present work, except in such long-range propagation as may occur with a radar or acoustic duct, when the scanning methods take on a fundamentally different form. And the theorem in the case of a definite-range law is trivially true.

It would be misleading to conclude that scanning should always be confined to the beam. In most cases it is imperative to detect the target *early*. For example, a surfaced submarine may submerge if not detected and attacked before it sees the searcher, or it may be expected to attack the searcher as soon as it sees it.

In concluding the treatment of this example, we point out an essential mathematical difference between it and those considered earlier: Strictly speaking, *no solution to the problem exists*. There is no function $\phi(\zeta)$ satisfying the conditions (51) and maximizing W. This does not matter in practice, since, as we have shown, any sequence of functions—those approaching increasing scan about $\zeta = \pi/2$ gives rise to a sequence of values of W that approach a common upper limit. This suffices to orient our choice of scanning methods. An obvious remark is that the problem does have a "solution," viz., proportional to $\delta(\zeta - \pi/2)$, the Dirac delta function. But this tells just as much and as little—theoretically or practically—as what has been stated above.

10. MULTIPLE OPTIMIZATION, LAGRANGE MULTIPLIERS, AND SUPPORT PLANES

The basic issue faced in this chapter has been one common to a large class of operational, economic, and similar questions: *to make an optimal decision when confronted with multiple measures of effectiveness*. In the optimal allocation of searching effort, one measure has been the probability of detecting the target, the other, the "economy" (or negative of the effort used). As we had stated the problem, the latter was given a fixed value $-\Phi$, the former was maximized. We could of course have switched our aim and sought to maximize the economy for a fixed probability of detection—with essentially the same results. More generally, we could have made what amounts to a linearly expressed "value judgment" with "tradeoff" and sought to maximize a weighted linear combination of these two measures. Thus if $u = -\Phi$, the economy, and $v = P[\phi]$, the probability of detection with the use of Φ, we could have maximized $Au + Bv$, where the constants express the tradeoff: $1/A$ pieces of u having an "equal value" to $1/B$ of v. When more than two measures of effectiveness are involved, e.g., (u, v, w) the corresponding ideas extend to them, using $Au + Bv + Cw$, etc.

These matters may be put in a graphical form in terms of sets and loci. Since we are forced to make a decision, we first direct our attention to the totality of possible decisions: it is a set Ω of elements ω, each one specifying a particular decision. In the cases treated in Sections 4 and 5, ω was an allocation of searching effort between n different regions, which could be specified by a set of n (nonnegative) numbers $(\phi_1, \ldots, \phi_n)$, and ω was a *point* in a region Ω of n-dimensional *space*. In the continuous cases of Sections 6–9, the decision ω was specified by a (nonnegative) function $\phi(X)$: Ω was a *function space* (hence, infinitely many dimensional).

To each decision ω in the "space" Ω of possible decisions corresponds a set of values (u, v), (u, v, w), etc., of our measures of effectiveness. In the case of allocation to the n regions, $u = -\Sigma\phi_i$ and $v = \Sigma Di(1 - e^{-W_i\phi_i})$. In the continuous case, these sums were replaced by integrals over the target region $\mathcal{R}$, or over the angle of scan in Section 9. As noted before, tactical problems in search may involve other measures of effectiveness as well, such as the degree of safety, earliness of detection, precision of localization, etc. But whatever the details of the special problem, the general fact is that Ω is *mapped* onto a set $\mathcal{S}$ in the space whose coordinates are the measures of effectiveness: the "point" ω of Ω going into the point (u, v), (u, v, w), etc., where u, v, etc. are the values corresponding to ω. Figures 6-3 and 6-4 are drawn for the case of a double-objective problem.

The first general principle to be inferred from these geometrical relationships is the common-sense one: *an optimal choice of ω will never lead to an interior point of* $\mathcal{S}$ (i.e., a point inside a neighborhood of points of $\mathcal{S}$), for one could always move such a point within its neighborhood so that all its coordinates are increased, and thus a better result obtained. This directs the attention to the boundary points of $\mathcal{S}$: those within every neighborhood of which there are points of $\mathcal{S}$ and also points of $\overline{\mathcal{S}}$ (i.e., not belonging to $\mathcal{S}$, and which therefore cannot be obtained by any decision ω of Ω). Points on the boundary may or may not belong to $\mathcal{S}$.

Figures 6-3 and 6-4 are schematic illustrations of possible cases, simple and complicated, when $\mathcal{S}$ is a region of the uv-plane. Evidently not all boundary points

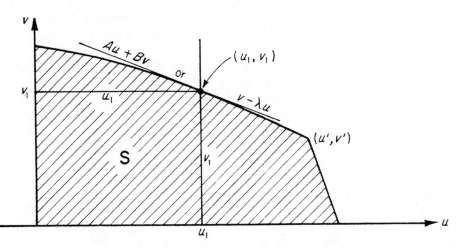

Fig. 6-3. Convex case.

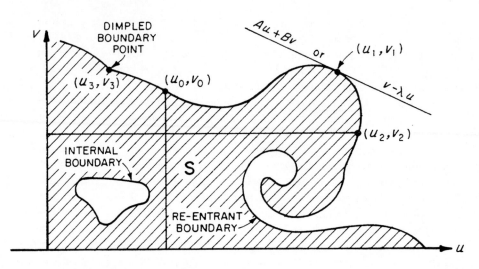

Fig. 6-4. More general case.

are relevant to the various optimization problems. The interior boundary and reentrant part of the exterior boundary in Fig. 6-4 do not correspond to optima.

Figure 6-3 shows that, with its type of boundary, the point (u_1, v_1) has the property that v_1 is the greatest v for the fixed $u = u_1$, that u_1 is the greatest u for the given $v = v_1$, and finally that the tangent through it, which has the slope $\lambda = -A/B$, corresponds to the greatest value of $Au + Bv$ for all the parallels of the form $Au + Bv = $ constant that have at least one point in common with S.

Figure 6-4 shows that a point such as (u_0, v_0), for which v_0 is the greatest v for fixed $u = u_0$, does not have the property that u_0 is the greatest u for fixed $v = v_0$, nor that of giving a greatest $Au + Bv$ for all parallels to the tangent at (u_0, v_0) and cutting S. Corresponding statements apply to (u_2, v_2). The point (u_1, v_1), which gives the greatest value of $Au + Bv$ for all S-intersecting lines of given slope λ, does in fact have the two other properties and thus corresponds to the (u_1, v_1) of Fig. 6-3.

Evidently the only boundary points relevant to the optimization of v for given u are those on the lower extremity of vertical half-lines entirely outside S; and for maximizing u for given v, extremities of horizontal half-lines outside it. Some boundary points, such as (u_3, v_3) of Fig. 6-4, can have both properties without the third one: that of maximizing $Au + Bv$ when $-A/B$ is the slope of the tangent at (u_3, v_3). To construct the locus of boundary points maximizing such linear combinations, we must apply the notion of convexity.

A region $\mathcal{R}$ in n-dimensional space (line, plane, solid, etc.) is *convex* if every indefinite straight line either has no point in common with $\mathcal{R}$, has just one point in common with it, or has a single segment (finite or infinite) in common with $\mathcal{R}$. Thus the shaded part of S in Fig. 6-3 is convex, and this makes the triple property of (u_1, v_1) intuitive geometrically—not only for that point, but for any other point on the boundary where a touching line slopes downward. To find the part of the boundary in the nonconvex case of Fig. 6-4 relevant to the maximization of linear expressions $Au + Bv$, we construct the *convex hull* S_c of S: the smallest closed convex region containing S. This is easily visualized as the plane region inside and on the boundary of a tightly stretched string (possibly infinite) containing the region S (as a rigid lamina). The points common to the boundary of S and of S_c are those that come into play in the maximization of $Au + Bv$. They are the points of contact of the string with S.

A *convex body* is a closed convex set; i.e., it includes all its (finite) boundary points. A *support plane* (or *line* in 2-dimensions, *hyperplane* in 4 or more dimensions) is one that intersects the boundary but has the whole convex body on one side of it or on it. It includes the case where this plane or line, etc., is tangent to the boundary at the point. It also applies to corner points such as (u', v') of Fig. 6-3 where there is a whole angle of support lines, which "touch" the boundary without being tangent to it.

The *Hahn–Banach* theorem states that through every point on the boundary of a convex body passes *at least one* support plane. This theorem, easily proved as an exercise in analytic geometry for bodies in finite dimensional space, requires a modified statement when it is infinitely many dimensional. For the latter see, e.g., Bourbaki [1]; it will not be needed in our work.

When S is a convex body (as in Fig. 6-3 when it includes its boundary points), the maximum v for fixed $u = u_1$ *exists*, i.e., it is obtained as the result of a possible decision ω of Ω (e.g., allocation of effort $-u_1$). The maximum u for $v = v_1$ also exists and has the value u_1. The boundary being smooth at (u_1, v_1) has a unique tangent of slope λ (< 0 in this type of case). Then the linear expression $Au + Bv$, where $-A/B = \lambda$ and (u, v) belongs to S, has an actual maximum at (u_1, v_1). It is important to realize that these statements say considerably more than the ones made earlier concerning this point (u_1, v_1) of Fig. 6-3. The earlier ones merely spoke of "greatest values," not "maxima"—the difference being that the maxima correspond to values that can be achieved by a possible selection of ω, whereas nothing of this sort had been implied by the previous statements. For example, in the problem of optimum scan of Section 9, the "optimum" corresponded to a boundary point that could not be obtained by any scanning procedure (i.e., by the choice of a definite ω), but had the useful property that it could be approached by a sequence $\{\omega_i\}$ of possible ones. In the earlier cases of search considered in this chapter, S was not only convex but closed, and the above triple property of (u_1, v_1) was guaranteed.

In a large proportion of actual cases in which Ω is finite-dimensional, as in those of sections 4 and 5, the measures of effectiveness are "smooth" and the region S possesses those parts of its boundaries relevant to the optimization. They are frequently given as the loci of the vanishing of certain Jacobian determinants. The region S is often not convex, however. It is to be noted that these convenient properties may often be lost if the natural formulation is replaced by one adapted to certain types of machine computation—then irregularities may occur as "artifacts" of the approximation.

Turning to the point (u_1, v_1) of Figs. 6-3 and 6-4, which, let us assume, belongs to S and has the triple maximal property, the use of $Au + Bv$, or its equivalent $v - \lambda u$, as the function to maximize, instead of v for $u = u_1$, etc., replaces a *constrained* problem of maximization by an unconstrained one: λ is the *Lagrange multiplier* familiar in classical treatments. Thus in the cases of Sections 4–7 we had $v = P[\phi]$ and $u = -\Phi$, so that the unconstrained problem was to maximize $P[\phi] + \lambda\Phi$, which we solved by the methods of J. W. Gibbs. Where Φ is so large that the constraint $\phi \geqslant 0$ does not have to be imposed, being satisfied automatically, the classical Euler–Lagrange methods are applicable.

To find the optimum by replacing the constrained by the unconstrained problem requires the eventual determination of λ. We have applied a geometrical or mechanical method in the cases of Sections 6 and 7, where the continuity of the change of λ with that of Φ was brought out. The same continuity can be proved in the cases of Sections 4 and 5, by computing its values as Φ approaches a "critical value" Φ', below which a region is not searched, above which some searching is done it it. The two values of λ approach the same limit as Φ approaches Φ' from above and from below. Moreover, in all these cases λ changes strictly monotonically with Φ (always decreasing when Φ increases), so that its value for each given Φ is determined—and often computable.

All this is illustrated in every case in which $\mathcal{S}$ is a convex body of the type shown in Fig. 6-3, but without corner points such as (u', v'). Every support line in the region considered is a tangent and has a negative slope: $\lambda < 0$. This slope decreases monotonically as u increases: *strictly* so, as long as the curvature of the boundary is not zero. Then each λ determines a point of tangency (u_1, v_1), at which each of the constrained optimization properties is valid. At flat segments of the boundary, or at corner points, this one-to-one correspondence $\lambda \leftrightarrow (u_1, v_1)$ would cease to be valid. However, it is valid in the problems of search with the detection law required for progressive searches by passive observation (Section 3); and it is precisely in these cases that we shall find its useful applications in Chapter 7.

The generalization to three or more dimensions is immediate.

The ideas and methods used in the present section are old. They have rather recently experienced an expanded range of application in the economic sciences. Recalling them from their past, the author [8] had outlined them in 1956 to make a point concerning the role of the decision-maker (value judgments involved in the "value" factors A, B) and their application to search theory. In 1963 Everett [5] applied the general Lagrange multiplier concept to optimal destructive bombing allocations and others, using the convex hull to secure a convex region $\mathcal{S}_c$. This could be handled in the step-function cases appropriate to machine computation. Recently (1975) Stone [13] made an intensive examination of the same ideas of convexity and Lagrange multipliers, treating by this means a large number of problems of search, as well as of many mathematically related ones, and with mechanical computability always considered.

Further interesting facts related to the subjects of the present chapter are found in references [11]–[13].

REFERENCES

1. Bourbaki, N. 1950. *Espaces vectorielles topologiques*, II. Paris: Hermann.
2. Dobbie, J. M. 1963. Search theory: a sequential approach. *Naval Research Logistics Quarterly* 4:323–34.

3. Dobbie, J. M. 1968. A Survey of Search Theory. *Operations Research* 16:525–37.

4. DeGuenin, J. 1961. Optimum distribution of effort: an extension of the Koopman basic theory. *Operations Research* 9:1–7.

5. Everett, H. 1963. Generalized Lagrange multiplier method for solving problems of optimal allocation of resources. *Operations Res.* 11:399–417.

6. Gibbs, J. Willard. 1928. On the equilibrium of heterogeneous substances. *Collected Works*, vol. 1, pp. 15–134, New York: Longman, Green & Co.

7. Koopman, B. O. 1946. *Search and screening.* OEG Report 56, Chapter 3.

8. Koopman, B. O. 1956. Fallacies in operations research. *Operations Res.* 4:425.

9. Koopman, B. O. 1957. The theory of search, III: the optimum distribution of searching effort. *Operations Res.* 5:613–26.

10. Koopman, B. O. 1979. An operational critique of detection laws. *Operations Res.*27–1:115–133.

11. Richardson, H. R. and Stone, L. D. 1971. Operations analysis during the underwater search for SCORPION. *Naval Res. Logis. Quart.* 18:141–57.

12. Richardson, H. R., Stone, L. D., and Andrews, F. A. 1971. *Manual for the operations analysis of deep ocean search*, prepared for the supervisor of salvage, Naval Ships Systems Command (NAVSHIPS 0994-010-7010).

13. Stone, L. D. 1975. *Theory of optimal search.* New York: Academic Press.

Chapter 7

Search in Time: Information and Jeopardy

The present chapter considers search that extends through a period of time sufficiently long to have a material effect on the operation and its results. Two assumptions are basic to the whole treatment: first, that the search is progressive and involves passive observations only; and second, that while the target may adopt procedures that reflect general knowledge of being searched, it does not react to specific details of the search. In most of the chapter it is further assumed that the search is subdivisible and localized, in the sense of Chapter 6, Sections 1 and 2, the latter extended to include time and its relaxation intervals. It follows that in these cases the general exponential detection law applies. On the other hand, to gain perspective and obtain some useful results, two quite different forms of progressive search are considered: search by the definite detection law of "clean sweep" (Chapter 3, Section 9); and search by repeated dichotomy in the set of states of a physical system. The minimum expected number of trials in the latter case leads to the classical *entropy* of the distribution; its negative, its *information*. Similarly, for fixed targets, the minimum expected searching effort used up by the moment of first detection is a numerical measure of the difficulty facing the searcher; its negative, the *jeopardy* to the target.

Two cases are considered. First, we consider progressive search for targets fixed in the plane of search. This plane may be geographically fixed, or it may be in uniform translation with the vector velocity common to the particular class of targets of interest, so that they can be treated as fixed in this plane. Second, we consider progressive search for a class of targets having more general types of motion. If a search in such cases is to be optimized, a sufficient degree of knowledge must exist to enable the searcher to make plans in a quantitative form. The general mathematical formulation is given, which is illustrated by some simple applications.

After such mathematical solutions have been obtained, it is necessary to have practical ones for their implementation. In the succeeding chapters the practical designs of searches for targets in transit under various possible conditions and with the use of different searching platforms will be treated as concrete problems. Theses will be illustrated by examples that were used with success during World War II. Practical guides for extending them to more modern situations, such as "sprint and drift" platforms and the longer ranges now involved, will also be outlined.

1. GENERAL FEATURES OF SEARCHES EXTENDING IN TIME

There is a difference *in principle* between the searches of the present chapter and those of the preceding one, which prevents a mere extension to three variables (x, y, t) of what was done for two (x, y), because of the target's *duration in time*. To bring this out, suppose that we are searching for a *target-event*—something that happens just once during a long period of time in the searched region $\mathcal{R}$. This might be an explosion, the launching of a peculiar missile, even a moment when an undetectable target becomes detectable during a long patrol. Then we could divide the "space-time" of the three variables (x, y, t) (corresponding with (x, y) in $\mathcal{R}$ and t in the period of interest) into small pieces (as in the definition of triple integrals in the calculus) and then assert that the target-event will be in one and only one piece, so that total probability can be applied. Thence the usual reasoning leads to an expression similar to (5) and (28) of Chapter 6, only with triple integration replacing double, (x, y, t) being the variables of integration, $p(x, y, t)\,dx\,dy\,dt$ being the probability that the target event will occur in $dx\,dy\,dt$ at (x, y, t). Such a $p(x, y, t)$ would be quite a different function from the one denoted by the same symbol used in this and in earlier chapters, in which $p(x, y, t)$ is a density in the (x, y) plane, t being a parameter: $p(x, y, t)\,dx\,dy$ is the probability that at the epoch t, the target will be in $dx\,dy$ at (x, y).

Since in the progressive searches for the persistently detectable target, we cannot say that the occurrence of the target in different pieces of the (x, y, t) space are mutually exclusive, we cannot apply total probability as in the case above. In fact our target is not a *point* in this space but a *curve*—a "world line"—cut by each plane, $t = $ constant, in a point. Furthermore, our one-parameter family of plane probability densities $p(x, y, t)$ is an altogether incomplete characterization of the target's statistics, and is quite insufficient for the purposes of search, as should have become evident in the subjects set forth in Chapter 5. There it is made clear that enough factors affecting the target's motion must be known so that not only a priori probabilities but *conditional* ones are determined—conditioned, for example, on a failure to detect the target on an earlier epoch, between which and the present one the target may have moved considerably. This is a characteristic feature of *stochastic processes*. The fact that the problems of the preceding chapter involved no such complications was due to the completely known law of motion of the targets: they were at (relative) rest. While the same assumption will be made in the next four sections, more general ones are introduced in the later ones. They will be given expression in practical terms in the succeeding chapters.

In order to define the local intensity of search at a given time t, the concept of three orders of size must not only be applied, as in Chapter 6, Section 1, to *distances*, but to *times*. As in Chapter 5, we had the "relaxation time" Δt, just as we had "intermediate sizes" of regions $\Delta\mathcal{C}$. For evidently during a time as small as a millisecond no organically complete amount of searching can occur. The eye cannot respond, there is no time for signal integration on a scope, and no effective searching motion can take place. Accordingly, our Δt is large enough to make these operations possible. As in the earlier case, a definite amount of searching effort $\Delta\Phi$ can in fact be applied in $\Delta\mathcal{C}$ during the period Δt, and the ratio $\Delta\Phi/\Delta\mathcal{C}\,\Delta t$ will not be sensibly different for different $\Delta\mathcal{C}$ and Δt—provided that, on the one hand, they contain the given point X and epoch t, and on the other hand, that they have the *intermediate* or *relaxation* size. This ratio, insensitive to such choices in $\Delta\mathcal{C}$ and Δt (provided, as we said, that they contain X and t) is essentially a function of these variables, to be denoted by $\psi(X, t)$ and called the *search density at X per unit time at the epoch t*. In spite of the fact that it is not the limit of a ratio in the strict mathematical sense, it can with adequate approximation be treated as if it were one, sums being replaced by integrals, etc. (with due precautions).

Thus the integral of $\psi(X, t)\,\Delta t$ over any region in $\mathcal{C}$ is the amount of searching effort done in that region during the interval $(t, t + \Delta t)$, and $\phi(X, t) = \int_0^t \psi(X, t)\,dt$ is the total intensity of effort at X expended during the interval $(0, t)$. Of course in dealing with a moving target that is in the piece $\Delta\mathcal{C}$ of $\mathcal{C}$ only for part of that time, the above time integral must be replaced by one taken over the corresponding part of the time. We shall return to this point in Section 7. Finally, the integral

$$\iint_{\mathcal{C}} dM \int_0^t \psi(X, t)\,dt = \iint_{\mathcal{C}} \phi(X, t)\,dM = \Phi(t)$$

is the total effort available up to the time t. Therefore $\Phi(t_2) - \Phi(t_1)$ is that which becomes available during the period (t_1, t_2).

The detection function $D(X, t, z)$ is defined as in Chapter 6, (1), but with the condition that the target is at X—i.e., in the neighborhood $\Delta\mathcal{C}$ of X—replaced in the case of a moving target by the condition that it is in this neighborhood during a certain part of the time $(0, t)$, the part over which $\psi(X, t)$ is integrated to give $z = \Delta\phi(X, t)$. Also, t as well as X must be included in the specification of the detection event occurring within this neighborhood $\Delta\mathcal{C}$ of X; e.g.,

(1) $D(X, t, \phi(X, t)) = P(\text{detection using } \phi(X, t)|\text{target given as stated}).$

We derive as before the exponential law of random search

(2) $D(X, t, \phi) = 1 - e^{-W\phi}, \qquad W = W(X, t), \qquad \phi = \phi(X, t),$

as in the proof of Theorem 1 (Chapter 3, Section 6), under the same hypotheses. Again $W = D(X, t, \Delta\phi)/\Delta\phi$ (small $\Delta\phi$) is a "coefficient of detectability" of the target at X and t, reducing to the sweep width when the tracks are of the simple forms of Chapter 3. Its possible dependence on t reflects such different conditions as day versus night visibility, variations of sonar conditions with time of day ("afternoon effect"), etc. As in every use of (2), here and in Chapter 6, the dimension of W is that of length if ϕ is measured as length per unit area, but as area per unit time (search rate) when ϕ is time per unit area, and so on. Thus $W\phi$ is always dimensionless.

In mathematical formulations of the various problems of optimal search, it is necessary to realize that in addition to the conditions of nonnegativeness of ϕ and of ψ, the latter function must be regarded as *bounded from above*: $\psi(X, t)$ cannot exceed a given constant, since there are always technical limits to the rate of application of searching effort at each time and place. Some tactical situations may justify a more flexible limit: a given function of (X, t), expressing the fact that the maximum rate may be different at different places in $\mathcal{C}$ and times t.

Of course from the practical point of view it would be useless to attempt to find an optimal search in cases of very general laws of dependence of the upper limit of ψ or of W on time, since in only a few simple cases can such functions be known with enough precision for advance planning of a search. Only one case of a time-dependent W will be considered, that of two different orders of visibility corresponding with two sorts of time interval, such as day and night. This will be studied in Section 4.

2. PROGRESSIVE SEARCH FOR FIXED TARGETS

The target searched is assumed fixed in the plane region $\mathcal{C}$ and the assumptions of the preceding section are made. *The optimal search is defined as the one minimizing the expected effort used up to the moment the target is detected.* This is the formulation of optimal search due to Dobbie ([2] of Chapter 6). No limit being imposed on the amount of effort $\Phi(t)$ *eventually* available, this expected value is finite. As we shall see, the time can be replaced by the variable $s = \Phi(t)$, so that restrictions in terms of ψ do not enter the formulas.

The problem is made meaningful (namely, meaningful as corresponding to a practical problem of preprogrammed search—not as a sequential decision process or as the purely abstract mathematical posits so frequently found in the contemporary publications; for examples and references to these, see Stone [7]) by virtue of the theorem of consistent iterative optimality of Chapter 6, Section 8, since if we optimize the available searching effort $\Phi(t_1)$ $(0 < t_1 < t)$ and then optimize the remaining effort $\Phi(t) - \Phi(t_1)$ on the basis of the a posteriori probability density $p'(X)$ (given nondetection in the first search), we obtain the same total distribution $\int_0^t \psi(X, t)\, dt$ as the optimal distribution of $\Phi(t)$. In other words, in the notation of the theorem cited,

$$\int_0^t \psi(X, t)\, dt = \int_0^{t_1} \psi(X, t)\, dt + \int_{t_1}^t \psi'(X, t)\, dt.$$

Thus (33), (34), and (35) of Chapter 6 give the solution of the problem of optimization in the sense of maximizing the probability of detection during the various given time intervals (of course with $\phi(X)$ and Φ expressible as the appropriate time integrals of $\psi(X, t)$ and $\Phi'(t)$).

Turning to the problem of optimization of the search in the sense of *minimizing* the expected amount of total searching effort $\Phi(T)$ expended up to the moment T of detection, this expected value $\overline{\Phi}$ is given by the following expression, which *does not involve the time* t:

$$(3) \qquad \overline{\Phi} = \int_0^\infty s\, dP(s) = \int_0^\infty sP'(s)\, ds,$$

where $P(s)$ is the probability that, at the epoch T of first detection, the total effort used will be $\Phi(T) \leqslant s$. In spite of the fact that no limit is being placed on the total effort *eventually* available $(\Phi(\infty) = \infty)$, it could be so *misapplied* that $P(\infty) < 1$, which would lead to $\overline{\Phi} = \infty$ (a positive probability of never finding the target). Nevertheless the formulas of the last chapter show that it *could be so applied* that $P(\infty) = 1$. Then (3) shows that the problem of minimizing $\overline{\Phi}$ is that of so distributing a unit mass of density $P'(s)$ along a line $(0 \leqslant s < \infty)$ that the resulting center of gravity (at $\overline{\Phi}$) will be as close to $s = 0$ as possible. Now whenever some of the mass is transferred from an interval (s_1, ∞) to an earlier one $(0, s_1)$ (other things not being changed), the center of gravity will move to the left (toward $s = 0$). Hence we shall diminish $\overline{\Phi}$ to the extent that we can crowd our mass to the left—up to the limit given by the maximization of the probability $P(s)$ for each s. This means that $P(s) = P_{\text{opt}}(\Phi)$ given by (35) of Chapter 6, i.e.,

$$(4) \qquad P(s) = \Pi(\lambda) - \lambda L(\lambda).$$

Naturally, the formulas above involving integrals and differentials are to be regarded as approximations to somewhat more complicated ones involving sums and differences, and closer to the reality of the "intermediate size" of Δt, $\Delta\Phi(t)$, etc. (see Chapter 6, Sections 1 and 2). Furthermore, even if certain search distributions could give rise to "lumpy" functions $P(s)$ (so that (3) has to be interpreted as a Stieltjès integral, etc.), no difficulty is produced in the essential argument leading to (4).

The next step in the evaluation of the minimum $\overline{\Phi}$ is the derivation of $dP(s)$ from (4) and the formulas of Chapter 6, Section 6. Evidently

$$dP(s) = \left[\Pi'(\lambda) - \lambda L'(\lambda) - L(\lambda) \right] d\lambda,$$

the accented functions being their λ-derivatives. To find them we must apply (32) to the increments $\Delta\Pi(\lambda)$ and $\Delta L(\lambda)$ produced by increasing λ to $\lambda + \Delta\lambda$. Taking $\Delta\lambda > 0$, we see that corresponding region $\mathcal{L}(\lambda + \Delta\lambda)$ has shrunk inside $\mathcal{L}(\lambda)$, and that in the difference region $\Delta\mathcal{L}(\lambda) = \mathcal{L}(\lambda) - \mathcal{L}(\lambda + \Delta\lambda)$ we have

$$(5) \qquad \Delta\mathcal{L}(\lambda) = \{ X : \lambda < p(X)W(X) \leqslant \lambda + \Delta\lambda \}.$$

Hence $\Delta\Pi(\lambda)$ and $\Delta L(\lambda)$ are the negatives of the integrals of $p(X)$ and of $1/W(X)$ over $\Delta\mathcal{L}(\lambda)$, by (32), and indeed

$$-\left[\Delta\Pi(\lambda) - \lambda\, \Delta L(\lambda) \right] = \iint_{\Delta\mathcal{L}} \left[p(X) - \lambda/W(X) \right] dx\, dy.$$

Dividing the inequality in (5) through by $W(X)$ and then subtracting $\lambda/W(X)$, we see that the integrand in the above integral is between 0 and $\Delta\lambda/W$. Hence by the law of the mean for definite integrals, the integral is between 0 and $\Delta A \cdot \Delta\lambda/W_{\min}$, where ΔA is the area of $\Delta\mathcal{L}$. Hence dividing by $\Delta\lambda$ and then letting $\Delta\lambda$ approach zero, we see that $\Pi'(\lambda) - \lambda L'(\lambda) = 0$. This assumes, of course, that $\Delta A \to 0$ as $\Delta\lambda \to 0$, always a valid assumption at all but a finite number of exceptional points: for these the result above is extended by continuity. It follows that

(6)
$$dP(s) = -L(\lambda)\, d\lambda.$$

To find λ in terms of s, we apply (34) of Chapter 6, setting $s = \Phi$. Again ds is the sum of the right-hand member of (34) calculated with respect to the change in the region of integration $\mathcal{L}(\lambda)$ and with λ in the integrand held fast, plus the differential calculated for $\mathcal{L}(\lambda)$ held fixed but the integrand varying. We will show as before that the former is zero, so that, differentiating under the integral sign and applying (32), we obtain

(7)
$$ds = -L(\lambda)\, d\lambda/\lambda.$$

The examination of the increment of the integral in (34) over $\Delta\mathcal{L}(\lambda)$ is made as before, applying (5), but now taking logarithms of all three (positive) members. This shows that the integrand is between 0 and $\log(1 + \Delta\lambda/\lambda)$, so the integral is between 0 and $\Delta A \cdot \log(1 + \Delta\lambda/\lambda)$; dividing by $\Delta\lambda$ and letting $\Delta\lambda \to 0$, we obtain the result stated.

Combining (6) and (7) we have $P'(s) = \lambda$, which leads to a geometrical interpretation of (3).

In Chapter 6, Section 10, it was observed that the region S when $u = -\Phi = -s$, and $v = P[\phi]$, was of the type shown schematically in Fig. 6-3 (without corner points, such as (u', v')), and that the slope of the optimizing part of the boundary $dv/du = -B/A$. It is more convenient in the present application to use the points of coordinates $u = \Phi = s$ and $v = P[\phi]$, producing a reflection of the former S in the vertical axis, giving S' (Fig. 7-1). The coordinates (s, v) are both nonnegative

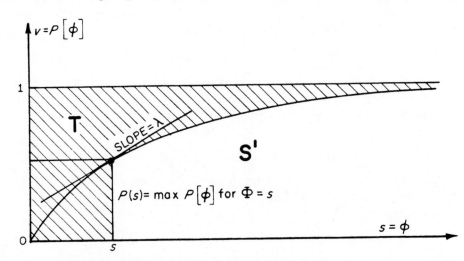

Fig. 7-1. Schematic relations in optimal search.

and v, being a probability, does not exceed unity, so that $\mathcal{S}'$ lies in the semiinfinite horizontal strip of unit width shown in Fig. 7-1. The slopes of tangents to the optimizing boundary of $\mathcal{S}'$ are positive and, as we have just shown, have the value $dv/ds = P'(s) = \lambda$. Finally, this curve approaches $v = 1$ as a horizontal asymptote.

Introducing this value in equation (3) we have

$$(8) \qquad \bar{\Phi}_{\min} = \int_0^\infty sP'(s)\,ds = \int_0^\infty s\lambda\,ds = \int_0^\infty s\frac{dv}{ds}\,ds = \int_0^1 s\,dv,$$

the last expression, by replacing s by v as the variable of integration. But this is the expression for the area of the complementary region $\mathcal{T}$ ($\mathcal{S}' + \mathcal{T} = $ strip), so that

$$(8') \qquad\qquad\qquad \bar{\Phi}_{\min} = \textit{area of } \mathcal{T}.$$

It may be important to know the standard deviation, $\sqrt{(\bar{\Phi^2})_{\min} - (\bar{\Phi})_{\min}^2}$; for this purpose we have the formula

$$(9) \qquad \bar{\Phi^2}_{\min} = \int_0^\infty s^2\,dP(s) = \int_0^1 s^2\,dv$$

$$= \text{area of } \mathcal{T} \times \text{center of gravity of uniform lamina } \mathcal{T}.$$

We note in closing that in many problems the expected length of time to detection $\bar{T}$ is the critical factor. When $\Phi(t)$ is proportional to t, the answer is contained in the above. In certain cases, however, $\Phi(t)$ is given but is not linear. This poses a different problem of optimization, mathematically equivalent to that of a time-dependent W.

3. APPLICATION TO THE NORMAL DISTRIBUTION WITH CONSTANT *W*

To find the minimum $\bar{\Phi}$ in the case of the normal distribution, we apply the results developed in Chapter 6, Section 7, based on the expression (36) for $p(x, y)$.

From (40) and (42) we derive the parametric equations for the optimizing boundary of $\mathcal{S}'$ of Fig. 7-1 in terms of the parameter ρ:

$$(10) \qquad\qquad v = P_{\text{opt}}(\Phi) = 1 - (1 + \rho^2/2)e^{-\rho^2/2};$$

$$s = \Phi = (\pi\sigma_1\sigma_2/4W)\rho^4.$$

These equations show that as ρ increases from 0 to $+\infty$, the boundary point (s, v) traces the curve, s increasing from 0 to $+\infty$, v from 0 to 1. Hence we can use ρ as the variable of integration, obtaining from (8')

$$(11) \qquad \bar{\Phi}_{\min} = \int_0^1 s\,dv = (\pi\sigma_1\sigma_2/8W)\int_0^\infty \rho^7 e^{-\rho^2/2}\,d\rho = 6\pi\sigma_1\sigma_2/W.$$

This is the *critical area* $2\pi\sigma_1\sigma_2$ times $3/W$. If W is a length (sweep width), Φ is also measured in units of length. If W is an area per unit time (search rate), Φ is measured in units of time.

The standard deviation is found from (9) and (10). We have

(12) $\overline{\Phi^2}_{min} = (\pi\sigma_1\sigma_2/32W)^2 \int_0^\infty \rho'' e^{-\rho^2/2}\, d\rho = 120(\pi\sigma_1\sigma_2/W)^2.$

Then subtracting $\overline{\Phi^2}_{min}$, we get $\sigma_{\Phi_{min}} = \sqrt{84}\ \pi\sigma_1\sigma_2/W = 9.17\pi\sigma_1\sigma_2/W$ or over half as much again as the expected expenditure Φ_{min}. Thus the latter is a decidedly dispersed quantity.

To give a concrete example, let us consider the one given at the end of Section 7 of Chapter 6: $\sigma_1 = \sigma_2 = \sigma = 100$ nautical miles, and $W = 5$ miles. But now the five 130-knot searching aircraft are available indefinitely on a 24-hour-a-day basis (presumably by continuous aircraft replacement). Measuring the effort $\Phi = \Phi(t)$ by the aircraft hours, we have $\Phi(t) = 5t$ from the starting time $t = 0$, so that the expected effort $\overline{\Phi} = 5\overline{T}$. The *sweep rate*, or area covered per unit time, is $vW = 130 \times 5$ per aircraft and hence 130×5^2 for all five. The detection probability per unit area per unit time is this quantity, but per unit *effort* (as measured, as above, for all five) it is one fifth of this, 130×5. Hence, according to the derivation of (2) from (1) in the last section, W must be replaced, not by 5, but by 130×5, so that the exponent is $130 \times 5\Phi(t) = 130 \times 5^2 t$. Then (11) gives $\overline{\Phi}_{min} = 6\pi(100)^2/130 \times 5$, corresponding to $\overline{T}_{min} = \overline{\Phi}_{min}/5$ hours or 2.42 days. This explains how ineffective the five-hour single-try search was, as examined in this case in Chapter 6.

The question of whether a 2.42-day search by five aircraft is useful or not would of course depend on the whole practical and tactical situation. In a salvage operation for a life-raft, it very well might be, whereas if only one aircraft were used, the time would be multiplied by 5 and be over 12 days, by which time the occupants of the life raft might easily have perished. If on the other hand the targets were hostile but disabled, it might gain assistance during the 2.42 days, thus entirely changing the tactical situation.

If the precision of initial target location were twice as good in the sense that σ were halved, the expected time to detection would, according to (11), be reduced to a quarter: 0.605 days or barely over $14\frac{1}{2}$ hours, a reduction which might entirely change the tactical situation.

While the precise quantitative examination of optimal search for a moving target when the law of motion is known to the searcher will be considered in Section 7, we can even at this point illustrate by a simple example the usefulness to a target wishing to avoid detection to introduce an element of random evasive motion while in a region in which it is exposed to the possibility of detection. We assume that its motion is that described in Chapter 5, Section 5, the simple diffusive case satisfying (19). If at $t = 0$ a perfect fix had been made, so that its probability is given by the right-hand member of (20) t units of time later, and that this represents the "time late" to the start of the second phase of the search (the first having given the fix), then this part will be conditioned by the subsequent motion of the target and the law of detection. We shall assume that after the time late $t = t_1$, the arrival of the searcher becomes known to the target, which immediately stops all its motion, for better concealment, and also that the subsequent search is subject to the law of random search and is optimized.

If the evasive motion had been in accordance with the first example given in Chapter 5, Section 7 (target at 12 knots randomly changing course every 15 minutes), the σ of the present formula (11) would increase as the square root of the time, and be $\sqrt{18t}$ until the start of the second phase, when it becomes fixed at $t = t_1$. Suppose that only one 130-knot aircraft is available with a sweep width of 5 miles, and hence a search rate of 130×5 square miles per hour. If Φ is measured in hours, we must set $W = 130 \times 5$ in (11), obtaining for the expected time to detection $\bar{T} = 6\pi \times 18t_1/130 \times 5 = 0.521t_1$. If then it had been 4 hours late, $T = 2.084$ hours. In fact the expected time to detection is proportional to the time late, by the factor 0.521.

Another application of the case above is to assume that the initial fix had been inaccurate, yielding for $t = 0$ a circular normal distribution of standard deviation σ_0. Then after t hours it would be given by the Pythagorean combination $\sqrt{\sigma_0^2 + 18t}$. If we *define* t_0 so that $\sigma_0^2 = 18t_0$, we can write the standard deviation as $\sqrt{18(t_0 + t)}$. If we take $t_0 = 18$ so that $\sigma_0 = 18$ miles (not a bad location error in many cases), we should have after a 4-hour time late, $\sigma^2 = 18 \times 22$ and hence $\bar{T} = 11.5$ hours.

The disadvantage to the searcher of a large $\overline{\Phi}$ and to a hostile target of a large $-\overline{\Phi}$ (jeopardy) should be made clear by these and similar examples.

4. THE DISTRIBUTION OF SEARCHING EFFORT IN TIME WITH VARYING *W*

Up to now we have excluded the effect of the variation of W with time during protracted periods of search. As stated earlier, the difficulties in such cases are due to the searcher's inability to predict such changes with enough precision, over long enough periods in the future, for the planning of an optimized search. There are cases, however, in which the variations of W are due to definite and predictable physical causes. One case is that of the search for a surface target by mainly visual means, W being greater in day than at night. Another case would be that in which the target is a submarine in direct transit at known speed between known points, and due to pass through waters of essentially known but different acoustic transmission characteristics. In a plane moving with the target's velocity, the effect on acoustic detection is that of a stationary target with a W changing with the time in a roughly predictable manner. In all cases the prediction of W is crude at best, so that simplified assumptions are appropriate. In the example to be studied here, of day-versus-night visibility, we shall treat the problem as an alternation of single-try searches, using probability of detection, rather than expected effort spent, as a measure of effectiveness. The transcription into the latter terms is an easy exercise in terms of Section 1.

A certain relatively narrow region $\mathcal{R}$ of the ocean has to be crossed by very fast enemy surface units. It takes each one a definite time T to cross $\mathcal{R}$, T being of the order of an hour or two. We wish to detect such units by means of aircraft patrolling the region $\mathcal{R}$: certain features of the tactical situations require them to stay within $\mathcal{R}$ at all times. We have at our disposal a fair number of aircraft of the same type, each capable of a definite number of flying hours during the twenty-four, 6 to 12, for example. Thus the total length of track of all aircraft during twenty-four hours has a fixed value of L miles, which is a measure of the total available searching effort. During the twelve daylight hours, radar search can be supplemented by visual, the combined power of detection being expressed by the value W_1 of the search width for each separate aircraft. During the twelve hours of darkness, radar is the sole means of detection, and the search width falls to a value W_2,

$$(13) \qquad\qquad W_1 > W_2.$$

One final assumption is fundamental: The enemy, not being aware of our search of the region $\mathcal{R}$, is as likely to cross this region at any one time as at any other. (The detection characteristics of present-day equipment reduce this example to an historical and illustrative one only.)

It may be assumed that for the best search the number of aircraft patrolling during any one hour of the twelve daylight hours should be the same as during any other. For if during a particular hour there are fewer patrols than during another, the loss of chance of detection during the former is not quite compensated for by the additional chance during the latter, on account of the tendency of overlapping (saturation effect), which is always present, but increases with increasing number of patrols in a given region. This situation is of course what is expressed mathematically by the exponential detection law (2). In conclusion, we may say that in any scheme of search to be considered there exists a constant number n_1 of planes airborne during the day, and, by corresponding reasoning, a constant number n_2 during the night. If v is the common aircraft speed, the total daytime and nighttime length of track flown is $12vn_1$ and $12vn_2$ miles respectively. Thus the following equation, expressing the limited total searching effort, must hold.

$$(14) \qquad\qquad n_1 + n_2 = \frac{L}{12v}, \qquad n_1 \geqslant 0, n_2 \geqslant 0.$$

Beyond this, n_1 and n_2 are at our disposal; they characterize the distribution of searching effort between day and night.

If the enemy unit crosses $\mathcal{R}$ during daylight, the total length of track flown while he is in $\mathcal{R}$ will be Tvn_1 (there are n_1 planes in the air, each of speed v, during the time T of passage of the enemy). Hence by the formula of random search the probability of detecting such a target is, if A is the area of $\mathcal{R}$,

$$1 - e^{-Tvn_1 W_1/A},$$

while the probability of detecting a target passing at night is

$$1 - e^{-Tvn_2 W_2/A}.$$

Since the chances of the enemy's crossing A by day or by night are the same, the sum of one-half of each of the expressions above gives the required probability of detection P (assuming for simplicity, and with satisfactory approximation, that the chance of a passage of A partly at night and partly in daytime is of negligible probability):

(15)
$$P = 1 - \frac{1}{2}(e^{-Tvn_1W_1/A} + e^{-Tvn_2W_2/A}).$$

Mathematically, our problem is to choose n_1 and n_2 subject to (14) so as to maximize P. The details of the work are altogether similar to those of Section 4, Chapter 6, except that n_1 and n_2 are the variables in the present case. The results are as follows:

Case 1. L is so small that

(16)
$$W_1 e^{-TLW_1/12A} \geqslant W_2,$$

then

(17)
$$n_1 = L/12v, \qquad n_2 = 0,$$

and all the flying must be done in daytime.

Case 2. L is large enough to make

(18)
$$W_1 e^{-TLW_1/12A} < W_2,$$

then both day and night searching must be done according to the equations [analogous to (17) of Chapter 6]

(19)
$$n_i = \frac{\log\left(\dfrac{TvW_i}{A}\right)}{\left(\dfrac{TvW_i}{A}\right)} + \frac{\dfrac{1}{W_i}}{\dfrac{1}{W_1} + \dfrac{1}{W_2}}\left\{\frac{L}{12v} - \left[\frac{\log\left(\dfrac{TvW_1}{A}\right)}{\left(\dfrac{TvW_1}{A}\right)} + \frac{\log\left(\dfrac{TvW_2}{A}\right)}{\left(\dfrac{TvW_2}{A}\right)}\right]\right\}$$

where $i = 1$ and 2.

As long as L is only moderately greater than the critical size expressed in equations (16) and (18), i.e., for which (16) becomes an equality, more searching should be devoted to day than to night ($n_1 > n_2$). But in the limit for increasing L, (19) shows that n_1/n_2 approaches W_2/W_1, which is less than unity; thus again we have the phenomenon of *reversal* signalized in Section 4 of Chapter 6: If a very large amount of searching effort is available, *more* searching should be done during the unfavorable period than during the favorable one!

It is assumed here again that the flights are at random. When the *direction* of the enemy targets across A is known, a more efficient disposition of aircraft-tracks is in the form of a crossover barrier patrol (Chapter 8). The formulas, *but not the ideas and essential results*, will then be changed.

5. EXPECTED AREA SWEPT CLEAN: JEOPARDY

The definite detection law was introduced in Chapter 3, Section 9, as a generalization of the definite range law when paths are curved or the searchers are numerous. While crude as an approximation to reality, it has the advantage of providing a general frame of reference into which many situations can be fitted before their "finer structure" can be known or realistically assumed. Furthermore, as was mentioned, it leads to certain useful *indices*.

We reemphasize that this clean-sweep law is not one that fits into the conceptions of Section 1 above or of Chapter 6, being essentially inconsistent with the preconditions implied in the definition of the local density of effort ϕ. It is possible, of course, to regard the definite detection law as a limiting case of the previous one as the detectability $W \to \infty$: (2) shows that $D(X, t, \phi) \to 1$ when $\phi > 0$, and $\to 0$ when $\phi = 0$; and (28) of Chapter 6 shows that $P[\phi]$ approaches the integral of $p(x, y)$ over the searched part of $\mathcal{C}$, viz., where $\phi > 0$. While these results are consistent with the definition of the definite detection law (clean sweep where $\phi > 0$), such mathematical manipulations have little physical basis and cannot be regarded as capable of furnishing cogent proofs. Thus (31) and (33) of the last chapter reduce to nonsense when $W \to \infty$.

We shall consider here the case of a stationary target with a given a priori distribution $p(X)$ and introduce as before ((51) of Chapter 3) the regions $\mathfrak{M}(z)$ where $p(X)$ exceeds given constant values z, as well as their complements and areas.

$$(20) \qquad \mathfrak{M}(z) = \{X: p(X) > z\}, \qquad \overline{\mathfrak{M}}(z) = \{X: p(X) \leqslant z\};$$

$$M(z) = \text{area of } \mathfrak{M}(z) = \iint_{\mathfrak{M}(z)} dx \, dy.$$

Clearly, $\mathfrak{M}(0) = \mathcal{C}$ so that $M(0)$ may be infinite. As z increases indefinitely, $\mathfrak{M}(z)$ shrinks and $M(z)$ decreases, approaching zero as z approaches $p_0 = \max p(X)$, which may itself be infinite. "Regularity" assumptions are made as usual. (We are setting forth the ideas in the case in which $p(X)$ is continuous and continuously differentiable, and with a graph having no "plateau" (positive area region of constancy). The consequence is that the area $M(z)$ is continuous and essentially continuously differentiable. In certain cases an approximation to $p(X)$ having different but equally simple properties may be more convenient [e.g., a step function]. The application of the ideas to this case is an exercise bordering on the trivial.

As stated in Chapter 3, Section 9, the *area R* of a region searched clean represents the given searching effort, and the single-try optimization leads to the determination of the unique z for which $M(z) = R$, and then a search of the corresponding region $\mathfrak{R} = \mathfrak{M}(z)$. This was explained in the same chapter, and also that with this type of search the property of consistent additive optimality is valid. Our present task is to evaluate the expected searching effort, i.e., the expected area $\bar{R}$, used up at the moment of first detection.

As in Section 1, $\bar{R}$ is given as Φ was, by (3); hence, we must find $P(s)$, the probability that the first detection will occur by the time an area $R < s$ has been searched. Evidently for a minimal $\bar{R}$ the search must at each stage proceed optimally. Hence $P(s)$ is the probability that the target will be in the region $\mathfrak{M}(z)$ where $M(z) = s$; in the rectangular coordinates $X: (x, y)$, this is the integral.

$$(21) \qquad P(s) = \iint_{\mathfrak{M}(z)} p(x, y)\, dx\, dy \quad \text{where} \quad s = M(z).$$

Note that as s goes from 0 to A, z goes from p_0 to 0. To evaluate $\bar{R}$ we must find $dP(s) = P'(s)\, ds$. If s is given a *positive* increment Δs, z obtains a *negative* one, $\Delta z < 0$. Hence, the region $\mathfrak{M}(z)$ expands by the incremental region $\Delta\mathfrak{M} = \mathfrak{M}(z + \Delta z) - \mathfrak{M}(z)$ within which $z + \Delta z \leqslant p(x, y) < z$, having the (positive) incremental area $M(z + \Delta z) - M(z)$, and we have

$$\Delta P(s) = \iint_{\Delta\mathfrak{M}} p(x, y)\, dx\, dy = z' \iint_{\Delta\mathfrak{M}} dx\, dy$$
$$= z'\big[\, M(z + \Delta z) - M(z)\,\big], \qquad z + \Delta z < z' < z,$$

by the law of the mean. From the assumed regularity of $p(x, y)$, $M(z)$ has a derivative $M'(z)$ (while our assumptions do not exclude the possibility that at certain isolated points z, $M'(z)$ is infinite, they do exclude the possibility that $M(z)$ fails to be the integral of $M'(z)$—which is the only important matter); hence, dividing by Δz and letting $\Delta z \to 0$, we see that $dP(s)/dz = zM'(z)$ or $dP(s) = z\, dM(z) = z\, ds$, the latter by (21). Hence, taking the "countermotion" of z versus s into account, we have

$$(22) \quad \bar{R} = \int s\, dP(s) = \int_0^A sz\, ds = \int_{p_0}^0 zM(z)\, dM(z) = -\int_0^{p_0} zM(z)M'(z)\, dz.$$

The ideas of Chapter 6, Section 10, being far more general than the assumption of the exponential detection law, may be applied to the present case. If we plot the points of horizontal coordinates $s =$ effort expended, and vertical coordinates $v =$ probability of detection with s, we obtain a region $\mathcal{S}'$ in the first quadrant, corresponding to the one shown in Fig. 7-1 of this chapter. It is bounded by the curve $v = P(s)$ given by (21), of slope $P'(s) = dP(s)/ds = z$ (this z corresponds to the λ in the exponential case). This slope is positive and decreases from p_0 (possibly $+ \infty$) to 0 as s increases from 0 to A ($+ \infty$ if area of $\mathcal{Q} = \infty$). Finally, the variable of integration in $\bar{R}$ can be replaced by the ordinate $v = P(s)$, which goes from 0 to 1 as s goes from 0 to A. The resulting expression is

$$(22') \qquad \bar{R} = \int s\, dP(s) = \int_0^1 s\, dv = \text{area of } \mathcal{T}$$

where $\mathcal{T}$, as in Fig. 7-1, is the semiinfinite horizontal strip with the region $\mathcal{S}'$

removed. As in the previous case, as the tangent to the optimizing boundary rolls in a clockwise direction, the expected effort used up at the moment of detection is the area of the above residual $\mathcal{T}$. Finally, the standard deviation of R is found from the formula for its second moment

$$(23) \qquad \overline{R^2} = \int_0^1 s^2 \, dv = 2 \text{ area}(\mathcal{T})\overline{s} = 2\,\overline{Rs}$$

where $\overline{s}$ is the horizontal distance to center of gravity of $\mathcal{T}$ regarded as a lamina of unit density—therefore a standard deviation of $R = [\overline{R}(2\overline{s} - \overline{R})]^{1/2}$. Which particular form of these equations (22), (22′), or (23) is used will depend on the application —viz., the function $p(X)$.

As before, $\overline{R}$ represents a difficulty or expense for the searcher; $-\overline{R}$ a degree of jeopardy for the hostile target, who benefits from its algebraic decrease.

Application to the normal distribution. We again make use of formula (36) and the notation of Chapter 6, Section 7: the region $\mathcal{M}(z)$ for which $p(x, y) > z$ is the interior of the ellipse with semiaxes $\rho\sigma_1$ and $\rho\sigma_2$, where ρ^2 is as in (38), but with W replaced by 1 and λ by z: $\rho^2 = -2 \log(2\pi\sigma_1\sigma_2 z)$. Consequently the area

$$s = M(z) = \pi\rho^2\sigma_1\sigma_2.$$

To find $v = P(z)$ we must integrate the normal $p(x, y)$ over this ellipse, most conveniently by making the change of variables (39) and integrating over the unit circle in the polar coordinates (ρ, θ). We obtain $P(z) = 1 - e^{-\rho^2/2}$. Thus

$$\overline{R} = \int s \, dP(z) = \pi\sigma_1\sigma_2 \int \rho^2 \, d(1 - e^{-\rho^2/2})$$

$$= \pi\sigma_1\sigma_2 \int_0^\infty \rho^3 e^{-\rho^2/2} \, d\rho = 2\pi\sigma_1\sigma_2.$$

But this is the area of the *critical ellipse*, of semiaxes $\sigma_1\sqrt{2}$ and $\sigma_2\sqrt{2}$, within which the target has the probability $1 - 1/e = 0.63$ of being.

Similarly we obtain for the standard deviation of R the quantity $2\pi\sigma_1\sigma_2$.

6. DICHOTOMY SEARCH IN STATE SPACE: ENTROPY

The searches considered throughout the main body of this book have been based on the geographical positions and motions of targets and the hours or days in searching for them; space and time gave the frame of reference. There is, however, another category of search and of problems of its optimization, in which these play no essential role. It is concerned with a *physical system* capable of being in any one of a given set of possible *states*, where no meaning is attached to distances between them, or to time intervals. It is a purely combinatorial situation, in which the probabilities of the states are the only continuous variables. The practical interest is to *coding* or to *code-breaking*, rather than to detecting and locating a submarine or other material target. The problem has the following simple statement:

Let the totality of n different possible states of the system S be identified by the integers $\{1, 2, \ldots, n\}$, and suppose that the searcher is given the n probabilities, p_i = prob. that S will be in state i. The searcher must determine the actual state of S by performing, as often as desired, a *dichotomy operation* of the following type: If at any stage, the previous operations have shown that S is in some particular subset of the n integers (the whole set of n, in the first operation), it may divide this subset in any manner it pleases into two parts—and then, at the cost of one dollar, be reliably informed in which of these two parts the state of S belongs. Suppose that the searcher's scheme of action is such that, if S is in the ith state, s_i dichotomies are required and hence, dollars spent. The expected cost of using this scheme is then

$$(24) \qquad G = p_1 s_1 + p_2 s_2 = \cdots + p_n s_n.$$

The problem of optimal dichotomy search is to find the scheme of dichotomies for which this expected cost is a minimum.

This problem coincides with that of *optimal coding* when two different letters, or symbols such as 0 and 1, are used in each unit-process of transmission (and when there is no "noise," viz., possibility of errors). If each unit-transmission costs one dollar, and if the probability that the ith message out of the totality of n possible messages will be transmitted is p_i, the average cost of that particular coding system that requires s_i transmissions for the message i is the G given by (24). Thus the problem of optimal dichotomy search and of optimal coding are mathematically identical.

This common problem has been completely solved, and the details are given by Fano [3]. They lead in a most natural manner to the formula for *entropy*, due to J. W. Gibbs (and applied to quantum mechanical observations by L. Szilard in 1924 and J. von Neumann in 1930, and then to communications engineering by C. Shannon). If $\log_a$ denotes the logarithm to the base $a > 1$ and $x \log_a x$ is extended to its limit 0 as x approaches 0 through positive values, then the definition of the entropy in the distribution p_i is

$$(25) \qquad H_a = H_a(p_1, \ldots, p_n) = -(p_1 \log_a p_1 + \cdots + p_n \log_a p_n).$$

We then have

Fano's Theorem. *For any distribution* $\{p_1, \ldots, p_n\}$ *the minimal G satisfies the inequalities*

$$(26) \qquad H_2(p_1, \ldots, p_n) \leqslant G(p_1, \ldots, p_n) \leqslant H_2(p_1, \ldots, p_n) + 1.$$

Both the proof and systematic methods of finding the optimal code or sequence of dichotomies are given in Fano [3].

This concept of entropy, and its negative, the numerical *information* in a distribution, have in recent decades experienced an almost explosive development. In 1950 several authors discovered the importance of a generalization based on a pair of distributions sometimes called their *cross-entropy* or *cross information*.

For references—as well as new statistical methods based on this concept—see Kullback [5]. Operational research has not remained unaffected by these developments; for a brief introduction to the theory of information from the point of view of the propositional calculus and some operational problems into which it enters, see Kimball and Koopman [4]. Further notions regarding applications to search are outlined briefly in Appendix A, Section 8.

7. OPTIMAL SEARCH FOR MOVING TARGETS: GENERALITIES

Up to this point the optimization of the use of searching effort has assumed that the target is at rest in the searched plane. The latter could be fixed geographically, or, in the case of targets belonging to a class all having the same fixed vector velocity, it could be a plane moving across the ocean with this common velocity of translation, relative to which plane the targets are at rest. It is necessary now to turn our attention to the important and much more difficult problem in which the targets are moving, but with a more general type of velocity than one that can be removed by such simple applications of relative motion as the one noted above.

Chapter 5 has been devoted to the various kinds of target motion and the conditions under which the evolving probability density of the target positions could be found with some useful order of approximation. It was emphasized that in any real search the only knowledge the searcher can have of the target's positions and possible motions must be based on the general physical factors acting upon it, as well as upon his intentions—objectives, tactical methods, and the like—and we must realize that "special information" may be available to the searcher. The searcher's reasoning about the target's reasoning will be considered in the next section.

Two approaches are possible to the formulation of the present problem. First, we could start with a given distribution of targets (the functions $N(X, t)$ or $p(X, t)$ of Chapter 5) and express mathematically the detection probability when the searcher moves along a particular path Γ for some period of time. Second, we could start with a particular *target path* C, and express the effect of a given time-evolving distribution of searching effort, $\psi(X, t)$. For our purposes in later chapters the second is the more convenient approach. The conditions leading to the exponential law given in Theorem I (4), Chapter 6, will be assumed.

To start from the beginning, we consider a single target moving in a definite track C, as in Chapter 3, Section 3 (Fig. 3-4), the coordinates X: (ξ, η) of the moving target being given by (11) and the probability $p(t)$ of its being detected during the interval $(0, t)$ by (6) of that chapter. We must, however, relate the earlier γ_t to our present function $\psi(X, t)$, and for this purpose a rederivation of the earlier formula (6) is useful.

Let $\bar{p}(t)$ be the probability that this moving target will fail to be detected during $(0, t)$. Suppose that at t it is at the point $X(t)$: $[\xi(t), \eta(t)]$, and that during $(t, t + \Delta t)$ it moves, but remaining in a neighborhood $\Delta \mathcal{C}$ of $X(t)$, both Δt and $\Delta \mathcal{C}$ being of "relaxation size." Then since the circumstance of failure of detection during the first interval cannot, according to our assumptions, give any reason to alter our appraisal of the probability of detection when it is in the latter interval, we have, by independent compound probability, etc.,

$$\bar{p}(t + \Delta t) = \bar{p}(t)[1 - D(X, t, \Delta\phi(X, t))]$$
$$= \bar{p}(t)[1 - D(X, t, \psi(X, t)\,\Delta t)].$$

This, combined with (2) (Section 1 above), dropping higher powers of Δt, leads to the differential equation $\bar{p}'(t) = \bar{p}(t)W(X, t)\psi(X, t)$, which, when solved on the assumption that $\bar{p}(0) = 1$, yields the following amplification of the (6) of Chapter 3:

(27)
$$p(t) = 1 - \exp\left(-\int_0^t W(X(t), t)\psi(X(t), t)\,dt\right)$$
$$C : X = X(t) = (\xi(t), \eta(t)).$$

The integrand is, therefore, the γ_t used in Chapter 3 (cf. also Chapter 6, Section 3).

Under certain conditions the functions involved in (27) depend on a finite set of parameters, $\alpha, \beta, \ldots$, in a known way, the latter having a known distribution of density $\pi(\alpha, \beta, \ldots)$. Then (27) is replaced by the mean:

(28)
$$P[\psi] = \int\int \cdots \left\{1 - \exp\left[-\int_0^t W\psi\,dt\right]\right\}\pi(\alpha, \beta, \ldots)\,d\alpha\,d\beta \ldots.$$

The searcher's real problem is that he knows too little about the target's track C (except in rather trivial cases). One method of obtaining, if not an *optimum*, at least a *minimally pessimum* distribution of search will now be described.

8. BLOCKADES AND THE PRINCIPLE OF THE MINIMAX

In a blockade the targets have the mission of going from a position or set of positions E to a second position or set of positions L, and in so doing must traverse a region $\mathcal{Q}$ in which hostile units maintain a continuing search. For any distribution of search rate per unit area, $\psi(X, t)$, and any path of transit C from E to L through $\mathcal{Q}$, the detection probability is given by (27). The geometry of the situation is shown in Fig. 7-2, while in the special case of circular regions, in Chapter 4, Fig. 4-1.

The blockade runners are under a physical constraint of speed. Indeed if they were not, they could achieve as low a probability of detection as they wish by making the time interval in the integration in (27) as brief as they like, so that $p_C(t) = 0$. We shall assume that they proceed at their constant maximum tactically feasible speed c. For the searchers maintaining the blockade, on the other hand, there must be a maximum possible total rate of search Ψ, which we shall assume to be constantly attained, so that the integral of $\psi(X, t)$ over $\mathcal{Q}$ always has this value. There is another constraint on $\psi(X, t)$ to be introduced later, and of course it is nonnegative. We shall assume further that because of the steady state of the whole operation, neither W nor ψ contain t explicitly: $W = W(X)$, $\psi = \psi(X)$.

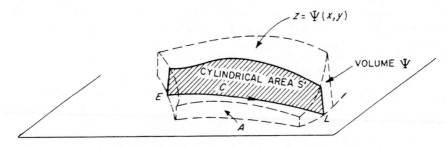

Fig. 7-2. Sea blockade of passage from E to L.

The next pair of assumptions is fundamental to the present application: *First*, that because the operation is a continuing one, the blockade runners are always able to know in advance the statistics of the searcher's function $\psi(X)$; *second*, that the searchers are aware of this fact and plan their searching $\psi(X)$ with the knowledge that the blockade runners will exploit every weakness of the blockade. As given by (27), $p_C(t)$ is a *functional* of C and ψ (a number determined when both of the latter are given). The object of the blockade runners is to use such paths C as to minimize it for each ψ; that of the blockaders is to maximize this minimum by their choice of ψ—a problem of *maximin*, or, for the complementary probability $\bar{p}_C(t)$, of *minimax*.

Formula (27) shows that both $p_t(C)$ and the integral in the exponent, $\int_0^t W[X(t)]\psi[X(t)]\,dt$, change in the same direction; hence the objects C and ψ which are obtained by the principle of the maximin applied to the former are the same as those when it is applied to the latter—a much simpler problem. Furthermore, since the speed $ds/dt = c$, a constant, we may use the arc-length s measured along C from E toward L as the variable of integration. The integral becomes that of $W[X(s/c)]\psi[X(s/c)]\,ds/c$ with respect to s from $s = 0$ on E to $s = s(C)$ on L. Taking out the constant factor c, the integral to which the maximin is to be applied is the following line integral

$$(29) \quad S[C,\psi] = \int_C W(X)\psi(X)\,ds = \int_0^{s(C)} W[x(s),y(s)]\psi[x(s),y(s)]\,ds$$

where $\xi = x(s)$, $\eta = y(s)$, are the parametric equations of C in terms of the arc length as the parameter, and of course $s(C)$ will in general be different for different curves C.

The first half of the problem—the choice of C to minimize $S[C,\psi]$ when ψ is given—is a classical one of the calculus of variations, going back to Fermat and Euler. Indeed it is the problem in geometrical optics of determining the paths C of light rays by applying *Fermat's principle of least time*: $n = n(X) = W(X)\psi(X)$ is the index of refraction of the medium, and $S[C,\psi]$ the time of travel of a vibratory phase along the path. The mathematical treatment is usually based on the *eikonal equation* $S_x^2 + S_y^2 = n^2$ satisfied by the *eikonal functions* $S = \min S[C,\psi]$, the curves S = constant being the wave fronts to which the rays C are perpendicular. Only in our first example can the treatment be completed on this basis; in the genuine cases of minimax, there is a profound difference.

The first example is that in which the searching units have so many complicated and unpredictable tasks and the area of $\mathcal{C}$ is so restricted that they merely patrol it uniformly: ψ = constant. Then the index of refraction n can be taken as $W(X)$; the paths will be straight when it is constant; otherwise curved so as to take advantage of regions of lower visibility. A similar determination of C would apply to the case in which $\psi(X)$ is not constant, but is chosen primarily for physical, tactical, or diplomatic reasons, and only in a secondary manner with the blockading object in view. The minimax reasoning is not determinative in such cases.

The second example returns to the maximin strategy of the searcher, but for simplicity is confined to the case of a constant W, so the principle is applied to $S' = \int_C \psi(X)\, ds$. The problem can be stated geometrically: The blockader's strategy can be represented by a surface $z = \psi(X) = \psi(x, y)$ above (or partly on) the region $\mathcal{C}$ in the xy-plane, and its constraint $\iint_{\mathcal{C}} \psi\, dx\, dy = \Psi$ means that the volume between this surface and $\mathcal{C}$ has the fixed value Ψ. The blockade runner's unfavorable quantity to be minimized, S', is the area of a cylindrical surface, traced by a vertical generating line as it moves along the directrix C and is cut off by the above surface. Accordingly, the geometrical statement of the problem is as follows: to deform the surface $z = \psi(x, y)$, never going below the xy-plane and always keeping the volume between it and the latter constant, in such a way that the cylindrical area determined by paths connecting E with L shall be as large as possible. See Fig. 7-3.

Whenever an application of this scheme is made to cases in which there is a constriction or pinching of $\mathcal{C}$ between E and L or at either of them (as in the circular regions of Chapter 4, Fig. 4-1), it results in a physical absurdity—that all the patrolling should take place on a 1-dimensional locus—a curve of least length cutting across $\mathcal{C}$ at its constriction. This absurdity has arisen, of course, because of

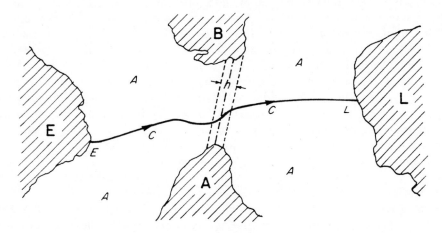

Fig. 7-3. Maximizing the least cylindrical area.

the lack of a further constraint on $\psi(X)$, namely that it should be physically realizable (consistently with the relaxation sizes that were at the basis of our definition of search rate density). The appropriate additional constraint is that there be a maximum search-rate per unit area, viz.: $\psi(X) \leqslant \bar{\psi}$, a constant. What this does geometrically is to introduce a horizontal plane $z = \bar{\psi}$, so that we must represent our surface by the formula $z = \min\{\psi(X), \bar{\psi}\}$—which effectively cuts off the top of the original surface. Then, in order to apply the full Ψ available, we must apply the coverage to $\mathcal{C}$. The geometrical picture would then indicate that as narrow a band-like region as possible must be patrolled at the constant density $\psi(X) = \psi_0$, the thickness of the band being constant h, where h is determined by the requirement that the area of the band times $\bar{\psi}$ shall equal Ψ. In the case shown in Fig. 7-2, the distance $\overline{AB}$ across the narrows is roughly determined and we have $\bar{\psi} \cdot \overline{AB} \cdot h = \Psi$ to determine h; this is shown by the dashed band in the figure. No patrolling is done outside the band. Calculating $\min p_t(C)$ by (27), we obtain

$$p_t(C) = 1 - \exp(-W\bar{\psi}h/c).$$

When the constriction of $\mathcal{C}$ is close to the place of entry E (or to that of exit L), as in the circular regions of Chapter 4, Fig. 4-1, a merely slight modification of this method is used. Thus we would determine a radius r greater than the radius r_E of E, by the area condition $\pi(r^2 - r_E^2)\bar{\psi} = \Psi$. The region between the circles of radii r_E and r is patrolled with the *maximum* density $\bar{\psi}$, and no patrolling is done outside; and the preceding expression is used for $p_t(C)$, with $h = r - r_E$. In this case, as explained in Chapter 4, Section 1, since the target probability density in the circular regions is inversely proportional to the radial distance, it might be supposed that the methods of search optimization of Chapter 6, Section 6, could be applied. *Such an application would be false.* The reasons have already been set forth in Section 1 of the present chapter: the persistency of moving targets in time means that we cannot assume that if a target is in one region $\Delta\mathcal{C}$ it is not in a quite different one $\Delta\mathcal{C}'$—an assumption upon which the methods of Chapter 6 were based.

The maximin solutions given in the last two paragraphs have been based implicitly upon the notion of *target flux* across a boundary, a concept discussed and applied in Chapter 5. Instead of considering the expected number of targets in an element of surface $\Delta\mathcal{C}$ at epoch t, we consider the expected number crossing an element Δs of arc of a bounding curve during a time interval Δt: this number divided by $\Delta s \cdot \Delta t$ is the *flux* in the direction of the normal to the curve, or expected rate of crossing per unit length. In many actual situations the target can cross the curve at only one point (e.g., on the line AB in Fig. 7-2), so that if it crosses through one element it does not cross through any different one. Total probability may be applied, and with it, the principles of Chapter 6—once the position of the curve and the flux through it have been determined. But a compromise must be made, because of the inevitable thickness of patrolled regions.

To turn back to the excluded case in which $W = W(X)$ changes markedly from position to position, the principles continue to apply, but to the more general refractive index $n = W(X)\psi(X)$. The graphical representation of Fig. 7-3 loses its simplicity, since the altitude, or length of the cylindrical elements, must be multiplied by $W(X)$, a different factor at each point. Furthermore, the required tradeoff between distances and detectability makes the assumption of the "all or nothing" search less convincing.

In Chapter 8, the practical implementation of the principles considered here will be made, starting with the barrier patrols that were used with success in World War II, and going on to the followup of a fix, etc. The screens discussed in Chapters 9 and 10 may also be viewed as transcriptions of the theoretical investigations of this and earlier chapters into practice—and with a historical record of success.

The history of the qualitative ideas of minimax, etc., must be as old as any use of cunning in conflict. They seem to have been first given mathematical expression by *Emile Borel* in a note to the *Comptes Rendue*, ca. 1925. They were applied to social games by *J. von Neumann* in 1929. Their present application to blockades was made by the author in a classified memorandum to the wartime OEG in 1943, and presented by him at the 1963 conference on search at the SACLANT ASW Centre (La Spezia, Italy), under the title "A Hide-and-Seek Game" (Unclassified), and published (along with classified material) in the proceedings of that conference. Of course, the applications to economics by Neumann and Morgernstern in 1944 were the starting point of the great subsequent activity in game theory.

REFERENCES

1. Dobbie, J. M. Some search problems with false contacts. *Oper. Res.* 21: 907–25.
2. Dobbie, J. M. 1975. Search for an avoiding target. *SIAM Journal of Applied Mathematics* 28: 72–86.
3. Fano, R. M. 1961. *Transmission of information.* Cambridge, Mass.: The Massachusetts Institute of Technology Press; and New York: Wiley.
4. Kimball, G. E., and Koopman, B. O. 1959. Chapter 9 in *Notes on operations research.* Cambridge, Mass.: The Massachusetts Institute of Technology Press.
5. Kullback, S. 1959. *Information theory and statistics.* New York: Wiley.
6. Stone, L. D., Sanshine, J. A., and Persinger, C. A. 1972. Optimal search in the presence of Poisson-distributed false targets. *SIAM Journal of Applied Mathematics* 23: 6–27.
7. Stone, L. D. 1975. *Theory of optimal search.* New York: Academic Press.

SUGGESTIONS FOR SUPPLEMENTARY READING

Brown, Scott S. "Optimal search for a moving target in discrete time and space." *Oper. Res.* (in press, probable appearance: 1979).
Chew, M. D. 1968. "A sequential search procedure." *Ann. of Math. Stat.* 38: 494–502.
Chew, M. D. "Optimal stopping in a discrete search problem." *Oper. Res.* 21: 741–47.
Hellman, O. 1970. "On the effect of search upon the probability distribution of a target whose motion is a diffusive process" *Ann. of Math. Stat.* 41: 1717–24.
Pollock, S. M., "A simple model of search for a moving target." *Oper. Res.* 18: 883–903.
Ross, S. 1969. "A problem of optimal search and stop." *Oper. Res.* 17: 984–92.
Stone, L. D. 1979. "General necessary and sufficient conditions for optimal search for moving targets." *Mathematics of Operations Research.*

Chapter 8

The Practical Search for Targets in Transit

The object of the present chapter is to show how a wide variety of problems in search and screening can be given practical solutions based on the principles developed in the earlier ones. In addition to the general limitations that can be expressed in simple mathematical form, such as those of relative motion in an approach, of restricted availability of searching effort, of limited ranges of detection, and many similar ones, a host of new constraints come into play that, while perfectly obvious to anyone engaged in carrying out the operation, are of so varied and irregular a nature that they defy precise mathematical formulation. A first class of such constraints comes from the nature of the *platform* bearing the detecting equipment. Whether it is an aircraft, surface, or subsurface craft, it can follow only a very restricted set of paths, and even when these paths can be planned in an optimal manner, the difficulties of navigation and keeping on course can prevent their being run with more than a limited precision (cf. Fig. 10-8 in Chapter 10).

Thus even after we have correctly calculated what the optimal distribution of a given amount of searching effort should be on a particular occasion, platforms cannot adopt courses that actually comply with such an ideal, except in quite a crude manner. A similar departure from a theoretical optimum will occur in every situation in the "real world." There is nothing peculiar to the theory of search in this; it affects every practical implementation of the theoretical results of operations research.

In spite of such discordance between what can be shown to be optimal and what can actually be done, the theoretical developments make, among others, three essential contributions to practical matters. First, they show directions in which the practicable operations should be changed in order to improve them. Second, by calculating a theoretical optimum or measure of effectiveness and then gauging the calculated or observed results of a practicable operation against such measures, they can indicate whether the former are unreasonably poor and ought to be improved. Third, they can serve a useful purpose in *limiting arguments*, often valuable in excluding basically fruitless operations.

By their very nature, the practical implementations of search theory are special and concrete operations, and have to be given in a realistic context. The greatest source of examples of this sort is historical—the naval operations against raiders and submarines during World War II. The present and two following chapters will contain many such cases, although certain updatings of the methodology of the past will also be given.

At the risk of repetition, we can state the general questions affecting search for targets in transit in the following terms.

In planning a search, the nature of the target is usually known, and its general position may be more or less known as a matter of probability (as in the problems of Chapter 6). But unless a fairly definite estimate of its motion can be made, the plan of search will have to be designed so as to be effective against a target having any one of a whole class of motions, as indicated by the tactical situation—rather than against a motion deemed to be the most likely and the only one to be considered, at the expense of effectiveness in regard to the others. The emphasis of this chapter is on the former principle, which is indicated when only the *intent* and the *capabilities* of the target are known. To know the intent of the target is to know where it is going: through what part of the ocean it passes, from what geographical locality it comes, to what place it is going, etc. And to know the target's capabilities is to have a reasonably good estimate of its speed u, as well as its endurance, etc. An essential part of such information can be put mathematically as follows: The target's vector velocity **u** is known at the different parts of the ocean where it is expedient to conduct the search. And since the main objective is to prevent the target's undetected accomplishment of its intention, success will be achieved even if the target is not detected but is forced to abandon its objective in order to avoid detection.

Attention will be confined in this chapter to the case where the detectability of the target does not change with the time, at least during long periods. Thus in the case of visual or radar detection, surface craft (including surfaced submarines) alone are considered; in the case of sonar detection, the submarine target is regarded as constantly submerged. This avoids the great complication that would occur, for example, in the case of a submarine whose tactics of submergence and emergence are not known and, since they may depend on the tactics of search, could only be evaluated by some form of "minimax" reasoning. Thus "gambits" are not considered here.

Three cases are of great importance in naval warfare and will be studied in the three parts of this chapter. In the first, the target's intention is to traverse a fairly straight channel (which may be a wide portion of the ocean), and the vector velocities at all points are parallel and equal (a "translational vector field"). Such a search is called a *barrier patrol*. In the second case, the target is proceeding from a known point of the ocean (e.g., a point of fix, an island, or a harbor), and the vector velocities are equal in length but are all directed away from this point (a "centrifugal radial vector field"). To this class of search belongs the *trapping square* and the *retiring search* when the approximate time of departure is known, and *closed barriers*, etc., in other cases. In the third case, the target's intention is to reach a definite point (e.g., the seat of a landing operation, an island needing supplies, a harbor), and the vector velocities are equal in length but directed inward toward this point (a "centripetal radial vector field"). Again the method of countering this intention may be the closed barrier. There are of course various cases closely allied to the three just mentioned, such as the antisubmarine or antishipping hunts conducted by carrier aircraft as the carrier sweeps through the ocean. But when the principles of this chapter are understood, the design and evaluation of such plans offer little difficulty.

In the case where the target intends to reach a point moving on the ocean (a ship, convoy, or task force), the vector field is of an entirely different character. The form of search used is then called a *screen*, which is the subject of Chapters 9 and 10.

Throughout the present chapter the effect of target *aspect*—the angle at which it is viewed—is disregarded. In the case of radar detection (see Appendix F), for example, the possibility may exist of securing a somewhat higher chance of detecting targets having vector velocities belonging to a particular class by using specially selected tracks, but the greatly added complication does not appear to warrant their consideration here.

Some recent searches for fixed sunken targets are referenced at the end.

Before entering upon the practical details, we reemphasize the importance of keeping in mind the assumptions implied, and that all the mathematical formulas and special procedures derived from them are deductions from hypotheses—and no more valid than the latter. It would be highly misleading to apply the procedures mechanically, as if they had *absolute validity*. Consider, for example, the drastic changes in the retiring searches described in Section 9 below if the hostile target were aware that it is being searched; if the search were no longer by passive observations, the whole velocity field would change completely.

Finally, it is emphasized once more that the search procedures exemplified herein apply to cases in which the detection ranges are short in comparison to distances covered by the searcher during the operation. New technology is beginning to lead to a set of search problems that will, in turn, require new solutions, namely the case in which the detection device produces long ranges of detection relatively to the distances that the platform covers during much of its searching motion. Furthermore, the detection regions may be annular in nature (using the term "detection region" rather in the sense of Chapter 3, Section 9). Finally, the detection probabilities may be highly dependent on searching speeds. The development of theoretically valid practical search plans for equipment possessed of such characteristics as the above is among the foremost endeavors now underway.

1. BARRIER PATROLS: CONSTRUCTION OF CROSSOVER BARRIERS

Under a wide variety of circumstances, the problem of detecting targets in transit through a channel by means of an observer whose speed v considerably exceeds the

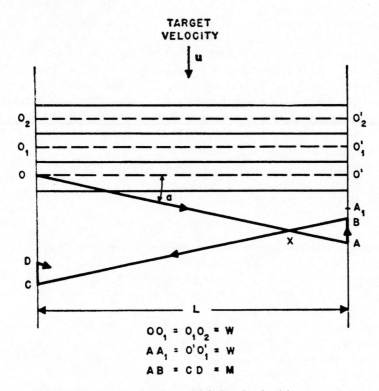

Fig. 8-1. The crossover barrier patrol designed to be tight.

speed u of the target (e.g., an airborne observer and ship target) can be simplified to the following mathematical statement. Given a channel bounded by two parallel lines L miles apart (the vertical lines of Fig. 8-1) and given targets moving through this channel and parallel to it at the fixed speed u (downward in Fig. 8-1), how shall observers fly from one side of the channel to the other and back, etc., in order to be most effective in detecting the targets? It is usually necessary to attach the flights to a fixed reference point O from which they start or take their direction. Thus O may be a conveniently recognizable point at or near the narrowest part of the actual channel (which will in general correspond only approximately to the mathematically simplified parallel channel shown in Fig. 8-1), O may be a harbor or air base, etc. It is convenient to draw the line OO' (dotted in Fig. 8-1) across and perpendicular to the channel, a purely mathematical reference line called the *barrier line*.

The reasoning leading to the construction of a barrier patrol was based, historically, on the definite range law of detection (see Chapter 3, Section 2; sweep width $W = 2R$). Since it leads in a natural manner to a form of patrol (the crossover barrier patrol) that turns out to be the optimum form from the point of view of any not-too-asymmetrical law of detection, it will be followed in detail in this section, while its more realistic evaluation will be considered in the following section.

For convenience of wording, the target will be referred to as a ship and the observer as an aircraft. While this corresponds to the most important case, others will be considered later. The same mathematical ideas apply in all cases.

Consider those targets that at the initial epoch ($t = 0$) are on the barrier line OO'. An observer starting from O when $t = 0$ and wishing to fly over these targets will not succeed in doing so if he flies along OO', except in the excluded case of targets at rest ($u = 0$). He will have to fly along OA, where the angle $O'OA = \alpha$, called the *lead angle*, is determined by the requirement that the observer reach each point on AB at the same time that the target that was initially on the point of OO' directly above it reaches that same point, i.e., $\sin \alpha = u/v$,

$$(1) \qquad\qquad \alpha = \sin^{-1} \frac{u}{v}.$$

When the observer flies along OA, he detects not only the targets initially on OO', but, in virtue of the definite range assumption, all those within a distance of $W/2$ miles on either side of OO'. The band of width W centered on OO' (Fig. 8-1) is swept clean; i.e., all the targets that may have been in this band when $t = 0$ are detected.

The observer now wishes to detect, on his return flight, all those targets that were, when $t = 0$, in a second band of width W adjoining the first one and directly above it. This band is centered on the line O_1O_1' of Fig. 8-1 where $OO_1 = O'O_1' = W$. The observer reaches A when

$$t = \frac{OA}{v} = \frac{L}{v \cos \alpha} = \frac{L}{\sqrt{v^2 - u^2}}.$$

At this epoch, a target initially at O_1', W miles above O', will have moved down to a point A_1, but continue to be W miles above the point A which the target initially at O' will have reached by this time: $AA_1 = W$. This is because if one target is W miles behind another, and if they both have the same speed and course, it will always be W miles behind. Obviously if the observer were to fly directly back to the left bank of the channel, he would not fly over the O_1' target (now at A_1), and hence not accomplish his purpose of sweeping the O_1O_1' band of targets. To do this, he must fly up the right bank, until he meets this O_1' target at a point denoted by B and determined by the condition that the time taken for the observer to fly from A to B equals the time taken for the target to go from A_1 to B, i.e., $AB/v = A_1B/u$. This equation, together with the fact that $AB + A_1B = W$, determines the *length of upsweep $M = AB$*. Solving these equations we find

$$(2) \qquad\qquad M = \frac{v}{v + u} W.$$

This flight takes $M/v = W(v + u)$ hours, so that the observer is at B when

$$t = \frac{L}{\sqrt{v^2 - u^2}} + \frac{W}{v + u}.$$

At this epoch, the targets, which when $t = 0$ occupied the O_1O_1' band, will be in a band of width W centered on the line (not shown in Fig. 8-1) through B perpendicular to the channel. From then on the situation is precisely similar to what it was initially: the observer will sweep this band clean if he flies back to the point C of the left bank, where the lead angle of BC has the same value α as before. And having arrived at C, he must make the upsweep $CD = M$ if he is to detect on his third crossing the targets which when $t = 0$ were in a third W width band adjacent to and above the O_1O_1', i.e., the band centered on O_2O_2', Fig. 8-1.

The time taken by the target to fly the *basic element OABCD* is denoted by T_0. The time computations of the preceding paragraph show that

$$(3) \qquad\qquad T_0 = \frac{2L}{\sqrt{v^2 - u^2}} + \frac{2W}{v + u}.$$

Another interval of time that is useful to consider is the time T_t that a target takes in moving from O_2 to O. Since $OO_2 = 2W$ we have

$$(4) \qquad\qquad T_t = \frac{2W}{u}.$$

Figure 8-2 illustrates the three possible cases. They are as follows:

In Fig. 8-2A, D is *below* O. Then T_t is *less* than T_0 (since the O_2 target and the observer reach D simultaneously), and the first crossover point X is to the *right* of the center of the channel (the second, to the *left*, etc.). The flights, *if continued by the same aircraft*, would take place farther and farther down the channel and thus lead to a *retreating element barrier*. This is the case for which Fig. 8-1 has been drawn.

In Fig. 8-2B, D coincides with O. Then $T_t = T_0$, and the point X is at the center of the channel and bisects OA and BC. The flights, *if continued by the same aircraft*, would repeat themselves exactly; the path $OABCD = OABCO$ would be flown over and over again, and thus the barrier would remain stationary. This is called the *symmetric* crossover barrier patrol or, less frequently, the *stationary element barrier*.

In Fig. 8-2C, D is *above* O. Then T_t is *greater* than T_0, and the first crossover point X is to the *left* of the center of the channel or, in extreme cases, may not occur at all (the second, to the *right*, etc.). The flights, *if continued by the same aircraft*, would take place farther and farther up the channel and thus lead to an *advancing element barrier*.

It is to be emphasized that all three barriers may be flown as stationary barriers by the device of repeating the elements by having successive aircraft start from O at epochs of T_t after one another. While the elements themselves may retreat or advance, the geographical position of the flights, and hence of the barrier as a whole, remains stationary. This will be illustrated by later examples.

The advancing barrier represents a situation in which more than enough flying is available (assuming the single aircraft's endurance is sufficient for the repeated flights) to produce the required coverage. Advantage can be taken of this circumstance to fly only during the favorable hours of the twenty-four (in daylight, if the greatest chance of detection or certainty of recognition is the main desideratum, or

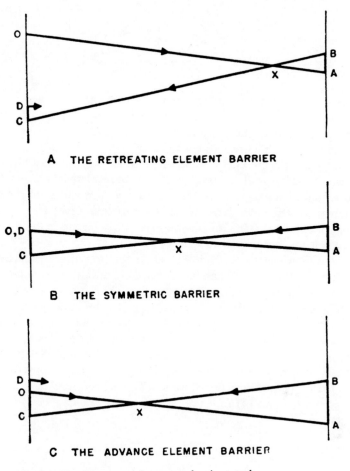

A THE RETREATING ELEMENT BARRIER

B THE SYMMETRIC BARRIER

C THE ADVANCE ELEMENT BARRIER

Fig. 8-2. The three cases of crossover barrier patrol.

at night with radar, if the element of surprise is more important, etc). For after advancing the barrier sufficiently during the favorable period, flights can be discontinued and the unswept waters (target positions) can be allowed to come down until their lower boundary reaches OO' (Fig. 8-1), whereupon the flights are recommenced. To find the time of no patrolling, one can reason as follows: If one basic element $OABCD$ is flown, but not a second, the central axis of the first unswept strip (the O_2O_2' strip of $t = 0$) will require the further time $T_1 - T_0$ to reach OO'; if N basic elements are flown, the further time $N(T_t - T_0)$ to reach 0. However, if the last upsweep is not flown, it will require $M/v = W/(v + u)$ more time, since the aircraft completes its patrol flights that much earlier. Hence the interval of time (after the aircraft reaches the left bank for the last time) during which no patrol flights (as distinguished from the return flight to base) need be flown is $N(T_t - T_0) + W/(v + u)$. With the aid of (3) and (4) we obtain the expression:

No Patrolling period =

(5)
$$N\left[\frac{2vW}{u(v+u)} - \frac{2L}{\sqrt{v^2-u^2}}\right] + \frac{W}{v+u}.$$

The symmetric barrier represents a situation in which the continued flying of the single aircraft is exactly enough to ensure the required coverage. It has a great advantage of simplicity over the asymmetrical cases, and the measures described later for making it applicable are frequently taken.

The retreating barrier represents a situation in which a single aircraft, even if its endurance would permit it to fly a large number of basic elements, is insufficient to maintain the required coverage, since the unswept area invades positions farther and farther down the channel. Under these conditions its flight has to be supplemented by that of other aircraft. One obvious way of doing this is to have a second aircraft leave O at the time when the target initially at O_2 reaches O, i.e., when $t = T_t = 2W/u$. This will be $T_0 - T_t$ hours before the first aircraft reaches D, and still longer before it returns to the base O. The second aircraft flies $OABC$, etc. But a better plan is to have n aircraft fly simultaneously abreast in a line perpendicular to their course and at the distance W apart. This has the effect of increasing the search width to the value $W' = nW$, and thus, if n is sufficiently great, leads from a retreating element barrier to a symmetric or an advancing one. Let us assume that with one aircraft $T_t < T_0$, i.e., the barrier element is retreating. What is the least number n of aircraft flying as described that will give rise to a nonretreating one? The answer is found by imposing the condition $T_t \geqslant T_0$ and replacing T_0 and T_t by their expressions in (3) and (4) *in which W' has been replaced by $W' = nW$.* We have

$$\frac{2nW}{u} \geqslant \frac{2L}{\sqrt{v^2-u^2}} + \frac{2nW}{v+u},$$

which is transformed algebraically so as to give the condition

(6)
$$n \geqslant \frac{L}{W}\frac{u}{v}\sqrt{\frac{v+u}{v-u}}.$$

Since n is an integer, it is taken as the lowest integer greater than or equal to the expression on the right, which is in general not an integer. Thus the number of aircraft is proportional to the width of channel and inversely proportional to the search width, and when v is so much greater than u that the radical can be regarded as unity, it is proportional to the target's speed and inversely proportional to the observer's speed.

It is remarked that when the width of channel L is not overwhelmingly greater than the search width W, an attempt is sometimes made to base the crossover patrol not on the boundary lines of the channel as in Fig. 8-1 but on two lines parallel to them and at a distance $W/2$ to the right of the left-hand boundary and $W/2$ to the left of the right-hand boundary, respectively. But all the discussion and formulas previously given apply to this case, provided L is replaced throughout by

$L' = L - W$. Thus (6) becomes

$$n \geqslant \left(\frac{L}{W} - 1 \right) \frac{u}{v} \sqrt{\frac{v + u}{v - u}} \; .$$

And we derive all the formulas needed to consider the altered channel case together with the case of n aircraft abreast, simply by replacing W by nW and L by $L - W$ in formulas (2) and (5). Thus, the length of upsweep formula (2) becomes

$$M = \frac{v}{v + u} nW,$$

and the conditions for the cases of Figs. 8-2 (A. $T_t < T_0$, B. $T_t = T_0$, or C. $T_t > T_0$) take on the forms

A. $$\frac{nW}{u} < \frac{L - W}{\sqrt{v^2 - u^2}} + \frac{nW}{v + u},$$

B. $$\frac{nW}{u} = \frac{L - W}{\sqrt{v^2 - u^2}} + \frac{nW}{v + u},$$

C. $$\frac{nW}{u} > \frac{L - W}{\sqrt{v^2 - u^2}} + \frac{nW}{v + u}.$$

We have seen in Fig. 8-1 how the bands swept clean according to the definite range law exactly cover the channel without overlapping or holes. That a plan of parallel flights, which, being intuitively simpler, might be tried instead of crossover

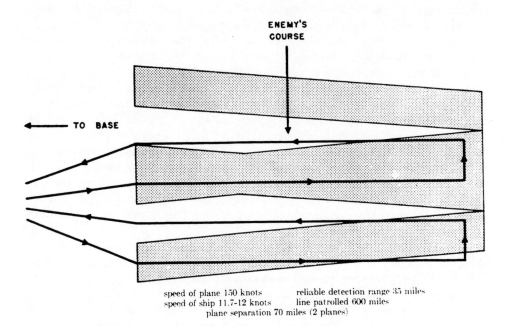

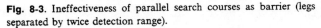

ENEMY'S COURSE

TO BASE

speed of plane 150 knots   reliable detection range 35 miles
speed of ship 11.7-12 knots   line patrolled 600 miles
plane separation 70 miles (2 planes)

Fig. 8-3. Ineffectiveness of parallel search courses as barrier (legs separated by twice detection range).

flights, produces overlapping and holes and thus a loss both of efficiency and effectiveness, is illustrated in Fig. 8-3. This and many similar figures (not given) contain an object lesson that was of historical decisiveness in an important operation of World War II. Here the problem was to set up a barrier effective against a 24-hour run at about 12 knots of enemy blockade runners in a known direction.

2. CROSSOVER BARRIERS WITH ANY LAW OF DETECTION

The assumption of a definite range law of detection, while affording a convenient basis for the construction of barrier patrols, leads to one fallacious conclusion, namely, that if designed as in Section 1 it is absolutely tight, providing a 100 percent chance of detecting the target, and, on the other hand, if it is designed with a slight overestimation of the search width W, it has holes. This in turn may lead to the practically disadvantageous procedure of exerting great effort to basing the barrier on a preconceived value of W, believing that nothing short of this tightness is adequate, while at the same time having a false sense of security when the ideal is achieved. The matter at issue is, in other words, just what it was in Chapter 3, when the importance of considering various more realistic laws of detection was stressed. The fact is that no barrier is 100 percent tight, whereas one falling far short of the ideal of the cleanly swept adjacent strips of Section 1 may have very real value; it may provide a very useful probability of detection. Thus if a barrier detects on the average even one-quarter of all targets, it will make it a very dangerous and costly procedure for the enemy to send his shipping through the channel.

In order to apply the machinery of Chapter 3 to these barrier patrols, we shall consider how the flights of Section 1 appear in space relative to the targets, i.e., in a horizontal plane moving down the channel with the speed u, "u-moving space," as we shall say for brevity. In such a space, all the targets are fixed. Thus the lines of targets OO', O_1O_1', O_2O_2', etc., are stationary horizontal lines, maintaining for all values of t their positions as shown in Fig. 8-1 for $t = 0$. And since, as we have seen, an observer flying the basic element $OABCD$ of the plan passes directly over the OO' and $O_1'O_1$ targets in the order of these letters, as well as up segments of the boundaries of the channel in passing from O' target to the O_1' target, and from the O_1 target to the O_2 target, the basic element flight will be along the path $OO'O_1'O_1O_2$ of u-moving space, as shown in Fig. 8-4. And as long as the crossover patrol is flown, more and more of the horizontal lines and their connecting segments of Fig. 8-4 will be traversed.

But this is simply the case of detection of a randomly placed stationary target by means of parallel sweeps, the problem considered in Chapter 3, Section 6. The fact that the distance between parallel tracks comes out as W in Fig. 8-4 is merely a consequence of the assumption of the definite range law made in Section 1 above, along with the desire of making the barrier 100 percent tight. The point to be emphasized is that *the crossover barrier patrol gives the best distribution of flights —uniformly spaced parallel sweeps.* This is why, in spite of rejecting one part of the assumptions upon which its design was based (definite range law), the form of patrol is still regarded as optimum. But in the interest of flexibility, to provide coverage by parallel sweeps when a sweep spacing of $S = W$ cannot be used, one must get away from this particular value of S.

Let the sweep spacing S be an arbitrarily chosen constant, one chosen without necessary relation to W or any other parameter of visibility. Is it possible to fly in such a way that the observer's path in u-moving space will be of the form shown in Fig. 8-4, but with

(7)
$$OO_1 = O_1O_2 = O_2O_3 = \cdots = O'O_1' = O_1'O_2'$$
$$= O_2'O_3' = \cdots = S,$$

and how are the flights to be described in the geographical space of Fig. 8-1?

The answer is simple: Fly the same crossover paths as in Section 1, only with W replaced throughout by S. For the relation between the geographical and the relative paths depends in no wise on the fact that S in Section 1 had the value W. The horizontal bands centered on OO', O_1O_1', etc., are now of width S, and merely lose their meaning of "regions swept clean." Moreover, all the formulas of Section 1 apply to the present case, provided W is replaced throughout by S. For convenience we shall write them down in the new (general) form here.

Length of upsweep for one and for n searchers abreast spaced S miles apart,

(8)
$$M = \frac{v}{v + u} S \text{ (one searcher)}$$

$$M = \frac{v}{v + u} nS \text{ (n searchers abreast).}$$

Time of flight of one basic element,

(9)
$$T_0 = \frac{2L}{\sqrt{v^2 - u^2}} + \frac{2S}{v + u} \text{ (one searcher)}$$

$$T_0 = \frac{2L}{\sqrt{v^2 - u^2}} + \frac{2nS}{v + u} \text{ (n searchers abreast).}$$

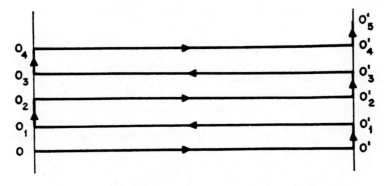

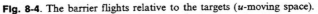

Fig. 8-4. The barrier flights relative to the targets (u-moving space).

Time taken for first target (on left bank) not flown over in the flight of the first basic element but which will be the lowest one flown over in the second basic element to reach O:

$$(10) \qquad\qquad T_t = \frac{2S}{u} \text{ (one searcher)}$$

$$T_t = \frac{2nS}{u} \text{ (n searchers abreast).}$$

Time of no patrolling after N basic elements (the last one without upsweep) are flown by n searchers abreast, from the end of the flights until the patrol flights must be resumed in order to maintain the uniform coverage of sweep spacing S in u-moving space:
No patrolling period

$$(11) \qquad\qquad = N\left[\frac{2vnS}{u(v+u)} - \frac{2L}{\sqrt{v^2 - u^2}} \right] + \frac{nS}{v+u}.$$

This assumes an advancing barrier, and no account is taken of the time for the aircraft to return to base.

As was seen in Section 1 the barrier element will be of the (A) retreating, (B) stationary (symmetrical), or (C) advancing types, according to whether $T_t < T_0$, $T_t = T_0$, or $T_t > T_0$ respectively. Using equations (9) and (10) and transforming the results algebraically, the following criteria are derived in the case of n aircraft flying in line abreast at spacing S.
Writing

$$k = \sqrt{\frac{v+u}{v-u}}$$

the condition for

$$(12) \qquad\qquad \text{A. Retreating barrier is } n < k\frac{L}{S}\frac{u}{v}.$$

$$\text{B. Stationary barrier is } n = k\frac{L}{S}\frac{u}{v}.$$

$$\text{C. Advancing barrier is } n > k\frac{L}{S}\frac{u}{v}.$$

The method of evaluating the probability $P(S)$ of detecting a particular target attempting to cross the barrier is given in Chapter 3, Section 7, equation (43) in particular. Figure 3-11 of the latter shows the relation between this probability and S (although the abscissa is the sweep density "n" $= 1/A$) in typical cases. If in particular an inverse cube law of sighting is assumed, $P(S)$ is given by (45)–(47) of Chapter 3.

$$(13) \qquad\qquad P(S) = \text{erf}\left(0.954\frac{E}{S}\right) = \text{erf}\left(\frac{\sqrt{\pi}}{2}\frac{W}{S}\right),$$

E being the effective visibility. In general, $P(S)$ has to be derived by approximate formulas or graphical methods, in connection with the material set forth in the appendixes on visual, radar, or sonar detection.

It may be remarked that if the target's speed u has been overestimated, the barrier flights will appear (relative to the target) not as the horizontal lines of Fig. 8-3 but as two sets of parallel lines, one set, corresponding to flights from the left bank to the right, being tipped slightly down to the right, the other set, corresponding to flights in the reverse direction, tipped down to the left. Also, all upsweep legs will be a trifle shortened. And thus the flights, while not giving as regular a picture relative to the target, will give one of more crowded paths, and hence the chance of detection will be *increased*. It will, however, not be as great as it would have been had the searcher planned his flights for the correct value of u.

If the target is moving obliquely down the channel, instead of exactly parallel to the banks as we have been assuming, the effective value of its speed as far as the tightness of the barrier is concerned is its downward component. This again tends to reduce the effective speed, with the result noted above.

There are, generally speaking, two methods of applying the results derived here. *First*, the probability $P(S)$, i.e., the tightness of the barrier, can be given which requires the number of aircraft needed to maintain a patrol of given sort (e.g., a symmetric one), the corresponding length of upsweep M (which determines the basic element), etc. *Second*, given the number of aircraft and type of patrol, find the probability of detection. In the first case, S is derived from $P(S)$ by an equation like (13), n is determined by (12), e.g., (B) or (C), then M is calculated from (8). In the second case, S is determined from (12), and then M and $P(S)$ from (8) and an equation like (13). But there are various mixed cases; the situation will be illustrated in Section 3.

We are now in a position to solve the problem, foreshadowed in Section 1, of the use of an advancing element barrier to avoid 24-hour flights. Suppose that for A hours out of the 24 it is expedient to fly the patrol, whereas during B hours it is inexpedient. (B might be the hours of darkness in cases where much dependence is placed on visual detection or recognition; $A + B = 24$.) Let us try to determine the number n of aircraft patrolling abreast and number N of circuits they must patrol together so that coverage at the sweep spacing S in u-moving space will be maintained constantly. For any given N and n, the time of no patrolling is given by (11), while the total patrolling time is $NT_0 - M/v$ (the $-M/v$ term, because the last upsweep is omitted). The sum of these two periods of time must equal 24 hours. Using (8), (9), and (11), one finds that

$$(14) \qquad\qquad nN = \frac{12u}{S}.$$

Now since the permissible no-patrolling time must be at least as great as B, (11) leads to the inequality

$$(15) \qquad N\left[\frac{2vnS}{u(v+u)} - \frac{2L}{\sqrt{v^2 - u^2}} \right] + \frac{nS}{v+u} \geqslant B.$$

By multiplying this through by $N(v + u)$, introducing the quantity k of (12), and replacing nN by its value given in (14), one derives the quadratic inequality

$$2LkN^2 - (Av - Bu)N - 12u \leqslant 0,$$

which (on completing the square, etc.) is readily shown to be equivalent to the following:

(16) $$N \leqslant \frac{1}{4Lk}\left[Av - Bu + \sqrt{(Av - Bu)^2 + 96Lku}\,\right].$$

It is noticed that this inequality does not involve S. And now we have the conditions (14) and (16) in all respects equivalent to (14) and (15) (one set is a necessary and sufficient condition for the other). Thus (14) and (16) are the necessary and sufficient conditions that N and n must satisfy to be solutions of the problem. They do not, however, fully determine N and n. The method for doing this is as follows: *First*, choose for N the largest integer satisfying (16). *Second*, choose a value for S which on the one hand makes $12u/NS$ an integer, and on the other hand gives an acceptably high value to $P(S)$ [by the use of (13)]. This last involves some trial and error; moreover, a value of S which has these properties may turn out to impose too great force requirements, and so one may have to be satisfied with a somewhat lower probability $P(S)$, i.e., use a larger S. When the value of S has finally been chosen, (14) gives n as a positive integer, and the problem is solved. It will be illustrated in Section 3.

3. PRACTICAL DEVICES USED IN SOME ACTUAL CASES

The following examples illustrate successful applications to intercepting five blockade runners through the South Atlantic during World War II.

1. It is desired to close a 600-mile channel by a barrier giving a 90 percent chance of detection. The speeds are $v = 130$ knots and $u = 12$ knots. The effective visibility is 20 miles, and equation (13) is assumed. (The value of 20 miles was too low for ships but was about correct for surfaced submarines.) How many aircraft are needed in order to have a symmetric element barrier, and how should the flights be specified?

Using (13), $\mathrm{erf}(0.954 \times 20/S) = 0.9$, and it is found from a table of error functions that $\mathrm{erf}(1.163) = 0.9$, hence $0.954 \times 20/S = 1.163$, so that $S = 16.4$. Since the inequality (A) of (12) must not hold, the number n of aircraft must be the smallest integer, not less than

$$\frac{L}{S}\frac{u}{v}\sqrt{\frac{v + u}{v - u}} = \frac{600 \times 12}{16.4 \times 130}\sqrt{\frac{142}{118}} = 3.7.$$

In other words, four aircraft are necessary. But with four aircraft, case (C) of (12) is in effect, not case (B): The barrier advances up the channel. To have a stationary one, the four aircraft may fly closer together than S, by an amount determined by solving the equation

$$4 = \frac{600 \times 12}{130S} \sqrt{\frac{142}{118}} \, ,$$

i.e., equation (12), case (B). We obtain $S = 15.15$ miles. With this reduced spacing, the barrier gains in tightness; in fact the probability found from (13) now becomes a 92.5 percent chance—all to the good. The length of upsweep given by (8) is $M = 55.5$ miles. Finally, the lead angle given by (1) is $\alpha = 5°18'$. The quantities determine the fundamental element, or rather elements, as four congruent symmetrical crossover paths flown, shown in Fig. 8-5.

But in determining force requirements it is not sufficient to have only the fundamental flights given; we must find how long their flying takes and consider questions of aircraft endurance. It is found from (9) (with $n = 4$, $S = 15.15$, etc.) that $T_0 = 10.14$ hours. Now only a long-range patrol aircraft such as a PBM or PB4Y could have an endurance sufficient for this one circuit of the fundamental element. It will have to be capable of well over 10 hours, since time must be allowed for investigation of contacts, the trip to and from base (which may not be at O, P, Q, R) etc. And it cannot be expected to make more than one circuit. Thus a new flight of four fresh aircraft must be readied and waiting at O, P, Q, R in order to take up the flights as soon as the first set returns to these points. The operation will therefore require eight aircraft, assuming maintenance to be quick and perfect. Actually, a few more should be on hand, as well as enough pilots and lookouts to ensure their being well rested at the outset of every new flight—an essential condition for their efficient operation, without which the effective visibility will fall far short of the assumed 20-mile figure.

2. Under the assumptions of the last example, let it be required to fly a barrier of the advancing type with n aircraft abreast during the $A = 12$ hours of light, to be discontinued during the $B = 12$ hours of darkness. Applying the method at the end of Section 2, we obtain from (16) that $N \leqslant 1.16$, and hence we take $N = 1$. Next we must take an S which gives $12u/NS = 144/S$ an integral value and provides an acceptable probability $P(S)$, while at the same time not using an undue number of

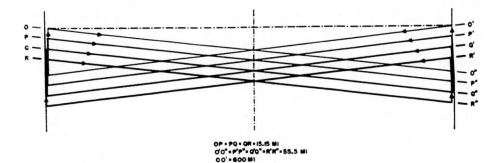

OP = PQ = QR = I5.I5 MI
O'O" = P'P" = Q'Q" = R'R" = 55.5 MI
OO' = 600 MI

Fig. 8-5. Symmetrical barrier flown by four aircraft abreast.

aircraft. We have seen that the value 16.4 gives a 90 percent chance of detection, and this suggests taking $S = 16$, for which $144/S = 9$ and $P(S)$ given by (13) is a probability of nearly 91 percent. Then $n = 9$: nine aircraft must be flown spaced at 16 miles abreast, one flight only being made per day. The time of patrolling is $T_0 - M/v$ (the last upsweep being omitted) which has the value [given by (8) and (9)] of $10 - 1/4$ hours, the remaining $13 - 3/4$ hours (including the 12 of darkness) not needing any patrol. The fact that the two periods are not each equal to 12 hours is of course due to the circumstance that since N and n are integers, (14) and (15) cannot be solved as equations but rather (14) as an equation and (15) as an inequality. The operation thus requires about the same forces as in the previous example. Which of the two methods is to be used depends on considerations of equipment (how good the radar is for search at dark, etc.) and tactics.

3. A channel 300 miles wide is to be barred by a symmetrical barrier flown by one aircraft of 6-hour endurance. How tight is the barrier, and how frequently does the aircraft have to be relieved? Assume again $u = 12$, $v = 130$, $E = 20$, and equation (13).

From equation (12), case (B), with $n = 1$, we obtain $S = kLu/v = 30.4$. From equation (13), $P = 0.644$: a 64.4 percent chance of detection. Eliminating S from equations (9) and (12), case (B), we have

$$(17) \qquad\qquad T_0 = \frac{2Lk}{v},$$

which, in the present case, gives $T_0 = 5.06$ hours. Evidently with an endurance of 6 hours, just one circuit can be flown, so we shall require about five flights a day, and between two and five aircraft available at the very minimum.

4. BARRIER WHEN TARGET SPEED IS CLOSE TO OBSERVER'S SPEED

So far it has been assumed that v considerably exceeds u; indeed, when $v \leqslant u$, the crossover type of barrier is kinematically impossible. This is no obstacle when the observer is airborne and the target is a ship, but when both observer and target are units of the same type (both ships or both aircraft), the situation excluded heretofore becomes important. Although many plans of barring a channel can be devised for this case, with particular emphasis on back-and-forth barriers, there are so many special factors of tactics, geography, environment, and variety of equipment that determine the best type of search that it would be meaningless to attempt to subsume the situation under general rules. Each problem must be treated individually.

5. CIRCULAR BARRIERS AGAINST A CONSTANT RADIAL FLUX OF TARGETS

In the case where enemy surface craft or submarines are attempting to leave a point of the ocean, such as an island or exposed harbor, and in the case in which they are attempting to approach such points or to close positions at which our forces are conducting landing operations, the vector velocity pattern is a radial one. It is "centrifugal" (directed away from the central point) in the former case and "centripetal" (directed toward the center) in the latter. But in each case it can be regarded as *constant in time*: over long periods, the density of outgoing or incoming craft is not expected to vary. The simplified mathematical model to be applied to such cases has been discussed in Chapter 4, Section 1, at the end of which the ideas are illustrated in Fig. 4-1. A more subtle "game-theoretic" one has been set forth in Chapter 7, Section 8.

It must be emphasized that the present situation is in strong contrast with that considered in later Sections 8–10, where the unit to be detected is, to be sure, proceeding radially away from a point of fix, but in which its likelihood of being at various distances from this point depends strongly upon the time elapsed since the fix. Corresponding to this latter circumstance, the layout of the search must provide for a progressive variation of the searched positions with lapse of time. The theory of such plans is far more complicated than that of the ones considered at present.

These barriers contrast also with the protection of a *moving* formation such as a convoy, to be considered later (in Chapters 9 and 10). The defended positions in the present chapter *are at rest*, and therefore the attackers have no tracking problem, and, moreover, can approach at any speed at which they find it convenient to operate and from any relative bearing. The defended position is constantly exposed to attack from any direction not effectively blocked by land masses or shoal water—or by mines.

Defense against targets moving toward a central objective is a specific type of problem that shares some of the tactical features of barrier patrols and escort formations, but, as noted above, has its own special kinematics. As in the case of convoy escort, the protection given may be of two kinds. Aircraft could engage in barrier patrols outside distances within which wholly submerged approach is possible (more than 60 miles out with the submarines of World War II). An intermediate aircraft screen may be provided to pick up submarines that may reveal themselves, to counter airborne weapons, or to monitor acoustic sensors. An inner screen of surface ships will patrol a barrier for submarines (submerged or surfaced) that may elude the aircraft screen. Details of each screen follow in Section 6. Mines may also be used.

One may need to abandon the design described in Section 1 in favor of a simpler plan. The lead-angle α which was a key element of the basic design given in Section 1 is required only because of the necessity to search parallel strips of space moving with enemy velocity **u**, patrolling with own velocity **v**, when the direction of search was *necessarily opposed* in alternating members of each pair of strips. If search of adjacent strips is always carried out in the same direction there is no need to use a lead-angle at all. The resulting searched strips in u-moving space will still be parallel but they will be inclined to the target track at an angle $(90° - \tan^{-1} u/v)$ instead of at 90 degrees, as a simple velocity diagram would show.

When a barrier is set up *around* an objective the closed barrier path may be made to contain the objective, and the lead-angle α can become zero. The resulting path is a simple circle, or more practically, a square. Such a path may be easier to navigate, or to evaluate, than a set of barriers set up on barrier lines that form the sides of a polygon.

The size of the square will usually be determined by tactical considerations, i.e., the distance at which interception would be achieved. For example, against submarines of W.W. II it was the distance within which approach while wholly submerged becomes possible. The distance the target can travel while the searcher makes one circuit, or between sweeps by equally spaced searchers on the same square track, becomes the track spacing S in u-moving space. For the simple case of a circular track this is

$$(18) \qquad\qquad S = \frac{2\pi r}{n} \cdot \frac{u}{v}$$

where r is the radius, and n the number of search craft employed. Since with a given effective visibility there is a contact probability corresponding to any value of S, formula (18) determines the number of searchers required to give any desired tightness.

For the more practical case of a square track of side b

$$(19) \qquad\qquad S = \frac{4b}{n} \cdot \frac{u}{v}.$$

This value of S corresponds to the *minimum* contact probability since with a square the target track will not always cross the search track at 90 degrees.

There is one important difference between this type of barrier and certain cases of the crossover type. S for a given size of square is determined wholly by relative target movement and the number of equally spaced searchers (S is proportional to u/nv), and no explicit choice as to its value determines the search path. In this respect it is like the continuous symmetrical crossover patrol. This raises the question as to how two searchers patrolling abreast should be spaced. If the definite range law is applied, search abreast at a distance apart equal to twice the range would be equal in effectiveness to search by each singly, equally spaced on one and the same square path. With any other kind of contact probability law the corresponding track spacing in search abreast is the value of S found by using formula (19) and the appropriate value of n. It will be noted that this is not equivalent to placing two or more searchers closely abreast on exactly the same track. They must be either equally spaced on an identical track, or, if abreast, spaced at right angles to that track by exactly the right amount. The effects of irregularities in spacing are, however, rather small. It should be noted that if the value of S/n is at all large, search abreast on square or circular paths cannot be carried out effectively because of the difference in the length of track for each observer. The effects of *search turns*, while not hard to calculate, may have to be evaluated.

It is apparent that the maximum size square is fixed by (a) the endurance of the searcher (endurance $> 4b$) and by (b) the number of searchers continuously available. When surface craft are employed against underwater targets it is very desirable that two or more patrol abreast. Since a large number will be required to cover a square of any size, it will be more practical to employ small groups (three to six) in crossover patrols on barrier lines that form a polygon with a convenient number of sides, rather than have them all patrol a single large square. Modern improvements in equipment will of course lead to modifications of these essentially World War II-type procedures.

6. PATROL AGAINST INCOMING SUBMARINES IN WORLD WAR II

Detailed application of the foregoing considerations to *air patrol* depended on the ranges of visual and radar detection, the latter on the radar gear installed on the aircraft. These in turn determined the interval that aircraft could patrol on the basic square track. The longer the radar range, the fewer aircraft need be employed, and the easier to navigate along the track. With S-band or X-band radar, navigation will be made very easy by the constant presence on the screen of check-points on the island.

The distance from the position being protected from submarines at which the patrol track will be placed will be the estimated submerged run consistent with effective weapon launching on the part of the submarines, and airborne radar ranges. With ASG radar used on patrol planes in World War War II this will result in flying a square with legs of about 180 miles to each side. With PBM aircraft the complete circuit of the square will then require six hours. Two complete circuits can be made by each sortie in twelve hours. Reference to formula (19) and standard tables of effective visibilities shows that only two 120-knot aircraft need patrol at one time equally spaced in order to give a 50 percent chance of contact with a 15-knot surfaced submarine. Four aircraft will give a probability of contact of 77 percent and six aircraft will give a probability of contact of about 90 percent. With the older and less effective ASB radar ($E = 8$ miles), however, six 150-knot aircraft patrolling a square with 150 mile sides will give a probability of contact of only 70 percent, and each sortie will be limited to a single circuit (four hours). Thus 18 TBF sorties give less protection than four PBM sorties. Today's *technology has changed these details—but perhaps not the principles.*

7. SEARCH ABOUT A POINT OF FIX

Here we shall give practical methods for implementing searches considered theoretically in earlier parts of this book, Chapters 4–7 particularly.

When an object of search on the ocean, such as a surface craft or downed airplane life raft, has had its approximate position disclosed to a searcher at a certain time, the searcher has the problem of disposing its subsequent searching effort (which is always limited) in such a manner as to maximize its chance of detecting the object, subject of course to the practical restrictions of navigation. The information regarding the object's approximate position may be derived from a DF fix, the report of a chance observation, by indirect inference, or, in the case of the life raft, from a radio communication from the aircraft about to crash. The point at which this information locates the target is called the *point of fix* and the time for which the information is given, the *time of fix*. It is assumed that the searcher is airborne and thus has a considerable speed advantage over the target.

If the fix were a perfectly accurate one and the target were at rest or moving in a known manner, the searcher's task would be simple. He would proceed to the point of fix in the former case, and would search the locus of points to which the target, initially at the point of fix, could be assumed to have moved during the intervening time. But such accuracy of fix is seldom if ever obtained. Only a probability distribution of target positions at the time of fix is actually given. This distribution will have its greatest density at the point of fix and fall continuously to zero at a distance. In an important group of cases, this distribution can be regarded as symmetrical about the point of fix and can indeed be taken with satisfactory accuracy as a circular normal one:

$$(20) \qquad p(x, y) = f(x, y) = f(r) = \frac{1}{2\pi\sigma^2} e^{-r^2/2\sigma^2},$$

where $f(x, y) \, dx \, dy$ is the probability that the target at the time of fix will be in the small region $dx \, dy$ at the point (x, y) at the distance r from the origin 0 (which is at the point of fix) and where σ is the standard deviation.

It should be remarked that DF fixes usually do not give rise to circularly symmetrical distributions (cf. Chapter 4, Sections 6–8) but under many conditions are of approximately this character. In any event, the assumption of a circular normal density will often result in a more realistic search effort than would an exclusive consideration of the mean.

Two cases are considered in this chapter. In the first, the target's motion is negligible, and so the target can be regarded as at rest. Equation (20) gives its distribution at all subsequent times. In the second, the target's speed is known but its direction is not, although it is assumed to be uniformly distributed in angle throughout the full circle. The distribution after the lapse of time t after the fix has already been derived in Chapter 5, equation (12). The solution in the second case will be related more or less directly with the first. It is to the second case that the geometrical schema of the centrifugal vector field mentioned in Section 5 of the present chapter applies exactly. In contrast to the cases of Section 6, however, the density of targets is not constant but, after being humped up about the center, spreads itself out into a thick ring cut normally by the vectors, with the lapse of time. See Chapter 5, Fig. 5-3, and the approximate equation (14).

8. SQUARE SEARCH FOR A STATIONARY TARGET[*]

In this case, as we have seen, equation (20) gives the probability density of the distribution of targets for all later time. If the total searcher's track length during

---

[*]In the 1946 edition, the present $W\Phi$ and $W\phi$ were denoted by Φ and ϕ, with corresponding differences produced in the intermediate formulas, but not in the final results.

the search is L miles and its sweep width W, then the quantity of searching effort as defined in Chapter 6 is $\Phi = L$. The problem of so disposing a continuous spread of searching effort of total amount Φ optimally has been solved in Chapter 6, Section 6, and for (20) in Section 7. *But here we are confronted by the practical problem of designing actual navigable flights that will maximize the probability of detection.*

The type of flight that it is expedient to use consists of a set of "expanding square" flights of the sort shown in Fig. 8-6. After passing over the point of fix O to a point S miles beyond O, the aircraft turns through a right angle (e.g., to the right), and after S miles it turns again through a right angle in the same direction, continuing $2S$ more miles before turning a third time. After flying $2S$ miles it turns again, and continues in this manner, always keeping adjacent parallel tracks S miles apart. After a certain number of legs have been flown, there results an approximately square figure covered by equally spaced lines, the space between them being the sweep spacing S. Such a figure will be called a "square of uniform coverage." The underlying scheme of the search is to fly a succession of superimposed squares of uniform coverage, each centered at O, and of successively large

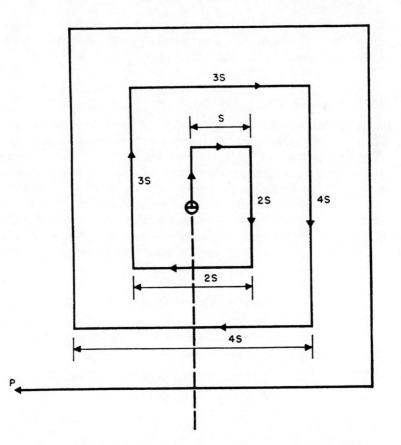

Fig. 8-6. Square of uniform coverage.

dimensions. This will furnish a practicable means of approximating to the theoretically optimum continuous distribution of searching effort derived in Chapters 6 and 7.

The first problem is to determine a desirable value of the sweep spacing S, up to now left arbitrary. The point of view adopted here is that S should be so chosen that on the initial square the probability of detection per unit time shall be a maximum (during the important part of the search, i.e., the beginning). Clearly such an S will, for a given law of detection, be a function of the parameters of detection and the standard deviation σ of the known or assumed target distribution. In the case of the inverse cube law of detection, S will be a function of E (or W) and σ. Since it can be shown that S will not be sensitive to the law of detection, it is permissible to assume the inverse cube one for convenience. As shown in Chapter 3, equations (26), (29), and (46),

$$p(x) = 1 - \exp\left[-0.092\left(\frac{E}{x}\right)^2\right],$$

where $p(x)$ is the probability of detection of a target of lateral range x from a straight aircraft track.

Consider the distribution (20) of targets before any flights are made. The probability of the target lying on the strip parallel to the y axis between x and $x + dx$ is found (by summing probabilities) to be

$$(21) \qquad\qquad dx \int_{-\infty}^{+\infty} f(x, y) \, dy = \frac{1}{\sigma\sqrt{2\pi}} e^{-x^2/2\sigma^2} dx.$$

The graph of the differential coefficient against x is the familiar normal law curve, reaching its maximum at the origin. Now suppose that an indefinite straight flight is made along the y axis and has failed to detect the target. In the light of this additional knowledge, the distribution of targets is altered, and the differential coefficient in (21) no longer represents the lateral density of targets [i.e., the probability in the $(x, x + dx)$ strip]. To find the new density, the use of Bayes' theorem is called for (see Chapter 4 introduction and Section 4). The "a priori probability" of the target's being in the $(x, x + dx)$ strip is given by (21). The "productive probability" of the event (viz., of not detecting the target on the sweep through O) is

$$1 - p(x) = \exp\left[-0.092\left(\frac{E}{x}\right)^2\right],$$

and hence the "a posteriori probability" density of probability of the target's being in the $(x, x + dx)$ strip is *proportional* to the product

$$(22) \qquad\qquad \exp\left(-\frac{x^2}{2\sigma^2} - \frac{0.092E^2}{x^2}\right),$$

that has its maxima at $x = \pm 0.65\sqrt{E\sigma}$. It is no longer humped at the origin but presents double humping with an intervening depression at the origin.

Where must a second indefinite sweep parallel to the y axis be made if it is to achieve the greatest probability of detecting the target? Since the distribution obtained above is skewed, the distance D between the first and the second track should be slightly greater than the distance $0.65\sqrt{E\sigma}$ out to the maximum of the new distribution. To find it precisely, we compute the probability of detection by multiplying the expression (22) with $p(x - D)$ and integrating over all positive x. It appears at once that in order to maximize this probability, D must make the function

$$\int_0^\infty \exp\left[-\frac{x^2}{2\sigma^2} - \frac{0.092E^2}{x^2} - \frac{0.092E^2}{(x - D)^2} \right] dx$$

a minimum. By trial it is found, in using numerical integration, that the approximate value of D is $0.75\sqrt{E\sigma}$.

Clearly, if the searching were done by means of infinite parallel equispaced sweeps, the sweep-spacing S would be taken equal to D if the chance of early contact is to be maximized. The square search of Fig. 8-6, while not exactly of this type, is near enough that an obvious choice of S is to give it the same value D. Accordingly, we shall use henceforth the sweep spacing

(23) $$S = 0.75\sqrt{E\sigma}.$$

Returning to the square of uniform coverage, it is seen that the three-circuit flight path of Fig. 8-6 can be inscribed in a square of side $2 \times 3S$. More generally, an N-circuit flight of this sort can be inscribed in a square of side $2NS$. The total length of tract from O to P is found (as an arithmetic progression) to be $L = 2S \times 2N(2N + 1)/2$. Hence the average density of searching effort (the ϕ of Chapter 6, Sections 6 and 7) is L/area, or

$$S\frac{2N(2N + 1)}{(2NS)^2} = \left(1 + \frac{1}{2N}\right)\frac{1}{S},$$

which is approximately $1/S$, the value to be adopted here.

Consider now a sequence of n squares of uniform coverage centered at O and of half-side s_k $(k = 1, 2, \ldots, n)$, where

$$0 < s_1 < s_2 < s_3 < \cdots < s_n.$$

If (x, y) is a point in some of these squares, let us say in those of side $s_{m+1}, s_{m+2}, \ldots, s_n$, then the mean density of searching effort performed by these squares is $(n - m)/S$. Thus the flights give rise to a searching effort function $z = \phi^*(x, y)$, the graph of which (in xyz space) is of the form of a tapered heap of square slabs of thickness $1/S$, piled upon one another and centered on the z axis. The total volume of this pile, $\int\int \phi^*(x, y)\, dx\, dy$, must equal the total searching effort $\Phi = L$; thus we must have

(24) $$4 \sum_{k=1}^n s_k^2 = SL.$$

It is by means of this function $\phi^*(x, y)$ that we must approximate the solution $\phi(x, y)$ obtained in Section 7 of Chapter 6. There it was shown that, outside the circle of radius a given by

$$(25) \qquad\qquad a^4 = 4\sigma^2 \frac{W\Phi}{\pi},$$

$\phi(x, y)$ is zero, while within this circle, it is given by

$$(26) \qquad\qquad \phi(x, y) = \phi(r) = \frac{a^2 - r^2}{2\sigma^2 W}.$$

The graph of $z = \phi(x, y)$ is thus a paraboloid having the z axis as axis of revolution, cutting the xy plane in the above circle, beyond which the paraboloid is replaced by the xy plane.

Thus, graphically put, our problem is to determine the quantities $n, s_1, \ldots, s_n$, subject to (24), so that the piled slab solid shall approximate the paraboloidal one. The heights of the two solids being n/S and $a^2/2\sigma^2$ respectively, n is determined by equating them,

$$(27) \qquad\qquad n = \frac{a^2 S}{2\sigma^2 W}.$$

Since n must be an integer, (27) means that it must be taken as the nearest integer to the right-hand member. To find s_k, consider the space between the two horizontal planes $z = a^2/2\sigma^2 W - (k - 1)/S$ and $z = a^2/2\sigma^2 W - k/S$. They contain the kth slab of the piled slab solid and hence cut from it the volume $4s_k^2/S$. They also cut from the paraboloid a volume of revolution readily found by integration to be $\pi(2k - 1)\sigma^2 W/S^2$. On equating the two volumes, we obtain

$$(28) \qquad\qquad s_k^2 = \frac{\pi}{4} \cdot \frac{W\sigma^2}{S}(2k - 1), \qquad k = 1, 2, \ldots, n.$$

Thus the volumes of the piled slab solid and the paraboloidal solid are equal [and hence (24) is automatically satisfied, since it expresses the required equality of this volume with $\Phi = L$, a requirement met by the paraboloidal volume, cf. Chapter 6, Section 7], and the two solids agree in position about as closely as possible.

The number and dimensions of the squares of uniform coverage are determined by equations (27) and (28), but except that they are all centered at O, their positions (relative orientation) have been left arbitrary. We now lay down the following rule.

The second square should be tipped so that its side makes 45 degrees with the side of the first, the third should similarly be at 45 degrees with the second (and thus be parallel to the first) and, in general, the $(k + 1)$ should be at 45 degrees with the kth [and parallel to the $(k - 1)$].

The justification of this rule is twofold:

First, a greater randomization of flights is achieved; i.e., there is less danger of passing over the same path twice in succession, with resulting loss of efficiency. The situation in this regard is illustrated by the following considerations. Navigational errors will most likely keep the second search from being flown along the optimum tract, which is approximately midway between and parallel to the legs of the first search. If $p(S)$ is the probability of detection with sweep spacing S, then the probability of detection with two searches when the optimum track on the second search is attained is $p(S/2)$. However, if the second search duplicates the first search, the probability of detection with two searches is $p(S/\sqrt{2})$ (assuming the inverse cube law). If the legs of the second search are inclined to those of the first search, so that the probabilities of detection on the two searches may be considered as independent, the probability of detection with two searches is $1 - [1 - p(S)]^2$. In general this latter probability will be slightly less than $p(S/2)$ but considerably greater than $p(S/\sqrt{2})$. For example, using the inverse cube law with $E/S = 0.1$, we have

$$p(S/2) = 0.212,$$

$$p(S/\sqrt{2}) = 0.151,$$

$$1 - [1 - p(S)]^2 = 0.203.$$

Thus, there seems to be more to gain than to lose by inclining the legs of the second search to those of the first search.

Second and more important, the $(k + 1)$ square flown according to this rule will sweep a maximum of important unswept water. Consider the situation after one square of uniform coverage has been flown without resulting in detection; the area which it is most important to sweep is the part of the circle circumscribing the late square but outside the latter. With the next square tilted at 45 degrees, a maximum of this area is covered. Moreover, with the tilted square the region of overlapping of two successive squares is least.

It remains to evaluate the probability P^* of detection by the square search described herein, and to compare it with the probability P for the optimal one of Chapter 6, Section 7. It is shown that a lower value of P^* is given by

$$(29) \qquad P^{**} = (1 - e^{-W/S})e^{-Wn/S} \sum_{k=1}^{n} e^{Wk/S} \operatorname{erf}^2 \sqrt{\frac{\pi W}{8S}(2k - 1)},$$

while P is given by

$$(30) \qquad P = 1 - \left(1 + \frac{nW}{S}\right)e^{-nW/S}.$$

These two functions are plotted in Fig. 8-7 for various values of n. The P^{**} curves are in solid line and the P curves are dotted; the P^* curves lie between.

Evidently, P^* will be less than the probability P for the idealized search, since P is the maximum probability that can be obtained with the given amount of searching (provided the assumptions of Chapter 6 are made).

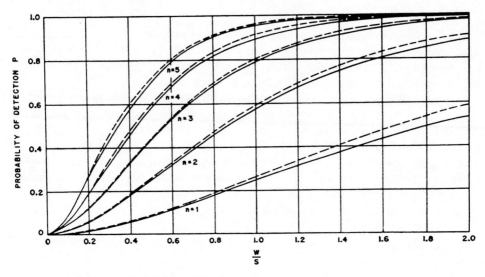

Fig. 8-7. Probability of detection.

Using the target distribution as given in formula (20) and the density of searching effort given in (26), the probability P of detection for the idealized case is obtained from formulas (40)–(42), Chapter 6, as follows, where $\sigma = \sigma_1 = \sigma_2$, and formula (25) above, relating a to the other quantities, is applied:

$$P = 1 - \left(1 + \frac{a^2}{2\sigma^2}\right)e^{-a^2/2\sigma^2}.$$

Using formula (27), P may be written in the form of equation (30).

The direct computation of P^* is difficult because each square is tilted 45 degrees to the preceding square and each square, except the first, is not included completely in the following square. To obtain a lower limit to P^*, consider the square distribution before the squares are tilted, i.e., when they are all parallel, and let P^{**} be the probability of detection with this distribution of effort under the assumptions of Chapter 6. Then P^* will be greater than P^{**}, for reasons already given above. By formula (28) of Chapter 6, the probability that the target will be in the square bounded by $x = \pm s_1, y = \pm s_1$, and will be detected by the n coverages of the square, is, where $\operatorname{erf}^2(\cdot) = (\operatorname{erf}(\cdot))^2$,

$$P_1 = \frac{4}{2\pi\sigma^2}\int_0^{s_1}\int_0^{s_1}(1 - e^{-nW/S})e^{-(x^2+y^2)/2\sigma^2}\,dx\,dy$$

$$= (1 - e^{-nW/S})\operatorname{erf}^2\frac{s_1}{\sigma\sqrt{\pi}}.$$

Similarly, the probability that the target will be inside the square bounded by $x = \pm s_k, y = \pm s_k$ but outside the square bounded by $x = \pm s_{k-1}, y = \pm s_{k-1}$ and will be detected by the $n - k + 1$ coverages of this area is

$$P_k = (1 - e^{-(n-k+1)W/S})\left(\text{erf}^2\frac{s_k}{\sigma\sqrt{2}} - \text{erf}^2\frac{s_{k-1}}{\sigma\sqrt{2}}\right).$$

Thus, P^{**} is given by

$$P^{**} = \sum_{k=1}^{n} P_k = (1 - e^{-W/S})e^{-nW/S}\sum_{k=1}^{n} e^{kW/S}\,\text{erf}^2\frac{s_k}{\sigma\sqrt{2}}.$$

Using formula (28), P^{**} may be written in the form of equation (29).

9. RETIRING SQUARE SEARCH FOR A MOVING TARGET: IMPLEMENTATION OF SECTION 7

The situation described in theoretical terms in Section 7 will now be given a practical operational implementation, which is, conveniently, by the use of a retiring square search. The initial ($t = 0$) probability density being the Gaussian one (20), the target's speed u being known, but not its direction, (equiprobable over 360°), the density $p(x, y, t) = f(r, t)$, t hours later, has been shown in Chapter 5, Section 4, to be given by (12) (graphed in Fig. 5-3) and for large t by (14) (assuming no alerting of the hostile target; cf. the next to the last paragraph in the introductory part of this chapter). Using u in place of w, these formulas become

(31) $$f(r, t) = \frac{1}{2\pi\sigma^2}e^{-(r^2+u^2t^2)/2\sigma^2}I_0\left(\frac{rut}{2}\right) \sim \frac{e^{-(r-ut)^2/2\sigma^2}}{2\pi\sigma\sqrt{2\pi utr}},$$

$$\sim \frac{e^{-(r-ut)^2/2\sigma^2}}{2\pi\sigma ut\sqrt{2\pi}}, \qquad \frac{utr}{\sigma^2}\text{ large, } r - ut \text{ close to zero.}$$

From the statements made in the last paragraph and the results of the preceding section we can construct a search for large values of the time T that has elapsed from the time of fix to the initiation of the search. In order to obtain the maximum probability of detection per unit time, the first circuit should be flown on the peak of the distribution (the peak is *circular*—it is the top of a ring); the second circuit a distance S as given in equation (23) inside or outside—say outside—the peak; the third, a distance S inside the peak; the fourth, a distance $2S$ outside the peak; etc. Since the peak of the distribution moves out approximately at the speed of the target, the ideal track on each circuit is an equiangular or logarithmic spiral.

We shall approximate each circuit by four legs with 90-degree turns, as shown in Fig. 8-8. Let the lengths of the legs be L_1, L_2, L_3, etc., and let the corresponding distances of the legs from the point of fix be r_1, r_2, r_3, etc. The time required for the aircraft to fly from A to B is $(r_2 + r_1)/v$, whereas the time required for the target to move from distance r_1 to distance r_2 from the point of fix is $(r_2 - r_1)/u$. The aircraft will just keep up with the target if these times are equal. In this way we find

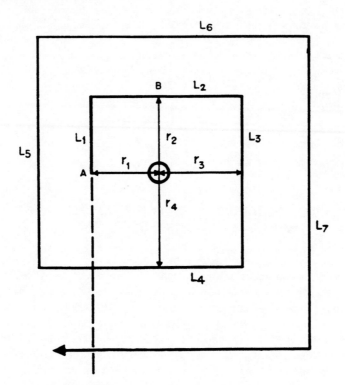

Fig. 8-8. Retiring search.

that

$$r_2 = mr_1, \; r_3 = mr_2, \; r_4 = mr_3,$$

where

$$m = \frac{v+u}{v-u}.$$

If we were to make $r_5 = mr_4$, the fifth leg would duplicate the first leg in space relative to the target. To make the fifth leg lie S miles outside the first leg in relative space, we must determine r_5 so that

$$\frac{r_5 + r_4}{v} = \frac{r_5 - r_4 - S}{u},$$

from which we find

(32)   where $$r_5 = mr_4 + a,$$

$$a = \frac{vS}{v-u}.$$

Continuing in this way, we obtain

$$r_2 = mr_1 \qquad r_8 = mr_7$$
$$r_3 = mr_2 \qquad r_9 = mr_8 - 2a$$
$$r_4 = mr_3 \qquad r_{10} = mr_9$$
(33)
$$r_5 = mr_4 + a \qquad r_{11} = mr_{10}$$
$$r_6 = mr_5 \qquad r_{12} = mr_{11}$$
$$r_7 = mr_6 \qquad r_{13} = mr_{12} + 3a, \text{ etc.}$$

A first approximation to r_1 is uT. However, the approximation to the spiral by straight legs requires that r_1 be slightly less than this value. Equating the average distance of the aircraft to the average distance of the peak of the distribution from the point of fix, the average being with respect to time spent by the aircraft on a leg of the plan, we obtain

$$r_1 = 0.9uT.$$

Since any changes of course of the target will reduce the outward component of its velocity and since the second circuit is to be flcwn outside the first circuit, we shall reduce r_1 still further and take

(34)
$$r_1 = 0.8uT.$$

Using the equation (33) and the obvious relations between the lengths of the legs and their distances from O, we have

$$L_1 = mr_1 \qquad L_7 = mL_6$$
$$L_2 = mL_1 + r_1 \qquad L_8 = mL_7 - 2a$$
$$L_3 = mL_2 \qquad L_9 = mL_8$$
$$L_4 = mL_3 + a \qquad L_{10} = mL_9 - 2a$$
$$L_5 = mL_4 \qquad L_{11} = mL_{10}$$
$$L_6 = mL_5 + a \qquad L_{12} = mL_{11} + 3a, \text{ etc.}$$

where r_1 and a are given by equations (32) and (34).

The search plan above has been devised for large values of T. For small values of T two questions arise:

1. What is the lower limit T_1 of T for which the search plan for large values of T may be used without any essential decrease in the probability of detection for a given amount of searching?

2. For T less than T_1, what modifications of the plan above for large values of T will give an essential increase in the probability?

The curves of Fig. 5-3 of Chapter 5 do not answer these questions. It is seen that when t is less than σ/u the distribution does not differ much from the initial distribution. However, there is a very rapid change in the distribution as t increases from σ/u to $2\sigma/u$. For t greater than $2\sigma/u$ the distribution has its maximum at

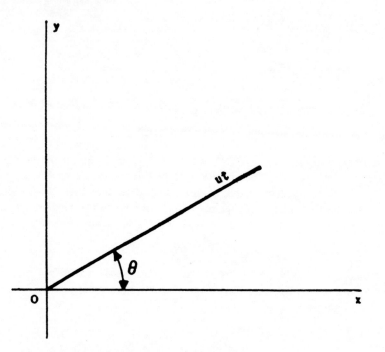

Fig. 8-9. The coordinate system for retiring search.

approximately $r = ut$ and moves outward at the speed of the target. This transition period between an essentially stationary distribution and a distribution moving at the speed of the target makes the problem difficult. ($u = w$ cf. Fig. 5-3)

The following derivation of equation (31) suggests a method of handling the problem. In terms of the rectangular coordinates (x, y) shown in Fig. 8-9 the initial distribution is

$$f(x, y) = \frac{1}{2\pi\sigma^2} e^{-(x^2+y^2)/2\sigma^2}.$$

If the target were known to travel at speed u in the direction θ, the distribution at time t would be

$$F(x, y; t, \theta) = \frac{1}{2\pi\sigma^2} e^{-(1/2\sigma^2)(x - ut\cos\theta)^2 + (y - ut\sin\theta)^2};$$

in other words, distribution (20) with a simple change of origin (translation). If, on the other hand, the target motion is random in direction, the distribution at time t is

$$f(x, y; t) = \frac{1}{2\pi} \int_0^{2\pi} F(x, y; t, \theta)\, d\theta$$

$$= \frac{1}{2\pi\sigma^2} e^{-(r^2 + u^2 t)/2\sigma^2} \cdot \frac{1}{2\pi} \int_0^{2\pi} e^{utr/\sigma^2 \cos(\theta - \alpha)}\, d\theta,$$

where $r^2 = x^2 + y^2$ and $\tan \alpha = y/x$. Using $\theta - \alpha$ as a new variable of integration and noting that the integral of a function of $\cos \theta$ from $-\alpha$ to $2\pi - \alpha$ is equal to the integral of the same function from 0 to 2π, we obtain the distribution given in equation (31).

For a given search plan and an assumed law of detection, we can apply the method above to find the searched distribution at any time t. We first find the effect of the searching upon the distribution function $F(x, y; t, \theta)$ and then average with respect to θ. To approximate this process, choose a small number of equally spaced directions θ from 0 to 2π, the number depending upon the degree of approximation desired. For each θ write on coordinate paper numbers proportional to the initial distribution and think of this distribution as moving in the direction θ. Then lay out the search plan relative to this distribution up to the time at which the distribution is to be examined. From the assumed law of detection, multiply the distribution numbers by the probability that the target will not be detected, taking into account the number of legs on which detection may occur and the distances from these legs. The result will represent the searched distribution for a given θ. The average distribution then can be obtained by averaging the numbers representing the searched distributions for each position relative to the point of fix and a given direction of reference.

In applying the method above it was assumed that four directions would give sufficient accuracy. A check was run by computing a distribution with four directions and with eight directions. It was found that the two distributions did not differ very much. Using a number of values for t and S, search plans were laid out and tested as follows: The first circuit was decided upon from the curves of Fig. 5-3, Chapter 5. Thereafter, each circuit was determined by examining the distribution at the end of the previous circuit. The following results were obtained.

1. If $T > \sigma/u$, the original plan for large values of T is nearly optimum.

2. If $T < \sigma/u$, the plan for large values of T is fairly good and may be used if the additional complication of another plan is not acceptable. However, an appreciable improvement can be obtained by slight modifications. Lay out the plan as in Fig. 8-8 with

$$
\begin{aligned}
L_1 &= mr_1 & L_7 &= mL_6 \\
L_2 &= mL_1 + r_1 & L_8 &= mL_7 + a_2 \\
L_3 &= mL_2 & L_9 &= mL_8 \\
L_4 &= mL_3 + a_1 & L_{10} &= mL_9 + a_2 \\
L_5 &= mL_4 & L_{11} &= mL_{10} \\
L_6 &= mL_5 + a_1 & L_{12} &= mL_{11} + a_3, \text{ etc.}
\end{aligned}
$$

and determine r_1, a_1, a_2, etc., as follows:

(35)
$$
r_1 = \frac{S}{m^2 + 1},
$$

$a_1 = a_2 = \ldots = a_k = vS/(v - u)$, $a_{k+1} = -(k + 2)a_1$, $a_{k+2} = +(k + 3)a_1$, $a_{k+3} = -(k + 4)a_1$, etc., where k is the positive integer nearest $2ut/S$. Here r_1 has been chosen so that L_1 and L_3 are separated by a distance S. This scheme seemed to be the best possible for the first circuit. The succeeding circuits then are flown outside this circuit until the point is reached at which it is more profitable to search on the inside of the distribution. If case T is so small that $2uT < S$, a slight improvement can be obtained by decreasing a_1 by 10 or 20 percent.

In the case of this section it is assumed that the target speed u is known exactly. The question naturally arises as to how much the probability of detection is affected by an error Δu in estimating u. From the asymptotic approximation to $f(r, t)$ for large values of t it is seen that the distribution function will be multiplied approximately by the factor $\exp(-t^2\Delta u^2/2\sigma^2)$. This is a very rough estimate of the factor by which the probability of detection will be multiplied. This, if $t\Delta u$ is small compared with σ, the probability of detection is not affected very much.

The effect of a speed distribution upon the target distribution can be obtained in the usual way. Let $g(u)$ be the probability density in speed. Then

$$\int_0^\infty g(u)\,du = 1$$

and the target distribution at time t is

$$\int_0^\infty g(u) \cdot f(r, t)\,du.$$

It is evident from the way in which u is involved in $f(r, t)$ that this integral will be difficult to compute for any continuous function $g(u)$ which represents a reasonable speed distribution. Consequently, the distribution curve was plotted from the curves of Fig. 5-3, Chapter 5, for particular values of t using the speed distribution

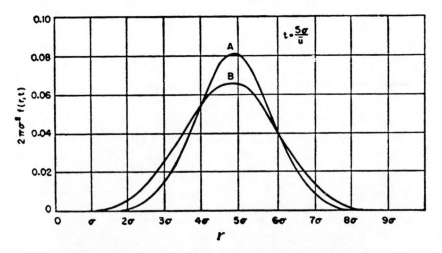

Fig. 8-10. Distribution curves for two assumed distributions of target speed. A: assumed speed $\bar{u}$ only. B: speed of $\bar{u}$, $0.8\bar{u}$, $1.2\bar{u}$ with speed $\bar{u}$ times as likely as $0.8\bar{u}$ or $1.2\bar{u}$.

function

$$g(u) = 0.25 \text{ for } u = 0.8\bar{u}$$
$$= 0.50 \text{ for } u = \bar{u}$$
$$= 0.25 \text{ for } u = 1.2\bar{u}$$

where $\bar{u}$ is the assumed speed. This curve for $t = 5\sigma/\bar{u}$ and the corresponding curve of Fig. 5-3, Chapter 5, are shown in Fig. 8-10. The new distribution curve has a smaller maximum value than the original distribution and is spread out more. However, the difference between the two distributions is not sufficient to justify any changes in the search plans.

In recent years the principles developed in the previous chapters have had many practical and effective applications, particularly to stationary under-water targets. For a brief account (with detailed references) to the searches for the H-bomb lost in the Mediterranean near Palomares (1966), for the missing United States nuclear submarine Scorpion (1968) and for wrecks and ordnance in clearing the Suez Canal, see L. D. Stone [1]; for recent presentation of methods based on computers, see Daniel H. Wagner Associates [2].

REFERENCES

1. Stone, L. D., 1975, *Theory of Optimal Search*, Academic Press, N. Y. pp. xi–xiii.
2. Daniel H. Wagner Associates, 1978. A Report made to the Office of Naval Research (ONR)— "Numerical Optimization of Search for a Moving Target."

Chapter 9

Sonar Screens: Old Examples and New Developments

When a surface formation of ships, such as a merchant convoy, military supply group, or task force, is transiting waters infested with hostile submarines, various methods of defense have been used ever since the submarine became an effective weapon. The defensive methods have evolved during the three major submarine campaigns of history: the U-boats in World Wars I and II, and the United States submarines in the Pacific. One method of defense was *avoidance* of places where the submarines were presumed to be gathering (through knowledge gained by methods of long-range observations, fixes, etc., and also by espionage and code breaking, the importance of which operations during World War II has been made public only since 1970). Another method was the use of *screens* formed of surface and air escorts, for both detection and attack on submarines approaching to firing positions. The traditional screens were of two types: *sonar screens* for either listening (used in World War I) or echo-ranging (chiefly in World War II); and *air escort* which, in addition to detecting and attacking surfaced submarines (or those otherwise giving evidence of their presence to aircraft), could *keep them down*. (Since the submarines of those times had restricted submerged endurance, and speed of about six knots, this constrained their operations severely.) More aggressive methods were the hunter-killer groups and direct attack on submarine pens. Furthermore, barriers of mine fields were applied successfully in World War I, and the use of antisubmarine submarines showed effectiveness in World War II.

The present chapter is devoted to sonar screens and is given concrete illustrations by their use in World War II. Any screen must be fitted to its precise task, and this in turn reposes on a set of assumptions of a highly specific sort applying to a particular historical era. This fact, together with the massive documentation available, has led us to concentrate on that war. Moreover, *the basic lines of the tactical analysis and reasoning are submitted as being far more general than that particular case.* To bring this out, we conclude (in Section 7) by casting a glance at certain generalities implied by the well-known state of more recent technology: submarines of high speed and endurance, cruise missiles, long ranges of detection, and the need for and kinematics of *sprint-and-drift* screening platforms. While avowedly leaving out a host of "special devices" and their implications, it will be sufficient to illustrate general principles—and keep the present book within its proper scope.

1. TORPEDO DANGER ZONES AND HIT PROBABILITIES

With World War II equipment, submerged submarines can only be detected at sufficient range by hydrophone or echo-ranging and can be located with sufficient accuracy only by echo-ranging. This detection must occur as far as possible from the convoy, both for its safety against torpedoes (whose ranges may exceed those of sonar detection) and to facilitate attacks on detected submarines. Consequently, it is necessary that the sonar equipment be carried on highly maneuverable and armed naval units of a relatively expendable nature, such as destroyers or destroyer escorts, which are to be appropriately stationed at a suitable distance from the convoy. Such a disposition of units is called a *sonar screen*. It has the dual function of detection and subsequent attack.

The first step in designing such a screen is to determine the region to be defended: a geometrical figure in the plane moving along with the surface formation. Since in World War II the torpedo was the longest range weapon of a submerged submarine, in designing antisubmarine screens it was also essential to determine the areas from which the submarine has a good chance of scoring a torpedo hit upon one of the units to be screened. Speaking loosely, the *torpedo danger zone* about an individual ship or group of ships is the region (thought of as moving along with the ships, i.e., it is fixed relative to them) within which a torpedo must be fired if it is to have any chance of scoring a hit. The shape and size of the zone will of course depend on the speed and type of the torpedo, as well as the speed and disposition of the ships. Speaking more precisely, there is a danger zone *for each given probability P.* It is the region from which the torpedo must be fired in order to have a chance not less than P of scoring a hit. It is bounded by a closed curve containing the ships, which is the locus of points from which the torpedo must be fired in order to have the given probability P of hitting. Such curves, one for each value of P, are the level lines of the *probability function* $p(r, \theta)$ and have as equation $p(r, \theta) = P$. The probability function $p(r, \theta)$ is the value of the probability of scoring a hit by a torpedo fired from the point of polar coordinates (r, θ) with respect to the reference point in the formation of screened ships (and in space moving along with them). It is a 2-parameter family of probabilities—not a density.

It becomes, therefore, our first object to evaluate this function $p(r, \theta)$. The present section is devoted to the description of various methods for doing this; subsequent sections, to carrying out the details in representative special cases. Modern computers could have greatly facilitated the process.

The primary factor involved in the determination of the enemy's chance of success $p(r, \theta)$ is the type of weapon he uses. If the lethal coverage of the weapon is high, the overall chance of success is correspondingly great. Consider, for example, three types of torpedo. The first runs at a 50-foot depth and explodes after a given length of run; the second, at 5 feet and explodes on contact; the third, at 5 feet, exploding on contact but is provided with a homing device such that whenever it passes within 500 yards of a ship it will home onto it and score a hit. It is obvious that the first will have a rather small lethal coverage, since only a ship near a certain point will be affected by the explosion. The coverage of the second is greater because any ship along the entire run of the torpedo may be hit. The homing feature of the third will give it by far the greatest coverage because the ships need be only within 500 yards of the torpedo track for a hit to be scored. These cases can be demonstrated qualitatively by a diagram like that of Fig. 9-1. The areas are shown for a torpedo proceeding at right angles to the ships. The areas shown have the property that any ship whose center lies in the area will be hit by the torpedo. For case (1) the area covered is slightly larger than the plan view of the ship, since a torpedo exploding up to about ten yards away might sink the ship.

Lethal coverage alone does not determine the enemy's chance of a hit. Firing errors must be taken into account, and if the errors are so great that there is only a

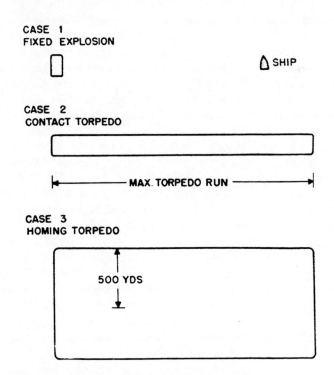

Fig. 9-1. Lethal coverage for various torpedoes.

small probability that the target will lie in the lethal area, the chance of a hit is correspondingly small. For any given accuracy, however, the weapon with the larger lethal coverage will be the more effective.

The foregoing discussion applies only to a single target. When fired at a convoy or group of ships, the torpedo will be successful if it hits any member of the group, i.e., if any of them lies in its lethal area. In general, the torpedo will actually be fired at a particular ship, but it may miss that ship and hit another one purely by chance. For long-range torpedoes fired at large convoys, the chance of such an event may be quite considerable. In such a case a torpedo may well be fired as a *browning shot* from a fair distance, aimed at the convoy as a whole on the chance of a random hit. Because of the importance of browning shots with large, closely spaced convoys, the probability of securing a hit on a merchant convoy is quite different from that on a single ship. The following discussion will deal with the case of the large convoy. The probability of hitting a single ship will be discussed in detail (in connection with the case of the task force) later in this chapter.

2. THE PROBABILITY OF SCORING A HIT ON A CONVOY WITH A SINGLE TORPEDO

While it has been the general practice to fire torpedoes in salvo, the probability that a salvo of a given number of torpedoes will hit, sink, or damage (to a given extent) a ship in the convoy, depends on *the probability of scoring a hit with a single torpedo*. It depends also, of course, on the assumed law of damage produced by a given number of hits (the damage being different, e.g., for merchantmen and for battleships). The one-torpedo probability becomes, therefore, the fundamental quantity to be found as a preliminary to any study of the probability of damage to convoys.

In this section, several methods applied in World War II of estimating this probability of a single torpedo hit will be described. The data from which such computations start are based on 1) the structure of the convoy, 2) the position of the firing point, and 3) the velocities of the units involved. And since the computation must be repeated for a large number of firing positions, an essential requirement is simplicity and speed of computation.

The first method is purely graphical and involves no computational difficulties beyond mere counting. We draw the convoy to scale with each ship of proper size and position. Radiating from the firing point, we draw a set of straight torpedo paths in convoy space, so chosen as to be spaced in angle with an angular density corresponding to the dispersion or error that it is intended to assume. If, for instance, twenty torpedo paths are to be drawn and the angular distribution is considered normal (Gaussian), they would be drawn at angles that divide the normal curve into equal areas, as shown in Fig. 9-2.

Thus we consider each track drawn as having a probability of 1/20 that a torpedo aimed at angle $= 0°$ will actually run along it. By superimposing the torpedo diagram on the convoy and counting the number of torpedo paths that hit

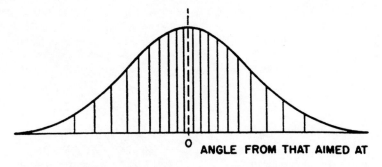

O **ANGLE FROM THAT AIMED AT**

Fig. 9-2. Torpedo firing errors.

ships, we can estimate the chance of a hit. In the example shown in Fig. 9-3, six out of 20 score hits so that the probability of a hit from that firing point is 30 percent.

In deciding on the probability of a hit from any particular point, however, it is necessary to pick out the submarine's best shot, whether it should aim at the ship as shown in Fig. 9-3 or at the closer one at the head of the starboard column, which presents a less favorable target aspect. It is usually possible to pick out the best shot by eye after a little experience, but sometimes both possibilities must be counted.

This method is extremely simple and direct, but it has a number of disadvantages. In the first place, it involves careful drawing and positioning of the diagrams. A great deal of inspection of diagrams is required. Since only a rather small number of torpedo paths can be drawn conveniently, the values are accurate only to the nearest 5 percent and may show considerable fluctuations for very small changes in firing position or aiming angle. In addition the estimated probability shows humps and valleys due to the screening effect of a regular arrangement of ships. From certain angles one ship hides a number behind it, while from slightly different ones all are presented as targets. The arrangement of ships in any actual convoy is not orderly enough to show such an effect, and therefore such variations must be smoothed out more or less arbitrarily in arriving at a final result: the level curves shown in Fig. 9-4.

The choice of torpedo firing error function depends on torpedo and predictor characteristics and firing doctrines; it will not be discussed here. It should be pointed out, however, that this error depends in general on the track angle of the torpedo, the angular error being small from ahead, large from astern. The length of torpedo path in *convoy space* is also variable—long from ahead, short from astern. When the convoy fired at is large, the variation in firing error is not very important and can be neglected quite satisfactorily, but the variation in track length must be taken into account, as shown in Fig. 9-5, which is based on the same constructions of relative velocities used so often in Chapter 2 [cf., e.g., Fig. 2-7(B)]; Fig. 9-3 conforms to this requirement. Since the chance of a random hit on a ship not aimed at contributes a considerable part to the total hitting probability, the variation of the error in aiming is relatively unimportant. This contribution depends on track length but not on aiming error.

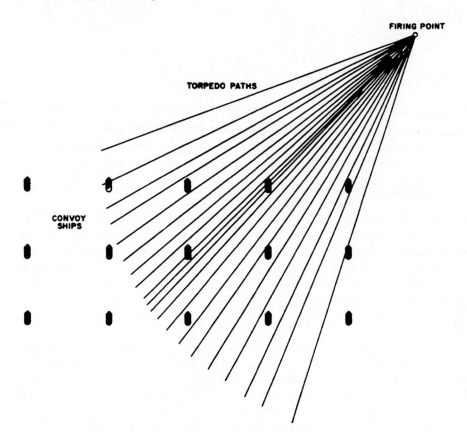

Fig. 9-3. Convoy and possible torpedo paths.

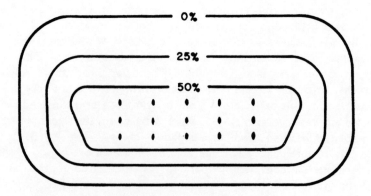

Fig. 9-4. Typical probability of hit contours.

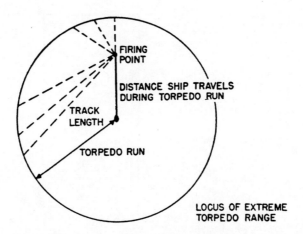

Fig. 9-5. Torpedo track length L in convoy space.

An obvious extension of this simple counting method can be used to reduce the fluctuations in calculated probability of hitting that are caused by the screening effect of a regular lattice of ships. We need only consider the possibility of irregularity in the convoy formation, that is, of ships being somewhat out of their proper convoy station. This can be accounted for by making each ship a "diffuse target" of length ℓ equal to the ship's length L, plus the amount the ship varies in position (thought of, for simplicity, as a fixed amount) relative to the ship's position as aimed at. Then the probability that a torpedo passing through the diffuse target will actually hit the ship is taken as $p = L/\ell$.

If we now consider the ith torpedo path ($i = 1, 2, \ldots, m$; m being 20 in the previous example) and the jth diffuse target ($j = 1, 2, \ldots, n$; n being the number of ships in convoy), we can define a number h_{ij} as the possibility that a torpedo traveling along the ith path will pass through the jth *diffuse* target. From a diagram analogous to Fig. 9-3, we evaluate the h_{ij} as being equal to either 1 or 0 by inspection (Fig. 9-6). Then the probability that a torpedo following the ith path will hit the jth *ship* is $p_{ij} = h_{ij}L/\ell$.

Hence the probability of *one* hit on the ith path being identical with that of *at least one* hit on the ith path is

$$p_i = 1 - \prod_{j=1}^{n} \left(1 - p_{ij}\right).$$

And the overall probability of a hit from the particular firing point is

$$p = \frac{1}{m} \sum_{i=1}^{m} \left[1 - \prod_{j=1}^{n} \left(1 - p_{ij}\right)\right].$$

This probability function is considerably smoother and more realistic than that obtained by the simple counting method. The diffuse target method is considerably more laborious, however, and involves a good deal of arithmetical calculation—drastically reduced, of course, by using modern computers.

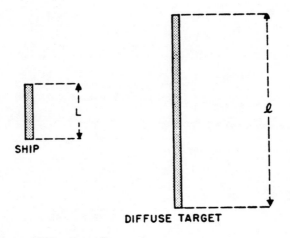

Fig. 9-6. "Diffuse target."

In addition to the three types of straight-run torpedoes having the lethal coverages or swept areas shown in Fig. 9-1, it was necessary in World War II to evaluate the effects of *curly* torpedoes: those which, after a straight run to the convoy, were programmed to *zigzag*, to *circle*, or to take some similarly irregular path through the convoy. Their distinguishing effect was thus that of a browning shot.

Many methods based on special assumptions were applied to find their hit probabilities $p(r, \theta)$ and the corresponding contours were traced. These are given in detail in the 1946 edition of *Search and Screening*. The general conclusion of that work is that the final and tactically useful results are quite insensitive to the "fine structure" of the assumptions. If curly torpedoes were judged to impose a threat in the future—and if Monte Carlo machine simulations were ruled out as being too expensive in time, money, or rigidity in their dependence on questionable assumptions—a good "rough and ready" evaluation could be made by reasoning as in Chapter 3, Section 6, and deriving an exponential approximation to a survival probability—here, survival from hitting, not from detecting.

Figure 9-7 shows the *swept area* of a zigzag torpedo, the areas corresponding to the lethal areas in Fig. 9-1. Denote it by B. Under the natural assumptions of random relations of the ship positions and torpedo path, the probability that a single particular ship in the convoy in the region of area A will be hit is B/A. Under the same assumptions of mutual disorder, the probability that the torpedo will score no hits when A contains n ships is $(1 - B/A)^n$. Introducing the ship density $N = n/A$ or ships per unit area, the probability of at least one hit is $1 - (1 - NB/n)^n$, which for the large values that we may assume of n is very close to $1 - e^{-NB}$. Figure 9-7 makes the computation of B in terms of relative velocities, etc. self-explanatory.

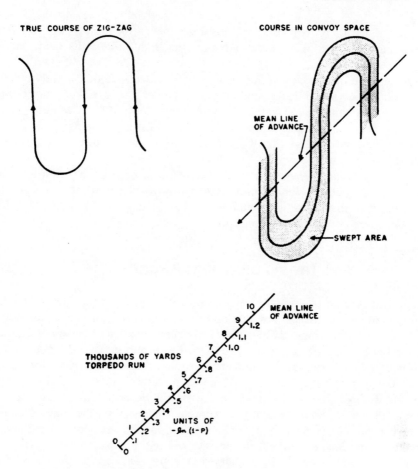

Fig. 9-7. Sweep rate for zigzag torpedo.

3. THE PROBABILITY OF HITTING A SINGLE SHIP OF A TASK FORCE

A task force represents a very different case from a merchant convoy. First, there are many fewer ships and their mutual spacing is much greater. Second, their military values are very different, usually containing one or possibly two *high-value* ships, such as aircraft carriers, the other units being present mainly to defend them. Third, their maneuvers are very different from those of convoys: they are either sailing at high speed, thus providing, during World War II, a considerable degree of protection from submarines; or they are discharging or recovering air-craft, creating very special problems. Their composition is heterogeneous. In addition to carriers, the task force includes antiaircraft cruisers, and destroyers provided with antiaircraft and antisubmarine weapons (and, in World War II, included aircraft for combat air patrol (CAP) and for antisubmarine patrol (ASP)). The classical formation during World War II was circular, the high value units being in the middle.

The 1946 edition of *Search and Screening* gave detailed methods, mainly graphical, but with some probabilistic modifications. Under the stress of the existing conditions of that time, there was little opportunity to verify the validity of the somewhat ad hoc probabilistic assumptions: they were used mainly as a test of sensitivity of the final results, after which verifications the graphical methods were used almost exclusively.

In view of the great changes that have taken place, both in the offensive and defensive, such as guided weapons and sprint-and-drift platforms, it would not be profitable to set forth the historic methodology for finding $p(r, \theta)$ any further. See Section 7 for more contemporary concepts.

4. THE PLACING OF THE SCREEN

The design and placing of a sonar screen is controlled by two main factors: the hit probability contours (under the assumption of either one or a salvo of N torpedoes fired), $p(r, \theta) = P$, delimiting the *torpedo danger zones* of various orders of danger, P, and the limited approach regions. Since in the former $p(r, \theta)$ is a conditional probability of a hit, given that the submarine reaches the position (r, θ), the actual danger to the formation is conditioned on the possibility that it will be able to reach such positions. Now we have seen in Chapter 2, Section 2, that if the speed u available to the submarine in making its approach is less than the speed v of the surface formation, a large part of the ocean is not a possible locus of starting points from which it can reach effective firing positions. For this it has to be in a forward sector, bounded on the sides by lines inclined at $\pm \sin^{-1}(u/v)$ with the direction of motion, called the *region of limited approach*.

In World War II, the speed u available to the submarine in approach to torpedo firing positions was the submerged speed, of about 6 knots, and hence less than even moderate convoy speeds. In more recent times, the submerged speeds, particularly of nuclear-powered submarines, has increased so greatly that this constraint would seem to have disappeared. However, in proceeding at high enough speeds to overtake a modern surface formation, their increased noise may make them unacceptably detectable by modern equipment, and hence constitute a severely limiting factor. Thus, the discussion to follow has more than historical or illustrative value. We shall return to such matters in Section 7, where some reasons for updating sonar screening procedure are given. In what follows we return to the earlier restrictions. Figure 9-8 shows schematically the principal elements upon which the sonar screens of World War II were based. The curve $p(r, \theta) = C$ around the convoy encloses the torpedo danger zone of order C.

Referring to Fig. 9-8, it is obvious that the task that the sonar screen has to accomplish is *at most* to intercept submarines that come from the submerged approach region R_0 (here R_0 is drawn corresponding to $p(r, \theta) = C$, the limit of the

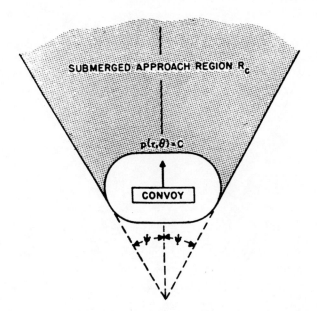

Fig. 9-8. Submerged approach region.

torpedo danger zone); other submarines do not constitute an immediate danger, as long as they remain submerged. Inasmuch as the line efficiency of the screen is greater the more escorts there are per unit length, the best way to intercept submarines entering the torpedo danger zone from R_0 is to dispose them in the shortest line connecting the limiting approach lines and lying outside the danger zone and inside R_0. Such a line is constructed by stretching a string around the forward part of the danger zone, its two ends being on the limiting approach lines and perpendicular to them ($S_0 S_0'$ in Fig. 9-9).

Such a screen would give 100 percent protection against submerged submarines if it were perfectly tight, i.e., if it had 100 percent line efficiency. Unfortunately the distances involved require $S_0 S_0'$ to be so long that no normally available number of escorts can provide a screen with anything like such a high line efficiency. The efficiency might, for example, turn out to be only 15 percent, which represents the only chance of preventing the submarine from approaching to within point blank torpedo range. Then consideration must be given to defending less of the torpedo danger zone with a shorter, and hence tighter, screen. If, for example, $C = 10$ percent, the level curve $p(r, \theta) = C = 0.1$ being smaller than $p(r, \theta) = 0$, a screen along $S_C S_C'$ would be shorter and hence tighter than $S_0 S_0'$. If its line efficiency were, for example, 25 percent, the submarine would have a *less* favorable chance of hitting the convoy than if the screen $S_0 S_0'$ were used. If it fires from outside the screen, its chance of a hit is, at most, 10 percent; if it attempts to cross the screen so as to be able to fire from a very favorable position, its chance of success is possibly as great as 75 percent. Obviously the submarine would do the latter

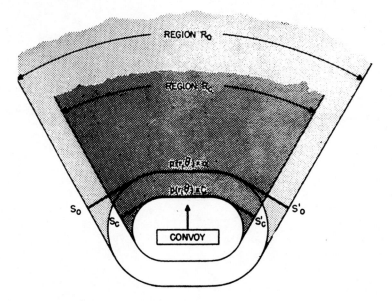

Fig. 9-9. Placement of screen.

(assuming that it is indifferent to its own safety and merely tries to maximize the chance of a hit). But in the previous case this course of action would have given an 85 percent chance of success for the submarine. Thus $S_C S'_C$ would be a better screen (Fig. 9-9). This contraction of the screen must, however, not be carried too far. If $C = 80$ percent, the level curve $p(r, \theta) = C = 0.8$ might well give a high (e.g., 90 percent) line efficiency. The submarine would simply fire from outside the screen and not attempt to penetrate it and would have as much as an 80 percent chance of making a hit. What value of C must be chosen to give optimum results?

This question was answered (about 1942) by applying the principle of the minimax, as in Chapter 7, Section 8.

Appendix G provides an outline of the physical facts of acoustic detection by a single element in a screen. The passive listening and active echo-ranging curves in Figs. G-10 and G-11 plot detection probabilities (essentially for a single glimpse; see Chapter 3, Section 2) as a function of true range. To obtain the lateral range curves under the assumption of independence (Chapter 3, Section 1), the usual methods of Chapter 3, Section 4, are applied (graphically or by numerical computation when no analytic expressions are known). To find the line efficiency (tightness) of the screen with a given spacing of units, the methods of that chapter are applied. Unfortunately for the simplicity of this method, a considerable body of operational and other evidence exists casting doubt on the assumption of independence. We must regard its results as somewhat crude approximations. In spite of various ad hoc methods of taking the dependence into account, little of proven worth has been accomplished. Screening is intrinsically a crude operation!

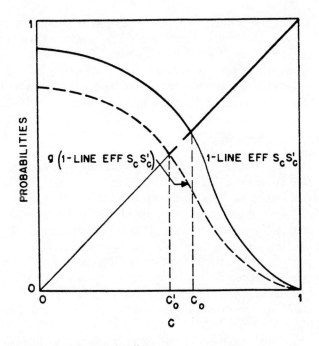

Fig. 9-10. Optimum tactics diagram.

Assuming always that the only consideration governing the way a submarine behaves is its desire to make a hit and that it has no primary concern for its own safety, then its best course of action is to attempt to penetrate the screen $S_C S_C'$ whenever $1 - $ (line efficiency of $S_C S_C'$) is *greater* than C, and to fire from just outside the screen if C is *greater* than $1 - $ (line efficiency of $S_C S_C'$). In either case its probability of scoring a hit (assuming that once it gets through the screen undetected it can certainly make a hit) is the *greater* of the two quantities $1 - $ (line efficiency of $S_C S_C'$), or C. The situation is visualized by the graph of each of these quantities regarded as functions of C (Fig. 9-10). The submarine's chance of hitting is evidently represented by the heavy line, i.e., $1 - $ (line efficiency $S_C S_C'$) for values of C less than its value, C_0, at the intersection of the two curves, and C itself to the right of C_0. The optimum screen is the one corresponding with the C that gives the submarine the least chance of hitting, $S_{C_0} S_{C_0}'$. This leads to the principle:

To obtain the best screen, use a curve $S_C S_C'$ of the type shown in Fig. 9-9 and bring it in (i.e., increase C) until the chance of crossing it undetected just equals the chance of scoring a hit from a point just outside it.

There are several qualifications to be made before accepting the above result, $S_{C_0} S_{C_0}'$.

First, submarines do give consideration to their own safety. Thus with the screen $S_{C_0} S_{C_0}'$ it would be more favorable to them to fire from outside the screen than to try to cross it. This would continue to be true even with the chance of undetected penetration, i.e., if $1 -$ (line efficiency $S_C S_C'$) is somewhat greater than C. Hence, from this point of view, the "best screen" would be somewhat farther out than $S_{C_0} S_{C_0}'$, just how much farther is difficult to estimate. Exactly the same reasoning can be made in different words, as follows: If we are going to have a certain chance of having one of our ships torpedoed, we would prefer to have a greater chance of getting the submarine; the best $S_C S_C'$ should be a little farther out than $S_{C_0} S_{C_0}'$. In whichever form this reasoning is given, it reposes on the fact that a submarine firing outside the screen is less likely to be attacked than one that tries to cross the screen first.

Second, it is not strictly true that once a submarine has crossed the screen undetected it is sure to score a hit. Again this tends to make the "best screen" somewhat farther out than $S_{C_0} S_{C_0}'$. If the chance of a hit at close range is g, $(0 < g < 1)$, to carry through the preceding reasoning we must replace the graph of $1 -$ (line efficiency $S_C S_C'$) by their product $g[1 -$ (line efficiency $S_C S_C'$)] plotted in the dotted curve of Fig. 9-10, and thus reach the best screen $S_{C_0'} S_{C_0'}'$.

Third, it is implicit that the submarine can fire torpedoes safely right up to the screen line. This was an acceptable assumption for World War II and a decade later, since detection ranges were short. Since then such ranges have so increased that the screen would appropriately be positioned several thousand meters inside the "best screen" line.

Fourth, it was assumed that a submarine encounters the screen with equal probability over its entire length. Yet it is markedly advantageous to the submarine —whether it wishes to penetrate the screen or not—to operate near the sides of the screen so as to facilitate its escape after firing. And the normal tracking procedure used by submarines tends to bring them into contact nearer the front *side* than the front center of a convoy of any size. For both these reasons it is important to avoid lessening the screen's line efficiency near its ends, i.e., abeam.

Fifth, in screening a fast ship or task group that may be zigzagging or maneuvering radically, the limiting approach angle is increased and the limiting lines spread out, and hence the screen must extend through a greater angle off either bow. But the principles remain the same.

The extreme case is that of the fast carrier task force that must be prepared to change its course radically, even to backtrack at short notice (e.g., in order to launch planes into the wind, or to avoid or surprise the enemy, etc.). Circular screens around the whole task force are frequently used in such cases, either with equally spaced escorts, or, more efficiently from the antisubmarine point of view, with closer spacing in the forward parts of the circle.

Even when as radical a measure as a circular distribution is not necessary, all turning of the convoy into unswept waters must be avoided. The screen should be extended in the direction the convoy expects to turn, so as to detect any submarines possibly present therein. This is particularly important in view of the tendency of tracking submarines to accumulate along the flank. In World War II they were surfaced while tracking, but they submerged and became a danger when the convoy turned.

Sixth, the submarine may be supposed to have more than one torpedo, whereas it was assumed implicitly in the foregoing probabilities that only one torpedo was involved. Having n torpedoes would have enlarged the level curves and also increased the damage done by a close-range submarine, and these two effects would affect the screen geometry in opposite directions. The significance of this factor does not become great until the *number* of torpedoes or salvos fired is *different* for submarines outside or inside the screen. A series of analyses conducted by the United States Navy in the 1960s concluded that a diesel submarine penetrating the screen would be able to get off two or three times as many torpedoes while it was in or under the convoy, and in the case of the nuclear submarine, even more. As a result, the development of new convoy formations is appropriate.

These facts emphasize the need of meeting the changing situations—both those that have become apparent in recent times and those that the future will inevitably bring forth—with the same rigorous logic as was applied in the past and illustrated by the foregoing examples.

This raises some general questions of methodology. For one thing, it might be objected that the reasoning upon which the choice of $S_{C_0} S'_{C_0}$ is based appears to assume that the submarine knows the values of the various probabilities involved, a thoroughly unrealistic assumption. But this use of the principle of the minimax (as also in the cases described in Section 8 of Chapter 7) does not invalidate the usefulness of the result. We are merely calculating the chance of success of the submarine if it did the best thing from its point of view. Its ignorance can only result in a—for it—less favorable course of action, thus diminishing its chance of success. Therefore our reasoning subsists but does not attempt to figure on the enemy's making a blunder. Rather than ask whether the submarine would know its best course of action, it is better to turn the question around: if early combat experience reveals a tendency of the submarines to attack at longer than their optimum range—or shows a preference to penetrate too close—then this may be *exploited* by the appropriate adjustment of the position of the screen. To figure in such a chance would carry the discussion to a higher order of tactical complexity than is warranted in the present general exposition.

Furthermore, our method has concentrated attention on the *probability of a hit* by one submarine with one torpedo and shown how to minimize it. Actually one might better aim first at minimizing the number of ships hit or sunk per submarine encounter (submarines using salvos and possibly many sorts of torpedoes, etc.). Then, with the results of that calculation in hand, aim to minimize the number of ships lost per submarine lost. But the present general treatment limits itself to laying down the principles for the plans and studies that dominated United States Navy defense of shipping analyses during the *recent* past.

5. PATROLLING OF STATIONS

When the number of escorts is insufficient to provide even a moderately tight screen without closing to unduly short distances of the convoy, it is customary for the escorts to "patrol their stations," that is, to take a course that causes their position to oscillate about their station sometimes quite a distance (e.g., 500 yards) to the right and then to the left of the point (fixed relative to the convoy) that represents the assigned station. The reasoning upon which this process is based is the following.

When there are too few escorts, the distance between two adjacent ones will be such that a submarine has a very good chance of passing through the screen undetected provided it goes about midway between the escorts; in other words, the screen has "holes." There are two possibilities: Either the submarine knows where such holes are or else it does not. If it does, it can profit by their presence, and thus the strength of the screen will have to be judged by its *weakest* point. If it does not know, it will enter the screen at a randomly chosen point, and thus the strength of the screen would be measured by its *average* strength, i.e., the average of its probability of detection. Now the object of patrolling stations is to deprive the submarine of the possibility of utilizing the holes, since, when it is near the screen, it is proceeding submerged and without being able safely to use its periscope. Of course the patrolling must have an irregular or random character. Thus patrolling the stations makes the second of the above possibilities the actual one. The average tightness of the screen is the valid index of effectiveness, and, low though it may be, it is much higher than the probability of detection in the hole.

Figure 9-11 shows the situation graphically. The ordinate represents the probability of detection at a point along the screen represented by the abscissa. Patrolling randomizes the situation with regard to the submarine, thus replacing the original curve (a) by the average ordinate horizontal line (b). The area under (a) equals that under (b).

The patrolling escort must recognize that in most practical screens it cannot hope to search out its assigned sector as in the barrier patrols described in Chapter 8. This fact is an immediate consequence of the relative velocities involved—the high speed of advance of the defended formation in comparison with the low lateral speed of the patrolling escorts. We reemphasize that the primary benefit of the patrol is the confusion to the submarine because of the different positions and aspects presented by the escorts. These deny the submarine the power to "split the gap" with relative ease, even when the patrolling escorts do not move far from the midpoints of their assigned sectors.

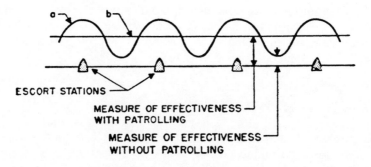

Fig. 9-11. The effect of patrolling of stations.

The advantage of patrolling stations is diminished with the increased speed of approach possible with nuclear submarines, which require fewer exposures of their periscopes for closing to firing range and which create a high relative speed, frequently greater than 30 knots. Furthermore, with modern sonars of increasing power and range, screen effectiveness is diminished as an escort approaches the limit of its sector, closing its neighbor so that their lateral ranges overlap. Taken together, the effect of these factors is that escorts in well designed screens should change course frequently and radically, but be constrained to a distance of about 500 yards from station.

6. PICKETS

The screen considered here is a line screen. One of a different sort and giving an effect of defense in depth (e.g., by alternate staggering of ships) would have the disadvantage of creating wake interference and difficulties of maneuvering. Nevertheless a line screen can be given some of the attributes of defense in depth by supplementing it with escorts stationed as *pickets* (1, 2, 3, 4), Fig. 9-12. These pickets accomplish the following tasks:

1. They act as visual or radar observers, particularly important when air coverage is lacking or very incomplete.
2. They investigate suspicious contacts and aid in attacking targets that may have seen detected by the screen or by having attacked a ship in the convoy: a so-called "flaming datum."

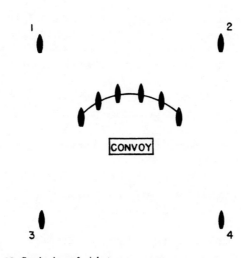

Fig. 9-12. Stationing of pickets.

7. THE NEW FACTORS AND THE NEW SCREENS

The decades elapsed since the close of World War II have seen a scale of technological improvements so vast and so radical that they have seemed to many observers to warrant jettisoning all the experience and operational analyses developed in the earlier era. An extreme view has been expressed that thermonuclear weapons have so altered the military picture that antisubmarine defense of overseas transport, as in the Battle of the Atlantic, will never have an occasion to occur—everything being ended so soon. This view might have been held during the brief period of extreme strategic imbalance, when only one nation or block of friendly nations possessed effective thermonuclear weapons, but with the present balance and spread of this power throughout the major nations of the world, one can take a quite different position: that the last thing any major nation wants to have happen is a thermonuclear war, and that any sizable military action it might take would be confined to very conventional methods, which might well involve adding blockades to other forms of economic pressure. Moreover, it is axiomatic that any position of weakness, such as lack of ability to defend sea-lift, will invite attack upon that very point. For such reasons as these, we deem it to be no waste of time to outline the new factors in the screening operation—in addition to those outlined earlier.

It is necessary—for many reasons—to confine the present scope of discussion to a very few and well-known cardinal points that affect submarine warfare of the present. The three favoring the submarine are the following:

1. High speed and long endurance and ranges of the nuclear-powered submarine. In retrospect, those of previous eras appear as mere submersibles—not submarines at all—having to be surfaced, and therefore subject to detection and attack during most of their mission, and laboring under major constraints when submerged.
2. Long ranges of weapons used by attack submarines. These include improvements in range, guidance, and homing ability of present-day torpedoes, but most spectacularly, those of cruise missiles, of many times the range of torpedoes, which demonstrated their effectiveness in the recent naval battles in the Near East.
3. Long-range detecting ability, whether through the use of satellites or sound channels to detect and locate large surface formations.

The factors favoring the defense against the submarine are the following:

1. Great improvements in hydroacoustic methods of detection, identification, and location of submarines. Passive listening is used, as well as active echo-ranging, which is applied with the modern understanding of the refractive properties of bodies of ocean water.
2. Greater ranges of attack weapons and greater accuracies.
3. Variety of platforms, both for detecting equipment and for weapons of attack. This includes increased ability for their coordination and indeed the whole electronic and computerized "central nervous system" of the operation.

Even from this rather limited "list of truisms" some conclusions can be drawn regarding the design of modern screens.

First, the *weapon danger zone* is much larger than it was in World War II, which was described as the *torpedo danger zone* in Section 1. It includes all points about the surface formation (and moving with the latter) from which a submarine-launched weapon has any chance of hitting an element of the formation; it still requires the evaluation of the hit function $p(r, \theta)$. The evaluation is simplified because of the simple circular nature of the weapon danger zone given in Fig. 2-9, Chapter 2, Section 3, portraying the fact that the high-speed missile is a threat independent of force motion.

However, the advantage of this simplification is more than offset by a new complication. It is important to distinguish between the *absolute* missile range and its *effective* range after detection, classification, and range determination by the attacking submarine have been taken into account. The target positioning for the enemy submarine may be aided by outside intelligence. In the absence of such intelligence, the effective firing range may be a fifth or less than the absolute range, and depends on surface formation speed (noise level) and other factors. As a result the threat extending radially from the formation is highly probabilistic. Mathematically it corresponds to the earlier torpedo hit probability $p(r, \theta)$ in which the fire control solution dominated. Now since the angle of bearing of fire is largely absent within the region of submarine approach, described below, the hit probability is a function $p(r)$; factors other than the fire control solution drive the dependence on range r.

Second, the attacking submarine(s), while capable of a submerged speed equal to or greater than that of the surface formation, will pay for increases in speed beyond very moderate ones (less than the speed of advance of modern convoys) by louder emitted noise, thus greatly increasing its range of detectability by modern sensors. If u is the maximum quiet submerged speed and v the surface craft speed, Fig. 2-9(c) of Chapter 2 gives the picture of the limited approach region when $u < v$; (b), when $u = v$. In case the submarine elects to increase its speed u to attack from any direction, we have 2-9(a), with no restricted approach.

Third, since the boundary of the danger zone, even under considerable restrictions on u, is much longer than could be given a defense by even the most advanced conventional surface units of a sonar screen, detecting the submarine before reaching it necessitates the use of modern long-range passive or active acoustic detectors. Strewing fields of sonobuoys ahead of the formation and using fixed "sterilized" lanes in the ocean have been given detailed study, but we shall confine the present section to cases more akin to the moving surface screens of the earlier sections of this chapter.

Fourth, to exploit their full capability (range, classification, and localization) the hydroacoustic detectors have to be *coupled with the ocean*. This implies more or less deep submergence of a fairly bulky system, and its use at rest or in restricted motion. This whole cycle of its use represents a *delay* in the advance of the platform.

Fifth, in order that the platform bearing the acoustic sensors, which has suffered the periodic delays mentioned above, be able to keep up with the surface formation moving at the speeds contemplated at present, it is necessary that this platform be capable of the operation of *sprint and drift*. "Drift" refers to the speed less than the formation's while going through the detection cycle; "sprint" means the higher speed needed to catch up with it. The earliest platforms considered for this process were helicopters. Later, consideration has been directed to platforms of greater capacity and endurance, particularly *hydrofoil* vessels and *surface-effect ships*.

In light of these considerations, both the placement of the sprint-and-drift screening units and the kinematics of the resulting screen will be very different from those of the simple line screens of the earlier era, described up to now in this chapter. An essential element in their design is the set of *isochrons*, or curves of constant time T taken by a submarine, moving at speed u and on its most direct course, to reach the boundary of the danger zone. The definition and construction of such curves has been given in Chapter 2, Section 3, and illustrated in Fig. 2-9. To exemplify their use in designing a sonar screen, suppose as in Fig. 2-9(c) that $u < v$ so that we have the angular region of limited approach. If a detection cycle takes the time ΔT, the screening units would be stationed on or beyond the ΔT isochron—beyond, if time to prosecute a contact is added. They might be posi-

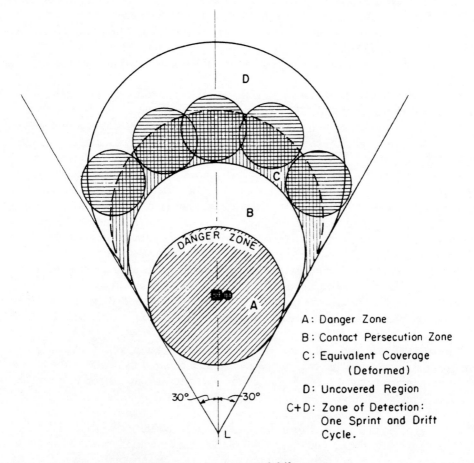

A: Danger Zone

B: Contact Persecution Zone

C: Equivalent Coverage
      (Deformed)

D: Uncovered Region

C+D: Zone of Detection:
        One Sprint and Drift
        Cycle.

Fig. 9-13. Equivalent areas in a sprint-and-drift screen.

tioned farther out, so as to place their detection coverage mainly between the isochrons T_1 and T_2, where $T_2 - T_1 = \Delta T$ and $T_1 \geqslant \Delta T$. Many further details can be worked out to correspond to the structure of the whole operation of detection and attack, etc. An example of a screen is shown in Fig. 9-13 for the case $u < v$, using the construction of isochrons of Fig. 2-9(c).

The evaluation of the tightness of such a screen could be an excessively complicated task. When it is to be done on the basis of operational realism, however, it can be greatly simplified, inasmuch as the specific quantities of all sorts are never known except in the crudest way in any actual situation. We may therefore proceed in three simple steps.

First, we estimate the effective area U covered by one escort unit during a single detection cycle. It is the "equivalent area" (in the sense used so often before in this work) of a *definite detection* law (or πR^2 of a definite range law, of range R) which detects on the average the same proportion of targets in a swarm of uniformly and randomly distributed ones, as the actual sensor. If there are n screening units between the isochrons for T_1 and T_2, and M is the area of the region they bound, evidently nU/M is a crude estimate of the upper limit of the effectiveness of the screen. It has the following interpretation: Suppose that the total area nU could be deformed to fit between isochron T_1 and $T_1' > T_1$, and fill this completely. Then if $T_1' \leqslant T_2$, the above ratio would express the probability of detection when our available detecting power—our quantity of searching effort $\Phi = nU$—is used optimally. Of course if $T_1' > T_1$, the ratio will exceed unity, but—as effort—this will not represent a waste, since it will give repeated chances to observe a target that could have been missed, in spite of the above calculation—which then takes the equivalence of the actual law with the definite detection law beyond its applicability. Crude though this upper estimate is, it can serve a very useful purpose. For if we suppose that nU/M turns out to be very low, we will realize that the screening operation, in the form assumed, is ineffective.

Second, we can obtain a more precise estimate of the screen's effectiveness through the application of the following model, which takes into account much of the inefficiency of overlapping of regions of detection. Suppose a piece of paper of area nU were cut up into very small bits of about the same size, and then sprinkled at random, like confetti, into the region of area M. Elementary and frequently employed reasoning (cf. Chapter 3, Section 6) shows that the expected proportion of M covered by at least one piece of confetti is very approximately $1 - e^{-nV/M}$, a quantity very close to nV/M when the latter is small. Even if some of the detecting regions (e.g., circles of radii R) have parts outside of the isochrons for T_1 and T_2, this can also be included in the area of the paper used, since they also represent areas of exposure of the target at an earlier or later cycle. In fact, this random exponential coverage formula has applicability to the case of "defense in depth" (screening units stationed in farther isochronal regions).

Third, the above exponential expression can often be modified to take advantage of special circumstances occurring at the sides, etc., but even as it stands it is a useful step in a rough appraisal.

In closing, we remark that some of the detecting platforms should be placed rearward of the formation, to detect the submarines that elect to go at high and noisy speeds—as well as for other reasons.

Chapter 10

Aerial Escort During World War II

An important practical application of many of the results established in the mathematical theory in Chapters 1–7 was the World War II design and evaluation of *air escort plans*. As in the two preceding chapters, these involve moving targets executing motions that are too complicated to be reduced to relative rest with respect to a conveniently moving plane (as in the case of steady barrier patrols), and the nature of which can only be inferred from their presumed tactical intent. The aerial escort of a transiting surface formation (to be termed the "convoy") is a supplement to the sonar screen of surface craft (including those performing sprint-and-drift), as explained in the preceding chapter on that subject. The present one is a condensed and altered version of Chapter 9 (Aerial Escort) of the 1946 edition of *Search and Screening*.

The reason for using this World War II illustration, in spite of the changed conditions of the present era, is the same as in the case of the two preceding chapters; it exemplifies a concrete and important operation that was actually carried out, tested, and evaluated, and it can be set forth in detail without security constraints. Furthermore, while the particular assumptions belong to a passed era, the presumable need for scientifically planned air escort of surface formations of the future is still of concern.

This chapter illustrates the development of successful operational plans, step by step: (1) careful theoretical analysis, (2) equally careful mathematical simplifications appropriate in the light of operational considerations, and (3) variations that were evolved as enemy tactics changed or became predictable.

As in the last two chapters, the calculations were carried out "manually." This naturally raises the question of the possible improvements that might have been obtained had modern computers been available. In so many branches of applied mathematics, such computers not only have dramatically facilitated the work, but have made certain investigations possible that could not have been done without them. Actually, however, the calculations were not the hard part of the present task. The greatest difficulties were in obtaining the physical and tactical facts and observational data. The mathematical reasoning based on the latter was of a familiar nature (to any experienced mathematical physicist); computers would have been irrelevant to this process. Once the steps above had been taken, however, modern computers might well have lightened the final work.

In view of the increasingly numerous attempts to short-cut the process described above by using *computer simulation*, it is necessary to emphasize once again the danger of such an approach. No simulation can give trustworthy results unless it is based on the painstaking tactical, physical, and mathematical analysis that certain of its users seem hopeful of avoiding. We have seen too many misleading (or exorbitantly expensive) results of such attempts. In certain cases these have been incorporated into officially sanctioned "models"—viz., computer programs—that are then "run" (possibly after "tuning") when answers are required. The danger of self-deception is all the more insidious because the *conception* of the problem is buried in a computer program—sheltered from that necessary part of the scientific method: rational criticism.

1. THE TACTICAL SITUATION

When a formation of ships (such as a merchant convoy in transit, a task force, or task group in cruising disposition) passes through submarine waters (i.e., waters possibly containing hostile submarines), safety can be increased by accompanying the formation with aircraft (carrier- or land-based) that perform systematic flights in its vicinity. Such flights are the subject of this chapter. They are called the *aerial escort*, the defended ships being termed in all cases the *convoy*. It is to be emphasized that the primary object here is *defensive*—to reduce the danger to the convoy —as contrasted with the primarily *offensive* purpose of flights such as the distant beam searches made by *Aircraft Carrier Escort* (CVE) killer groups, where the destruction of the maximum number of submarines is the primary aim (yet in World War II many U-boats, lured to the convoys, were sunk by these "defensive" escorts). To put it in slightly different terms, if a submarine is present, the success of the aerial escort is measured by its ability to prevent the submarine from damaging the convoy. While the most satisfactory result undoubtedly is the sinking of the submarine, the escort must also be regarded as successful if its mere detection of the submarine permits the convoy to avoid it, or even if its presence induces the submarine to submerge and remain submerged in a region from which no submerged attack upon the convoy can be delivered.

In order to attack a convoy, a submarine must 1) detect the convoy, 2) make an approach (usually with tracking) to firing range of the convoy, (3) fire its weapons effectively, and (4) withdraw to safety. Aerial escort is chiefly instrumental in obstructing the first and second of these operations. Its first function (prevention of detection) can be called the *scouting* effect; its second (prevention of approach), the *screening*.

In any definite situation there will be a maximum range R at which a submarine, using all its facilities, can detect the convoy. Visual detection of a nonsmoking convoy in ideal weather occurs at a distance limited only by the earth's curvature and atmospheric refraction, but it can be greatly lowered by adverse meteorological conditions and increased by convoy smoking. Radar detection of convoys is dependent on the equipment. In World War II it did not exceed good daylight visual detection. Hydrophone ranges depend on sound conditions and sea state, as well as size and speed of convoy. Under World War II conditions they were not much in excess of 15 miles, but under ideal conditions with a large, fast task force they could attain 50 miles. The greatest of all these ranges, R, measured from a reference point O fixed in the convoy and thus taking into account convoy size, had in most cases values between 15 and 30 miles. The circle of radius R and center at the reference point O is the *detection circle*, which may be described as the region inside which submarines have an appreciable chance of detecting the convoy, and outside which they have little.

Figure 10-1, which is drawn relative to the convoy (in which, therefore, reference point O remains fixed), shows the tactically relevant features: the convoy and its surrounding *torpedo danger zone* (shaded; that now becomes the *weapon danger zone*; cf. last section of preceding chapter), *the area of submerged approach* (see Chapter 9), and the detection circle. There is also shown (bounded by dotted lines) the area within which the ships of the convoy and its escort could detect a surfaced submarine. The convoy is heading up the page at the *speed made good* of v knots. The region $ABCD$ is called the *danger zone*. If a submarine has reached it, it is in contact with the convoy and can submerge at will and then make a submerged approach undetected by the aircraft. To reach the danger zone is a usual tactical objective of attacking submarines.

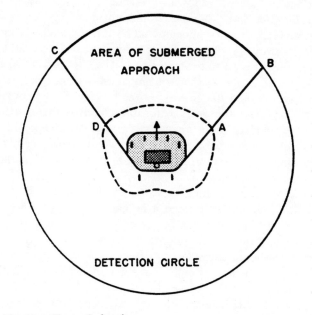

Fig. 10-1. The tactical regions.

The figure is drawn on the assumption that the submarine's submerged speed is less than the convoy's speed. In the contrary case, the solid curve $CDAB$ may have to be drawn much farther back of the torpedo danger zone—corresponding to the locus within which the endurance of the submarine submerged just suffices to close the torpedo danger zone. Or the restriction may not exist, when this endurance is very great. In this case the danger zone will be the ring-shaped area inside the detection circle and outside the dotted curve. (This paragraph in the 1946 edition reflected the knowledge of the advent of certain new types of U-boats then under development: type 21 [snorkeling] and closed-cycle types, Walter boats, etc. Nuclear power now gives submarines unlimited tactical endurance.)

In order to have scouting effectiveness, i.e., in order to prevent the submarine from gaining contact with the convoy (so that it will either not know that the convoy is present, or, in case it has been directed to the convoy by means other than its own immediate detection, have no precise knowledge of the position or course of the latter), it is necessary that the aerial escort fly a sufficient amount directly outside the detection circle, particularly in the forward regions, which are those in which submarines are most likely to be encountered by the circle (Chapter 2, Section 5). A method of evaluating numerically the *scouting* effectiveness of any given flight plan will be set forth in Section 2 below.

In order to have *screening* effectiveness, the escort flights must be made so that the tracking and approach procedures normally carried out by a surfaced submarine are impeded. Essentially this means that entrance to the danger zone must be barred and that this area itself must be covered so that even if a submarine has entered it and submerged, it will have a material chance of being detected should it momentarily surface or otherwise show its presence. The importance of barring the arc BC is due to the fact that a submarine in front of the convoy but unaware of the latter's presence is likely to be encountered by this arc as the latter moves over the water with the convoy, by which time the submarine will detect the convoy and then be in a favorable position to submerge and deliver an attack. The importance of barring AB and CD is due to the fact that these will normally be crossed by submarines that have tracked the convoy on the surface. Such submarines cannot enter the area of submerged approach nearer to the convoy than A or D since they would be detected by surface units, and an attempt to enter beyond B or C would require their loss of contact with the convoy. Methods of evaluating scouting effectiveness are given in Section 2; screening effectiveness is the subject of Sections 3–6.

When aerial escort accomplishing these results is maintained day and night, maximum protection is obtained. Should it be necessary to discontinue the flights at night, it is important that predark flights of a scouting character be made at greater distances around the convoy in order to clear the waters through which the convoy will pass in the night as well as to detect submarines that may be stalking the convoy, intending to close it at night. The characteristics of such flights will be examined in Section 7.

The only practicable flight plans for regular aerial escort (all those flown continuously during a length of time, but excluding predark flights) are *periodic* ones. After the period of T hours the plan of flight is repeated, the paths flown during the next T hours being identical (as seen relative to the convoy) to those of the preceding T hours. This continues as long as the plan is flown. The period T should be of the order of one or two hours. Thus the plot of every regular plan relative to the convoy consists of one or more closed circuits, the whole being flown every T hours. The geographic plot is not closed, but is of an advancing recurrent nature, the length of the recurrent figure flown by each aircraft being T times the aircraft's ground speed (or average ground speed, in case of variations in the latter due to wind or other causes).

One assumption is presupposed in the quantitative probability reasoning concerning any aerial escort plan: that *the submarine does not know the plan*. Otherwise any plan using a normally restricted number of aircraft would be ineffective. Actually, it is difficult to imagine that the enemy could ever obtain sufficiently detailed information concerning the plan to be enabled thereby to penetrate undetected.

2. THE SCOUTING EFFECTIVENESS

A measure of the effectiveness of any aircraft escort plan as a method of scouting is the *probability* it affords of detecting (visually or by radar) submarines that are moving so that they will eventually enter the detection circle—detecting them, that is, before they enter the circle. It is assumed that these submarines are proceeding surfaced (or snorkeling) in a straight course at speed u. The probability will depend on this speed, as well as on the position of the submarine's path. It should be noted that the word "scouting" is used in the present study to indicate a primarily defensive operation, in contrast to a frequent and more offensive connotation of the term.

Another measure of a related effectiveness is the ability of the aircraft to force the submarines to submerge outside the detection circle, and thus greatly to reduce their chance of operating against the convoy. This does not require the aircraft to detect the submarines but, rather, the submarines to detect the aircraft. Since this detection depends on the amount of flying in the various areas outside the circle (in much the same manner as the aircraft's probability of detecting the submarines does), the probability of the latter affords a significant norm for evaluating the plan, thus dispensing with the need for its separate study.

At this stage it is important to emphasize that submarines outside the detection circle are to be regarded as unalerted and either ignorant of the convoy's existence or insufficiently informed of its position to be enabled to make a systematic approach. Consequently they may be regarded as *random submarines*; all courses are equally likely. And when attention is confined to submarines on courses leading eventually to their entry into the detection circle, they continue to be random submarines but with appropriately altered distribution of courses.

For expediency of computation, the probabilities of interception before entry into the detection circle are evaluated for targets of each *velocity* class (see Chapter

2, Section 5). In practice this means that, after having estimated the probable cruising speed u of an unalerted surfaced (or snorkeling, as the case may be) submarine, a track angle ϕ is selected. Then attention is fixed on the class C_ϕ of surfaced submarines of speed u that (1) proceed at the selected track angle ϕ and (2) have tracks relative to the convoy that enter the detection circle. Then the probability P_ϕ that such submarines will be detected by the aircraft is calculated. This is essentially a problem of barrier patrol evaluation but pertains to the case of barriers in which the aircraft flights, though periodic, are very irregular. The principles of the treatment have been given in Chapter 3, Sections 6 and 7, and Chapter 8, and we confine ourselves here merely to setting forth a simple method that will usually give sufficient accuracy.

Step 1. Draw the escort plan to scale relative to the convoy, and draw the detection circle. See Fig. 10-6 below.

Step 2. From ϕ, u, and the convoy speed, find the relative course θ and speed w with respect to the convoy (see Chapter 2, Section 1, Figs. 2-1 and 2-2). Trace the two tangents to the detection circle making the angle θ with the convoy course. (Note the present use of u to denote the *surface* speed).

Step 3. Measure the total length L_ϕ of that part of the aircraft path that lies outside the detection circle, between the two tangents drawn in step 2, and that is situated on the side of the circle corresponding to entrance into the circle by submarines of class C_ϕ.

The required probability is then

$$P_\phi = 1 - e^{-WL_\phi/2RwT},$$

where W = effective sweep width for the detection of surfaced (or snorkeling) submarines by the aircraft.

This calculation of P_ϕ is carried out for a set of angles covering the full circle. These may be taken equally spaced either in ϕ or in θ, at for example 15 degree intervals (or larger if less complete information suffices). They are conveniently exhibited by marking each P_ϕ off radially along a line starting at the origin and making an angle $\theta - \pi$ (and hence directed *toward* the incoming submarine) with the direction of the convoy. When the resulting points are joined by a smooth curve, a *polar diagram* (to be called the *scouting diagram*) is obtained. A corresponding polar diagram of P_ϕ plotted against ϕ or $\phi - \pi$ can be drawn, but being less directly related to the relative picture of the flight plan it gives a less clear indication of its scouting tightness.

It is noted that in the case of fast convoys whose speed v is greater than the surfaced (or snorkeling) cruising speed u of the submarine, the polar curve is a closed loop lying ahead of the polar origin O. This corresponds with the fact that along a given θ (represented as the radial line at angle $\theta - \pi$ with the convoy's course), there are two velocity vector angles ϕ, one corresponding with submarines proceeding toward the convoy, the other to those headed away from it but overtaken by it. Thus the loop is cut in two points by the above radial line. When $v < u$, there is only one point of intersection, the loop enclosing O. When $v = u$, O is on the loop.

Actually, the chief use of the scouting diagram is in obtaining the *scouting coefficient*, now to be defined. In appraising the scouting effectiveness of a plan, consideration must be given to the total detected fraction f of all the submarines whose motion will lead them into the detection circle. The number of submarines of C_ϕ entering the circle per unit time is equal to the area $2Rw$ in relative space that contains them, times the density of members of C_ϕ (by the randomness, independent of ϕ). Thus their number is proportional to $w[w = w(\phi)]$. Of these, a number proportional to wP_ϕ is detected on the average. Hence, the total number detected is proportional to the integral

$$\frac{1}{2\pi} \int_0^{2\pi} w(\phi) P_\phi \, d\phi,$$

which is conveniently found by taking the arithmetic mean of the numbers $w(\phi)P_\phi$ found as above for equally spaced angles ϕ. If every submarine were detected ($P_\phi = 1$), the above would reduce to

$$\frac{1}{2\pi} \int_0^{2\pi} w(\phi) \, d\phi.$$

To obtain the required fraction, the first expression is divided by the second, giving

$$f = \frac{\displaystyle\int_0^{2\pi} w(\phi) P_\phi \, d\phi}{\displaystyle\int_0^{2\pi} w(\phi) \, d\phi},$$

a weighted mean of the quantities P_ϕ. This can be computed by taking the equally spaced angles $\phi_1, \phi_2, \ldots$ and obtaining

$$f = \frac{w(\phi_1)P_{\phi_1} + w(\phi_2)P_{\phi_2} + \cdots}{w(\phi_1) + w(\phi_2) + \cdots},$$

or by using previous results [Chapter 2, equation (4)] to evaluate the denominator. In the notation of the reference, this gives

$$f = \frac{\text{arithmetic mean of } w(\phi_1)P_{\phi_1}, \; w(\phi_2)P_{\phi_2}, \cdots}{(u + v)(2/\pi)E(\sigma)},$$

where v is the convoy's speed.

The number f, called the *scouting coefficient*, is in the nature of a measure of effectiveness of the scouting of the aerial escort plan. The values are reasonably insensitive to possible misestimations of u but depend very materially upon the value of R.

Certain modifications of the procedure above may be useful in special situations. Thus in the case of certain submarines having extra batteries, a high submerged speed may make the submerged overtaking of the convoy possible, although only at relatively short distances, on account of limited battery endurance at such speeds. This means that the danger zone may be bounded in the rear by a curve passing a few miles, e.g., ten, to the rear of the convoy and gently concave in its direction, and intersecting the detection circle at points near each beam. Then an evaluation of the scouting diagram and coefficient, with the detection circle replaced by the composite curve consisting of the forward part of this circle joined to the above rear limiting approach curve, may be useful. Such an evaluation proceeds along similar lines to the earlier one, except that the distance D between the tangents now depends on ϕ: $D = D_\phi$ rather than $D = 2R$ must be used in the denominator of the exponent in the formula for P_ϕ. This procedure has a certain inaccuracy, inasmuch as it counts submarines inside the detection circle but behind the rear limiting approach curve as random, whereas they can be expected to have gained enough knowledge of the convoy's location to change from an accidental to an intended approach. There are cases, however, where this inaccuracy may be ignored.

3. THE SCREENING EFFECTIVENESS

A measure of the effectiveness of an aircraft escort plan as a screen is the probability it affords of detecting surfaced submarines that are making a systematic approach to the convoy (the 1946 edition had reference to visual or radar detection; today *sonobuoy* detection is at least as important and does not require exposure of the submarine above the surface). Such submarines not only are alerted but they have a fairly precise knowledge of the convoy's location, course, and speed. Their approach may include a tracking procedure, and some form of closing (e.g., along a normal approach course or a collision course) to a favorable position for submerging and thence making a submerged close approach and attack. Their surfaced approach course may therefore be quite complicated, and since the probability of detection depends on its geometrical shape, as well as upon the phase of the aircraft's motion (i.e., its position on its circuit when the submarine is at a given distance from O), the evaluation of all such probabilities is not feasible. Hence the importance of the following line of argument, intended to establish as a useful norm of screening effectiveness the probabilities of detection calculated for *collision courses only*. With the reference point O in the convoy as center, a circle is drawn so large that it includes the whole aircraft escort track so far within it that there is no probability that any of the aircraft will detect a submarine outside it. This circle, in general much greater than the detection circle, will be called the *reference circle*. Any approaching submarine will cross the reference circle at some (last) point A at the bearing θ relative to the convoy's course. This is shown in Fig. 10-2 drawn relative to the convoy motion. One parameter of the submarine's path is θ; another is the distance from the convoy at which it submerges. Figure 10-2 shows three paths, AB (the collision approach), AB_1, and AB_2, all corresponding to the same θ and same distance from convoy of point of submergence (thus B, B_1, B_2 are all on the same "submergence circle"). (We are assuming that the boundary of the submergence region is a circle, thus considering only the simplest case. Were the tactical situation known in more

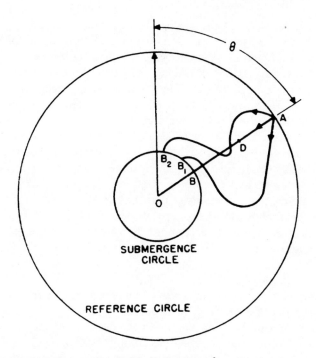

Fig. 10-2. The reference figures in an approach.

detail, some other region might be more appropriate. For example, the danger zone has been used in analyzing the plan of Fig. 10-6, but the principle of the reasoning remains the same.) How do such paths compare in their probabilities of detection? Again it must be emphasized that the submarine is assumed not to know the aerial escort plan: the most it knows is that aerial escort is being flown. Otherwise aerial escort with any normal number of aircraft could not be assumed to be useful, inasmuch as the submarine could be presumed to know how to get in undetected. Consequently, the paths AB, AB_1, etc., are randomly situated with respect to the aircraft paths. Now of all the submarine paths AB, AB_1, etc., the *collision course AB is the one that takes the least time for the submarine to get from A to the submergence circle.* If therefore the density of air coverage is substantially the same throughout the regions through which AB, AB_1, etc. can be expected to pass, the probability of detection for AB is *less* than that for AB_1, AB_2, etc. On account of the intention of tracking the convoy before closing and then of entering the submerged approach region (Fig. 10-1), many submarine paths may be expected to be of the type of AB_1. Hence, if the probability of detection of AB is to represent a genuine conservative estimate (lower limit) of the probabilities of detection of AB_1, AB_2, etc., *the flight plan must provide adequate barring of crossing the line AB of Fig. 10-1.*

Consider now two collision courses: AB and AO (Fig. 10-2). The probability of detection of AB is obviously less than that of AO (at most equal to AO, in the case when all flying is done well outside the submergence circle). If the density of flight were essentially the same at all the places through which the collision course of bearing angle θ passes, out to a point D, and then fell to zero, the probability of detection of AB would be given by multiplying that for AO by the factor BD/OD. If there were more flying farther out along OD than at points nearer to O, the factor would be *greater* than BD/OD; if less flying far than near, the factor would be less than BD/OD, and, indeed, the probability of detection of AO gives little information about that of AB when the flying is highly concentrated near the convoy. But such plans are bad plans (since they duplicate the sighting operations of the surface escorts and since they cover regions where the submarine can be expected to be already submerged) and therefore need not concern us here. Their exclusion is part of the task of the design of a plan (Section 6 below). Thus, with reasonable escort plans, the probability of detection of AO is a satisfactory index of the tightness of the screen along the line of bearing θ. We may add that the probability for AO is the same (on account of the way in which the reference circle was drawn) as that for a collision path of bearing θ but extending to infinity instead of to A.

In conclusion it is here posited:

Under the proviso that (1) the entrance to the submerged approach region be adequately guarded (so that probability of detection of AB_1 is not less than AB), and (2) the flying be not unduly concentrated near the convoy, the probability $p(\theta)$ of detection of a collision course submarine coming from infinity to O along the bearing θ calculated for various representative values of θ is *a norm of the screening effectiveness*. The polar diagram $r = p(\theta)$ is called the screening polar diagram. Its construction is the subject of Section 4 below.

A modified procedure is to take the polar diagram in which probabilities of detecting collision course submarines outside the danger zone are plotted, instead of probabilities of detection all the way into O. This occasionally gives useful indications, *but its value is mainly in scrutinizing poor plans*, i.e., those in which an undue amount of flying is done close in. In a well-designed plan, the diagram as it has been considered earlier should not be too different from the modified case mentioned here.

4. THE SCREENING POLAR DIAGRAM: GENERAL CONSIDERATIONS

As in Section 2, the period T of the flight plan is ascertained, and the diagram of the plan is drawn in convoy space. The problem is to find the probability $p(\theta)$ of detecting a surfaced submarine approaching on the collision course which in convoy space is the radial line drawn out from O at the angle θ with the convoy course. In order to see precisely what is involved, we shall give the exact formulation of $p(\theta)$, and afterward study methods for its approximate evaluation.

Let t denote the time (hours) *before* a particular submarine reaches O (at O, $t = 0$). Marking an x axis in the direction of the convoy's heading (the reference point O in the convoy being the origin) and a y axis in the starboard direction (Fig.

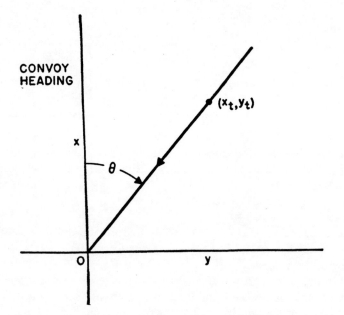

Fig. 10-3. Collision approach: the coordinate system.

10-3), the submarine's position at any time t is (x_t, y_t), and if $w(\theta)$ is its relative speed, we have

$$x_t = w(\theta)t \cos \theta, \qquad y_t = w(\theta)t \sin \theta,$$

which are, in fact, its equations of motion.

If (X_t^i, Y_t^i) are the coordinates of the ith aircraft at time t, this aircraft's equations of motion are of the form

$$X_t^i = X^i(t), \qquad Y_t^i = Y^i(t),$$

where the two functions $X^i(t)$ and $Y^i(t)$ are each periodic and have T as a period. Indeed, T is the smallest *common* period of all the functions $X^i(t)$, $Y^i(t)$ for all values of i (i.e., the least common multiple of the periods of all aircraft circuits of the plan). Of course some of the aircraft may repeat their circuit more often than others, so smaller numbers, such as $T/2$, may be periods of some of the pairs of functions $X^i(t)$, $Y^i(t)$. It must be realized that to give the escort plan is to give these functions, and vice versa.

Let $\gamma(\sqrt{(x - X)^2 + (y - Y)^2})\, dt$ be the instantaneous probability of sighting a target (surfaced submarine) at (x, y) by an observer [aircraft at (X, Y), see Section 2 of Chapter 3], giving the probability of sighting the submarine on its entire collision course by the ith aircraft as (adjusting the variable of integration t so that it increases as the submarine approaches):

$$1 - \exp\left\{ -\int_0^\infty \gamma\left[\sqrt{(x_t - X_t^i)^2 + (y_t - Y_t^i)2}\ \right] dt \right\},$$

and the probability that at least one of the aircraft will sight it as

$$1 - \exp\left\{ -\sum_i \int_0^\infty \gamma\left[\sqrt{(x_t - X_t^i)^2 + (y_t - Y_t^i)^2}\ \right] dt \right\},$$

the summation in the exponential being over all values of i that occur (e.g., from 1 to 3 if there are three aircraft flying the plan.) (Effects of target aspect and bearing on this probability are being ignored in thus assuming γ is a function of the distance between observer and target.)

This is not yet the value of $p(\theta)$.

Suppose that a second submarine is following the first at a distance $w(\theta)\tau$ behind it (i.e., τ hours later). If $\tau = T, 2T, 3T$, etc., its chance of detection is the same as before, because of the periodicity of the plan. But if $0 < \tau < T$, it will arrive at the various points of its path when the aircraft are at a different phase in their circuits from those of the previous case, and thus the probability of detection will be different. To find its value, we have but to write the equations of motion of the second submarine (x_t', y_t'),

$$x_t' = w(\theta)(t + \tau) \cos \theta = x_{t+\tau},$$
$$y_t' = w(\theta)(t + \tau) \cos \theta = y_{t+\tau},$$

and substitute these expressions into the formula above in place of (x_t, y_t), i.e., replace (x_t, y_t) by $(x_{t+\tau}, y_{t+\tau})$. Now the value of $p(\theta)$ is the probability of detecting a submarine chosen at random on the line of bearing θ. Its position is characterized by the value of τ, which is uniformly distributed in the interval $0 \leqslant \tau < T$. Thus to obtain $p(\theta)$ we must average the *probabilities* obtained as before for each τ; we have then finally

$$p(\theta) = \frac{1}{T} \int_0^T \left\{ 1 - \exp\left[-\sum_i \int_0^\infty \gamma(r_i)\, dt \right] \right\} d\tau,$$

$$r_i = \sqrt{(x_{t+\tau} - X_t^i)^2 + (y_{t+\tau} - Y_t^i)^2}$$

[cf. (33) of Chapter 7, Section 7].

The exact computation of $p(\theta)$ would be a formidable task and is not warranted, in view of the fact that any explicit expressions for γ and $w(\theta)$ are at best only very approximate, while at the same time there is bound to be considerable navigational inaccuracy in flying the plan. Fortunately, approximate methods exist whereby $p(\theta)$ can be evaluated. The earliest method was to use a *definite range law* of sighting and treat the problem graphically. This method, except as giving very crude indications, has had to be abandoned. It not only gives an unsatisfactory degree of approximation, but, more important, it frequently yields a value $p(\theta) = 1$, thus giving the impression that a perfect barrier could be established (corresponding with the idea of "sweeping the ocean about the convoy clean"). This is an

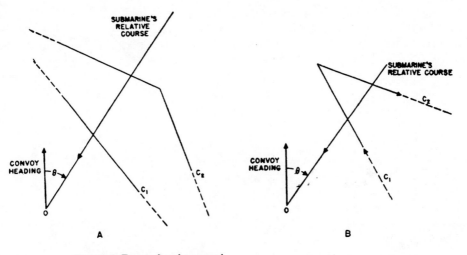

Fig. 10-4. Types of paths crossed.

illusion. Every plan gives the submarine a finite (though possibly small) chance of an undetected surfaced passage through the aircraft screen, provided the velocities make such an approach kinematically possible. A much better method, for the visual case at least, is the one based on the inverse cube law of sighting. This law is used illustratively by means of examples in Section 5, below. Here we merely outline the general principles of the approximation to $p(\theta)$, whatever the nature of γ and thus applying equally to any law of visual or radar detection.

As the first step in the approximation, suppose that the submarine crosses (i.e., either actually intersects, or passes in close enough proximity to afford an appreciable chance of a sighting) two partial paths C_1, C_2, of the plan (and possibly others). This may occur, as in Fig. 10-4A or B.

The distinction is that in (A) the paths are either flown by different planes or by the same plane at considerably different epochs, and therefore, because of the irregularities in the flights and in the submarine's motion, etc., *the detection by the aircraft on C_1 and the detection on C_2 may be regarded as statistically independent events*, whereas in the case (B) *such independence may not be assumed*. Furthermore, detection on any of these paths will not occur (i.e., occur with but a negligible probability) at a considerable distance from the submarine's path, for example on the dotted portions of C_1 and C_2 and beyond. Thus we may at our convenience either suppress all this more distant part of the paths or alternatively (when it is mathematically simpler) produce the straight lines to infinity away from the submarine's course. It then becomes a much simpler problem to calculate the probability of detection by C_1 and then by C_2 separately in (A), and by the combination $C_1 + C_2$ in (B). And we are thus led to the following first simplification in the computation of $p(\theta)$.

For each given θ, separate the aircraft's paths into coherent pieces [C_1 and C_2 separately in (A), $C_1 + C_2$ joined in (B)], and regard each piece simplified at its distant parts either by suppressing them or producing them to infinity as straight lines. Then compute the probability of detection for each part by the methods to be

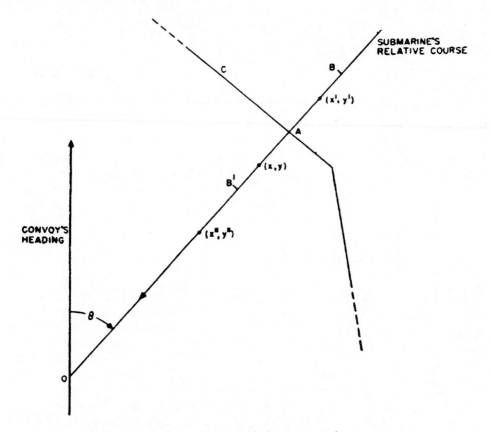

Fig. 10-5. Successive positions seen during an approach.

developed below. Last, combine the probabilities of the different parts as independent probabilities. Thus, in (A), if $p_1(\theta)$ and $p_2(\theta)$ are the probabilities of detection by C_1 and C_2, and if no other paths are crossed, we have

$$p(\theta) = 1 - [1 - p_1(\theta)][1 - p_2(\theta)].$$

The second step in the approximate computation of $p(\theta)$ concerns the evaluation of the probability of detection $p'(\theta)$ for a single coherent part of track ($p' = p_1$ or p_2 in the previous example). Figure 10-5 shows the situation schematically. The coherent part of track is C (which may also be thought of as bent back, as in Fig. 10-4B, where $C = C_1 + C_2$).

Since the aircraft flying C has a much greater speed than the submarine, the latter will move only very slightly during the time it takes the aircraft to traverse that part of C (the solid line) that is close enough to the submarine's path to give any appreciable chance of detection. Hence the approximation: *Regard the submarine as stationary* [e.g., at the point (x, y)] *while the aircraft makes a given flight C.* This sanctions the use of the formulas of Chapter 3 for the detection of targets at rest in relation to the searcher. Thus for the single flight depicted in Fig. 10-5 our expression for the detection probability takes the simpler form (with $s = vt$):

$$p' = 1 - \exp\left\{-\int_C f(r)\, ds\right\},$$

where v is the aircraft speed, s is the distance along its path C measured from any fixed reference point, and $\int_C$ denotes integration over the whole of C. $\int_C f(r)\, ds$ is the contact potential (Chapter 3, Section 3), r being the distance between the target at the fixed point (X, y) and the observer (aircraft) at the moving point (X, Y). A further approximation is involved here, in that the average ground speed v is taken as the aircraft speed in convoy space. Now C is flown regularly every T' hours, where $T' = T$ or an integral submultiple thereof (e.g., $T' = T/2$).

Hence if at one epoch (time when the aircraft is at a fixed reference point on its path C such as A, Fig. 10-5) the submarine is at (x, y), T' hours earlier it was at (x', y'), and T' hours later it will be at (x'', y''), where

$$x' - x = x - x'' = T'w(\theta) \cos \theta,$$
$$y' - y = y - y'' = T'w(\theta) \sin \theta;$$

and there will be other earlier and later positions of the submarine corresponding with multiples of T'. The probability of detection in at least one of these positions is

$$1 - \exp\left\{-\sum_n \int_C f(r_n)\, ds\right\},$$

where

$$r_n = \sqrt{(X - x_n)^2 + (Y - y_n)^2},$$

(x_n, y_n) being the nth position of the submarine, e.g., $(x_n, y_n) = (x, y)$, (x', y'), (x'', y''), etc., and $X = X(s/v)$, $Y = Y(s/v)$, the coordinates of the (moving) aircraft. As before, this must be averaged over a complete set of representative positions of (x, y), e.g., over all positions specified by

$$[x + \tau w(\theta) \cos \theta, y + \tau w(\theta) \sin \theta], \quad 0 \leqslant \tau < T'.$$

Thus

$$p'(\theta) = \frac{1}{T'} \int_0^{T'} \left\{1 - \exp\left[-\sum_n \int_C f(r_n)\, ds\right]\right\} d\tau.$$

The third step in the approximate evaluation of $p(\theta)$ consists in ignoring certain complicating but quantitatively unimportant differences between the actual finite segments of aircraft tracks and infinite or semi-infinite ones, to which the appropriate lateral range formulas of Chapter 3 apply. Dropping distant (dotted) tracks by extending them indefinitely has been mentioned; furthermore, the formulas of Chapter 3 to be used already contain the results of the averaging over the phase T shown in the preceding formula.

5. PLOTTING THE SCREENING POLAR DIAGRAM: INVERSE CUBE LAW

To bring out the effect of relative motion, as well as to illustrate one step in the evaluation process, we consider the (absurd) case of a single aircraft flying a circular path C centered at O in Fig. 10-1 and of radius R_1 somewhat less than R. A submarine approaching O along a radial path will be moving with a relative (surfaced) speed w given by the constructions in Fig. 2-2 and formulas (1) of Chapter 2. If the flight period is T it will move a radial distance wT between successive crossings of OA by the aircraft. We may usually assume that the arc of C on which the submarine is visible from the aircraft is short enough to be regarded as straight, and that the aircraft performs sufficiently many circuits of C during the submarine's approach from A to B to justify the use of the formula of parallel sweeps of spacing $S = wT$; see Chapter 3, Section 7, (43). If the inverse cube law is applied, (43) reduces to (45) so that $p(\theta) = \text{erf}(W\sqrt{\pi}\,/2wT)$, W being the sweep width of the aircraft against the surfaced (or otherwise detectable) submarine. Because of the rapid decrease of the error function $\text{erf}(x)$ with the decrease of x, it would appear that the large values of w in the forward sector would give low screening probabilities in the places where most protection is needed, while giving high effectiveness in the rear where it is of little usefulness.

To give a numerical illustration, suppose that $W = 5$ naut. miles, that $u = 15$ and $v = 9$ knots, and that $T = 1$ hour. A submarine approaching from dead ahead $(\theta = 0)$ will have $w = u + v = 27$; from hard on relative flank $(\theta = \pi/2)$ $w = \sqrt{u^2 - v^2} = 9$; from dead astern $(\theta = \pi)$, $w = u - v = 3$. The tables of $\text{erf}(x)$ (e.g., B. O. Peirce's) show that the detection probabilities are, respectively, 0.18, 0.51, and 0.96. Clearly such a path places its main effectiveness where it is least needed, in spite of being geometrically located in what might appear to be a reasonable place. With a 120 knot aircraft, C would have a radius $R_1 = 60/\pi$, about 19 miles (near the second circle in Fig. 10-6).

To build up the screening effectiveness where it is most needed—and to give an example of an evaluation—evidently most of the flying must be done in the forward regions, and the simplest element would be a plan containing a straight leg making an angle ψ with radial lines of approach. The distance of radial advance between successive flights along this leg is still wT, but because of the angular tilt, the sweep spacing is now $S = wT \sin \psi$. Thus we now have $p(\theta) = \text{erf}(W\sqrt{\pi}\ \csc \psi/2wT)$, and this rapidly approaches unity as ψ approaches zero. In the numerical example considered before, if $\psi = 20°$ the detection probability dead ahead is increased from 0.18 to 0.5.

Figure 10-6 shows a flight plan for a single escort; it was intended to put protection where it was most needed. Figure 10-7 shows its evaluation by the screening polar diagram. A scale of probabilities given under the numerical assumptions there is representative of many World War II situations. (These figures are quite different from those of the preceding examples, which would have given an absurdly large circle with R_1 exceeding R). Clearly it is weak dead ahead

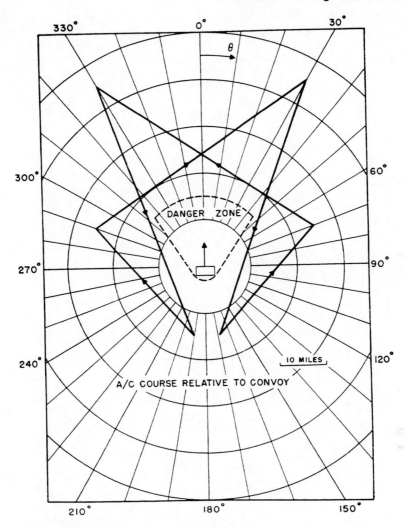

Fig. 10-6. A possible aircraft escort plan.

but is more effective in the important 30° relative approaches. It was obtained by examining various approaches and applying the inverse cube formula when it seemed appropriate.

Considerable experience in World War II showed the difficulty in securing strong screens with very modest numbers of aircraft. Their demonstrated tactical effectiveness seems to have been due to their scouting effect, and in "keeping the subs down." The situation was quite different in the air escort of carrier task forces, with their great number of escorts and offensive capabilities, yet their air screens were often much improved by applying the scientific analyses exemplified above.

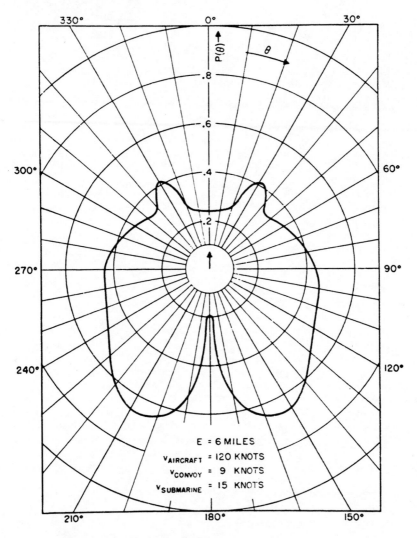

Fig. 10-7. Screening polar diagram.

6. PRACTICAL INSTRUCTIONS FOR OBTAINING A POLAR DIAGRAM

Broadly speaking, the first step in the polar evaluation of a given screening plan is to draw, on its plot relative to the moving convoy, selected representative radial directions of collision approach, such as OA, Fig. 10-2. They are "representative" first in not going through such peculiarities of the path as angular points and such isolated peculiarities, and second in giving a sample of all the various sectors of possible approach. The next step is to apply to each approach line the appropriate detection formula of Chapter 3 (or whatever improvement that can be established). Often there are enough repeated flights crossing the target's closing path to justify using the formulas of parallel sweeps, singly or by combining two or more as independent events. In some cases the parallel sweeps lie so much on one side of the target that the sighting potential (see Chapter 3, Section 3) has to be halved. This is equivalent to replacing the full parallel sweep probability p by $1 - \sqrt{1 - p}$. In some further cases, only one or two sighting encounters with the

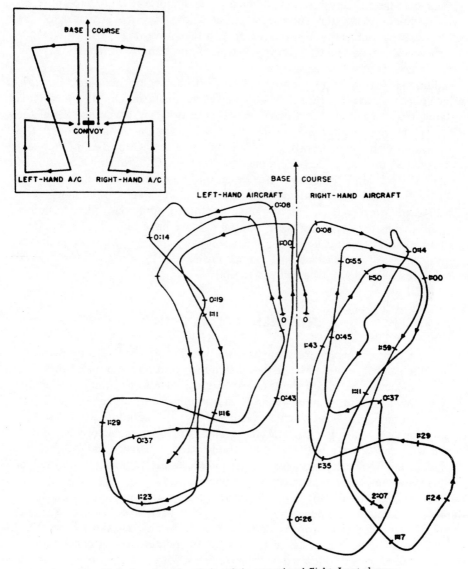

Fig. 10-8. Actual tracks of aircraft in operational flight. Inset shows search plan being used.

surfaced submarine are possible because of the relative velocities involved. Then the lateral range curve may have to be used directly.

After finding the values of $p(\theta)$ for the representative approaches in this manner and plotting them radially in polar coordinates, a smooth curve is traced through the resulting points—a sort of graphical interpolation. This will necessarily leave out much of the "fine structure" of a diagram drawn with meticulous exactness (assuming that such an object has a meaning). The use of the rougher interpolation is more than a matter of convenience—or of treating roughly known data with the roughness that they deserve. It is justified by the important fact that under no known conditions could the submarine either know the fine structure of the effectiveness of the screen, or if it did, be able to take advantage of it. In effect, it has to operate against a "moving average," its mean probability of detection over a sector of at least five or ten degrees.

An additional reason for the appropriateness of the rough interpolated diagram described above is shown in Fig. 10-8, which gives two pictures. On the upper left is the relative track of an air escort plan for two aircraft flying on either side of the convoy; on the right is shown a relative trace of the paths actually flown. The actual positions of the two aircraft were obtained by radar sightings at the frequent times marked on the trace, taken from the escort carrier (CVE) during a crossing of the Atlantic in the war. This lack of "parade-ground regularity" is a constant factor in real life—both in military and civilian operations of any degree of complexity.

The 1946 edition of *Search and Screening* contained numerous rules, formulas, tables, and graphs for obtaining polar diagrams. If we have judged it unnecessary to reproduce them here, it is because under the greatly changed present conditions, numerical details of the past could be more misleading than useful. The general principles are the burden of the present sections.

7. THE DESIGN OF A PLAN

As in all questions of this nature, there are two possible viewpoints. Either we may lay down the tactical results to be achieved (scouting and screening) and then find a plan that achieves them with the least expenditure of effort (number of aircraft and flying time); or else we may fix the total amount of effort available and seek the plan that maximizes the tactical results. Now the solution of the second problem furnishes that of the first since it automatically informs us of what can be achieved with one aircraft, with two aircraft, etc., and it remains only to pick the first plan in this sequence that gives the required result. Accordingly it shall be from this viewpoint that the problem is approached here.

Let the number n of aircraft be given together with their capabilities of speed v, endurance, and detection. The convoy's speed v_c (in the sense of mean course made good) is also supposed to be known. Before there can be any question of the "best" plan, a decision must be made as to how much relative importance must be attached to *scouting* as compared with *screening*. Now this is a purely tactical question. It must be settled on the basis of presumed enemy tactics and submarine capacities, as well as of our own defensive capabilities and our vulnerability. For example, against a submarine capable of high submerged speed and endurance, screening could be expected to be less effective than scouting, whereas the reverse might be true if the submarine were of the older type without these capabilities. When this decision has been reached and the relevant speeds and distances have been estimated, five conditions must be satisfied:

1. The entrance to the submerged approach region must be adequately guarded.
2. Flying must not be unduly concentrated about the convoy.
3. The circuits must be closed in convoy space, i.e., the aircraft must automatically meet the convoy.
4. The time between successive meetings of the convoy must not be excessive (never more than two hours; one hour is much better than two).
5. The plan must be navigable with reasonable ease. This means that one involving many turns must be avoided.

Now obviously it is not feasible to deduce an exact plan from these data and the requirement of maximizing scouting and screening. It is necessary *first* to invent plans and *afterward* to test, modify, and select until a satisfactory one is obtained, and to exhaust all visible possibilities of improvement. *Such a procedure is an art quite as much as a science.* It is advisable to make the designs first relative to the convoy rather than in space fixed with respect to the ocean, since the former picture is simpler and more direct in its illustration of relevant features, but eventually it will be transferred to geographic space, where the last refinements can be made.

When a satisfactory plan has been designed for one speed ratio $r = v/v_c$, it is usually desirable to extend it without changing its fundamental character, so that it will be applicable to broader ranges of r. This should be done without changing the angles of the courses in the original plan, if possible, but rather by varying certain leg lengths. It is simply the kinematic problem of bringing all planes back to the convoy periodically every T hours, given the new values of r. It is solved by simple trigonometry as follows: Draw a full period of the plan in geographic space, i.e., the figure that repeats itself every T hours. Consider the part of the plan flown by one aircraft. Let it be desired to vary two particular leg lengths, x and y, maintaining the others constant (values given). Let z be the distance the convoy moves in the time T. Then the three variables x, y, z are related by three equations of the first degree: first, the requirement that the length of the flown path (vT) divided by z $(v_c T)$ be equal to $v/v_c = r$; second, that the algebraic sum of the projections of the legs on the convoy path shall be z; and third, that the algebraic sum of the projections on a normal to the convoy path be zero. Solving these equations, x, y, z are obtained as functions of r and, of course, T. Tables of the results are furnished with the plan. Of course, it is necessary to reexamine the plan (calculating scouting and screening diagrams anew, at least at critical places) for the extreme values of r used, in order to be sure that the necessary protection is maintained.

Since the effectiveness of a plan depends on the conditions of detection (visual or radar), reasonable and conservative estimates of visibility should be made in making all these calculations. It may be necessary to repeat such calculations for other visibilities. However, it is unlikely that a plan that is better than another at one visibility will be worse than it at a different visibility, unless the change of visibility entails an essential change in the tactical situation.

To sum up, first design a plan complying with the obvious requirements set forth above and in the light of the experience gained in the calculations made in the earlier sections—and of the operational lesson of Fig. 10-8—and then evaluate the plan's scouting and screening effectiveness.

8. FINAL SWEEPS

As long as the convoy is in submarine waters, maximum protection is obtained by flying the escort plan without letup. But it is often necessary to discontinue the flights for a protracted period of time, for example, during the hours of darkness. The danger incident to this can be minimized by flying *final sweeps* at a greater distance than the normal flights, immediately after the latter are discontinued. These final sweeps are essentially of a scouting character, which aim at detecting submarines that might constitute a menace to the convoy at a later period, after aerial escort has been discontinued.

The first thing to realize is that it is not normally possible to detect, by flights made at the time ($t = 0$) of discontinuance of aerial escort, all the submarines that could possibly close the convoy during the next H hours of escortless travel, for it would be necessary to sweep the area of the ocean in which such submarines must be. This, in the case of $u > v_c$, is the shaded circular region of Fig. 10-9, obtained by multiplying all lengths of the circular diagram of relative speeds (vector $\mathbf{w}$) by H. This means that an area of $\pi u^2 H^2$ would have to be swept. For example, if $u = 12$ knots and $H = 8$ hours, the area is 29,000 square miles. With an aircraft of 130 knots and sweep width 10 miles, a time of $29.000/1,300 = 22.3$ hours would be required. Even with four planes, 5.6 hours would be needed; and more, if the difficult track problem of covering the area is taken into account, with the resulting loss of efficiency. If less than this coverage is available, what should be covered and what neglected? This is essentially the question answered in Chapter 6, Section 6. Indeed, during the relatively short time for the final sweeps, the targets can be regarded as essentially stationary.

Taking a system of rectangular coordinates with origin fixed at the convoy reference point O (and hence moving with the convoy), and axis of abscissas in the direction of convoy motion, we must evaluate the function $p(x, y)$, where $p(x, y) \, dx \, dy$ is the probability of there being a "dangerous" surfaced submarine in a $dx \, dy$ region at the point (x, y) (at the initial epoch $t = 0$), where by a "dangerous" submarine is meant one that will surely come in contact with the convoy (i.e., enter the detection circle of radius R, center O) during the subsequent H hours. Next, we must evaluate the amount of coverage or searching effort Φ

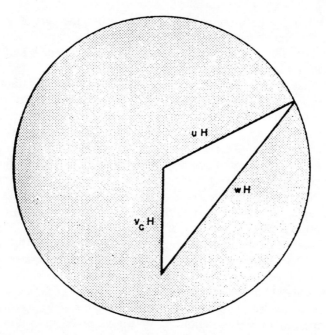

Fig. 10-9. Circle of possible future contacts.

available. Thus if we have the use of n aircraft for h hours each and if their speed is v and effective search width is W, $\Phi = nvh$, and according to the results of Chapter 6, Section 6, we are warranted only in searching the region $A_b = L(\lambda)$ defined in (32), where we are writing $b = \lambda/W$, so that this A_b is the region for which $p(x, y) \geqslant b$. The value of b is determined by (34), which is equivalent (in the present case of constant W) to

$$\int_{A_b} \int \left[\log p(x, y) - \log b \right] dx \, dy = \Phi$$

and which has a simple geometric interpretation in terms of volumes, as the general case of variable W had in Chapter 6 in terms of masses. Searching should be confined to A_b and distributed therein according to (33), which here takes the form $W\phi(x, y) = \log[p(x, y)/b]$. But in practice, such refinement is not apt to be possible, and the best procedure would be to use any practicable search, of a more or less uniform sort, in the estimated region A_b. Of course, the whole of the detection circle itself must be included in the search to detect submarines already in contact with the convoy, particularly trailing behind and tracking on the flanks.

The estimation of $p(x, y)$ is difficult, not because of the mathematics involved (a crude mathematical formulation is quite sufficient) but because it depends on the correct appraisal of the tactical situation regarding the submarine. Three extreme cases may be considered as examples.

Case 1. The submarines are uniformly distributed over the part of the ocean of interest and are cruising at an estimated speed of u knots in any direction (i.e., in uniformly distributed random directions; see Chapter 2, Sections 4 and 5). This is the case in which the submarines are picked up purely by chance and not as the result of any systematic patrolling on their part. The problem of finding $p(x, y)$ in this case has been solved in Chapter 2 [see Section 6, problem 3, together with Figs. 2-12 to 2-16. The $\Phi(r, \beta)$ of this reference is not to be confused with the "amount of searching effort" Φ used above]. In this reference, the probability $P(r, \beta)$ is found [(r, β) are the polar coordinates of (x, y)]; unlike $p(x, y)$, this is not a probability *density* but a *probability*, namely, the probability that the target given to be at (r, β) [or (x, y)] when $t = 0$ shall subsequently enter the detection circle. But if the mean density of submarines is N, there will be $N\, dx\, dy$ submarines *in all* in the $dx\, dy$ region at (x, y), of which the fraction $P(r, \beta)$ will enter the circle; hence the relevant expected number of submarines in $N\ P(r, \beta)\, dx\, dy = N\ P(r, \beta) r\, dr\, d\beta$. Now as in the discussion in Chapter 6, Section 6, the constant of proportionality N is immaterial in the final results. Hence the material given in that chapter applies with the former $p(x, y)$ replaced by $P(r, \beta)$. Finally, in the problem of Chapter 2 the time before contact was not limited, whereas we are restricting it to H hours. But with the searching effort normally available, only regions within an H-hour submarine run of the detection circle can be searched, and so the time restriction applies automatically.

Let us consider as example the case $v_c/u = k = 2/3$, e.g., submarine cruising surfaced at 15 knots, convoy at 10 knots. The level curves of constant probability $P(r, \beta)$ (i.e., the boundaries of A_b for different values of b) are given in Fig. 2-14 of Chapter 2. Let the detection range of the submarine on the convoy be $R = 20$ miles. This gives the scale in Fig. 2-14, Chapter 2, of 20 miles to the inch. With two 130-knot aircraft available for two hours and assuming the search width $W = 10$ miles, we have $W\Phi = 2 \times 2 \times 130 \times 10 = 5,200$ square miles of searching coverage effort available. To determine the probability contour of Fig. 2-11, within which the search must take place, we have to invoke (34) of Chapter 6, which becomes (in the form given above):

$$\int\limits_{A_b} \int \log P(r, \beta) r\, dr\, d\beta - A_b \log b = W\Phi = 5,200.$$

The values of $P(r, \beta)$ for $k = 2/3$ would have to be drawn from Fig. 2-14, Chapter 2, and the integration and calculation of the area A_b performed for different values of b, the arc finally chosen. Then a plan of search would be devised as much as possible in accordance with the preceding modified formula (33) of Chapter 6.

The following rough graphical version of this process illustrates the principles of the method in a form that can be carried out without unreasonable trouble in practice and that provides about all the accuracy our rather dubious tactical and numerical assumptions would appear to warrant.

With a planimeter (or an approximating ellipse) calculate the areas of the various A_b regions of Fig. 2-14 (Chapter 2), remembering that $b = 0.1$ for the 10 percent region, $b = 0.15$ for the 15 percent, ..., $b = 1$ for the detection circle. We find approximately for the A areas, and the ΔA rings between successive regions:

$$
\begin{aligned}
A_1 &= 1{,}260, & \Delta A_1 &= A_1 \quad -A_{0.4} = 150, \\
A_{0.4} &= 1{,}410, & \Delta A_{0.4} &= A_{0.4} - A_{0.25} = 1{,}710, \\
A_{0.25} &= 3{,}120, & \Delta A_{0.25} &= A_{0.25} - A_{0.15} = 3{,}030, \\
A_{0.15} &= 7{,}050, & \Delta A_{0.15} &= A_{0.15} - A_{0.10} = 8{,}950, \\
A_{0.1} &= 16{,}000.
\end{aligned}
$$

To find the graph of the function

$$
f(b) = \int\!\!\int_{A_b} \log P(r, \beta)\, r\, dr\, d\beta
$$

against b out to $b = 0.1$, we may multiply each ring area by the arithmetic mean of the (natural) logarithms of the probabilities of the two bounding level curves (except initially, the area of the detection circle is multiplied by $\log 1 = 0$), and then add the results out to the ring bounded by the value of b in question. The curve for $f(b)$ is then drawn through the resulting five points. Next, the function

$$
F(b) = 5{,}200 + A_b \log b
$$

is graphed, taking the five values of A_b given above and multiplying by $\log b$, b being the value corresponding to the boundary; a smooth curve is then passed through the resulting points. These curves are found to intersect at about the point $b = 0.13$, i.e., $f(0.13) = F(0.13)$; but this is the above form of equation (34) of Chapter 6. See Table 10-1.

Now since one cannot hope to search in accordance with equation (33), Chapter 6, rewritten as above, the best practical recommendation is to cover a region extending a little beyond the 15 percent curve of Fig. 2-14 (Chapter 2), for example, by a sector search. The probability of detecting the target by a random search of the 15 percent curve, is, by (40) of Chapter 3,

$$
p = 1 - e^{-LW/A} = 1 - e^{-\Phi/A_{0.15}}
$$

$$
= 1 - e^{-5{,}200/7{,}050} = 0.52.
$$

Table 10-1.

b	Avg log $\log b$	b	A $(A_1 = 1{,}260)$	$b \times \Delta A_b$	Avg log $f(b)$	$F(b)$
1.0	0	0		0	0	5,200
0.4	−0.91	−0.45	150	−68	−68	3,910
0.25	−1.49	−1.20	1,710	−2,060	−2,128	550
0.15	−1.89	−1.69	3,930	−6,650	−8,778	−8,100
0.10	−2.20	−2.04	8,950	−18,300	−27,078	−30,000

Thus, there is a little over half a chance that a given submarine in the 15 percent region will be detected. Therefore, the search is decidedly useful, but by no means as good as having regular escort flown through the night.

Case 2. The submarines are mounting guard along the route of the convoy (as they estimate it). If several submarines are acting as a coordinated group, they may form a line patrol across the convoy path of a type illustrated by the following example: Submarines are placed in a line across and at right angles with the convoy path patrolling stations 20 miles apart; each submarine proceeds at a low speed ($u = 10$ knots) and is never more than half an hour's run from its station. [This was a German plan described in the British Monthly Anti-Submarine Report (secret), November 1942.] Submarines acting alone may patrol at greater distances about their stations, but in all cases the distance is limited by the objective of intercepting convoys moving along the line.

This case is easier to treat—at least mathematically—than the first, since the only dangerous submarines here lie in a band whose middle line is the convoy's future course and whose total width is $2(R + d)$, where d is the presumed distance of lateral patrol of the submarines, while R is (as before) the submarines' detection range on the convoy during the time of discontinuance of the normal aerial escort (e.g., at night). For a submarine at lateral range more than $R + d$ on either side of the convoy's course would be unlikely to constitute a threat; $p(x, y) = 0$ outside the band, $p(x, y) = $ constant > 0 within the forward length of the band of Hv_C miles. Thus, this whole piece of band must be swept. This is a feasible operation. With $R = 20$, $d = 10$, $v = 8$, $H = 8$, the rectangular band's area is 3,840 square miles; one plane of 130 knots and 10-mile search width would require $3,840/1,300 = 2.95$ hours. With two or three planes, not only this area but a somewhat wider one, including the daytime detection circle, could easily be swept in a very reasonable time, at the last hour or so of daylight.

But in setting up this search, it is essential to know in advance what deceptive steering is intended during the night. Convoys usually make a deceptive change of course shortly after dark; the band may have to be a bent one under such circumstances.

Case 3. This is another tactic carried out in many cases by the U-boats in World War II. They would follow the convoy at their surfaced cruising speed and out of its sight during the day, closing the range to its rear as night approached, and then advancing surfaced along one or both sides during darkness to a position within the limited submerged approach region, only to submerge and deliver an attack at night or early dawn. This called for *final aircraft sweeps to the rear* of the convoy before the aerial escort was discontinued at night. Such an operation was often highly successful and resulted in the destruction of many U-boats—and their eventual abandonment of this particular tactic.

Appendix A

The Probability of Physical Events

"Probability," as applied in common parlance to a surmise, indicates a perception of its "likelihood," "reasonability to suppose," "chance of being true," and appears in a host of similar expressions. Reflecting a quantitative aspect of this intuitive or "subjective" perception, De Morgan has termed it the "degree of rational belief." It always contains the implication that some knowledge exists bearing on the surmise, but not enough to determine its truth or falsity. Thus it is perfectly consistent for its "probability" to change as this body of knowledge changes, and for different people possessed of different knowledge to appraise it differently. While no generally accepted *definition* of "probability" has ever been given, the concept is used or implied in most practical decisions in daily life. (For a mathematical development of probability as an intuitive partial ordering of statements, with a derivation of their numerical probability, see Koopman [8].)

This appendix is directed to the very restricted situations in which probabilities can be measured numerically and obey simple mathematical laws. The numerical results are not submitted as *definitions* of the probabilities, but as objectively determined *values* of something already understood. The literature on probability is massive—and contains a host of opposed schools of thought at the philosophic level. We can side-step all such matters, and confine ourselves to their common core—all that is needed by science and, in particular, the scientific theory of search. A few possibly useful references are given at the end, with orienting comments.

1. PHYSICAL EVENTS AND THEIR COMBINATIONS

Probability, as a *quantitative* science, was developed by induction from special cases; it has always sought a degree of precision of its concepts and required some restriction in its fields of application. In the early phases, in the seventeenth and eighteenth centuries, numerical probability was concerned with games of chance and the various combinations of their outcomes. The material used (dice, cards, etc.) had enough *mechanical symmetry* to enable "common sense" to infer a symmetry of probabilities. "Equal chances" could be counted; Laplace could measure the probability of the outcome of a trial as the number of favorable ways divided by the total number of possible ways—the latter, because of the symmetry of the mechanism, being judged "equally probable." In the nineteenth century, a science of numerical probability was developed on the basis of statistics; the repetition of observations under "similar conditions" would be found to yield a more or less fixed proportion of outcomes of a prestated type, and this ratio was used to measure the probability of such an outcome. Here again, repetition "under similar conditions" implied some form of symmetry (with respect to translations along the time axis). Bernoulli's theorem and his law of large numbers brought the Laplacean and the statistical conceptions together; see Section 4 below.

A fundamental extension of probabilistic concepts—of particular significance to operations analysis and search theory—started in the nineteenth century and continued in a dramatically expanding form into the present one. It came about through the applications of probability to the physical sciences, particularly to the molecular theory of matter. Statistical mechanics saw the introduction of the concept of *entropy*, coextensive with *information*; quantum mechanics, which required probability for the very statement of its laws, also contributed a new concept—that of *compatibility* versus *incompatibility* of observations—a concept that had been strangely neglected in the classical theory of probability, but which we have applied in the present work (passive versus active observations, etc.).

Throughout all these developments in its history, one concept has been central to the science of probability, that of *event*. This has been based, more or less explicitly, on the *observation of an occurrence involving a physical system* (conventional matter, radiation, etc.), which may involve living beings, as in its applications to biology, operations research, economics, etc. Moreover, the observation need not actually be carried out, but it must be possible in principle. It is an *operation* in the sense of P. W. Bridgman (Preface [1]); to be precise, an event is a *contemplated statement concerning the result of such a trial or observation, applied on a particular occasion*. It has also been termed an *experimental proposition*. Such a statement or proposition can be discussed without necessarily asserting or denying its truth, or indeed whether we know whether it is true or false; the only condition is that it be *meaningful* in the context of the discussion. We shall return to certain points of the definition in Section 4, when it will be contrasted with a different one, used in the purely abstract modern mathematical theory of probability, and equivalent with it only under special assumptions.

Among the simplest notions of logic are that, from certain meaningful statements, others can be obtained, but such operations as *denial* (from α we derive $\bar{\alpha} =$ not α), *conjunction* or logical product of two (from α and β we derive $\alpha\beta =$ "both α and β are true"), and *disjunction* or logical sum ($\alpha + \beta =$ "at least one of α and β is true"). [Other notations increasingly used are $\neg\alpha$ or α' for $\bar{\alpha}$; $\alpha \wedge \beta$ and $\alpha \vee \beta$ for $\alpha\beta$ and $\alpha + \beta$; lower-case Greek letters and 1 and 0 denote our "statements."]

It is precisely at this point that a new issue is raised, not noted by Boole or his followers in the development of symbolic logic—that of *compatibility*. It is perfectly possible to define, individually, two experimental propositions α and β in completely meaningful terms, without its being possible to do so for $\alpha\beta$ or $\alpha + \beta$. For example, we might propose certain possible experiments to be made on a particular strange new mutant of a rat, and α could be the statement that when inoculated exclusively with toxin A it dies at once, and β, that this happens when its sole inoculation is with toxin B. Clearly $\alpha\beta$ and $\alpha + \beta$ are meaningless (without drastic redefinition); they imply mutually exclusive operations. Similarly, if α and β are precise statements concerning the position and conjugate momentum of an elementary particle in quantum mechanics, the laws of this subject show that they are based on incompatible observations. In Chapter 1, Section 5, an incompatibility has been noted in cases when two "active observations" of a target are combined.

2. THE LAWS OF PROBABILITY

From each of the various conceptions of probability mentioned at the beginning of the last section, which led historically to the general theory, the *laws of probability* are easily inferred. (i) The probability of an event is a number between 0 and 1 (inclusive); an impossible (e.g., self-contradictory) event has the probability 0, while one certain to occur (e.g., implied by what is known) has the probability 1. (ii) The probability that at least one of two mutually exclusive events will occur on a trial is the sum of their individual probabilities (the law of total probability). (iii) The probability that both of two events will occur on a trial is the product of the probability of either one, times the conditional probability of the other, given the former—in either order (the law of compound probability). These are the laws by which, from given probabilities, others are derived. In the usual practical applications, the events of interest depend in a known way on simple events (i.e., are expressible, explicitly or implicitly, as logical combinations of the simple ones), and the simple events have probabilities that can be found (by arguments of symmetry, statistical experience, physical laws, etc., etc.). Therefore, the laws of probability enable us to find needed probabilities from other probabilities that we know. In more difficult cases, there are not enough known probabilities to determine the desired answer. Supplementary principles, such as that of "stability" under irregular disturbances, must be introduced, leading to entropy maximization and, in a conflict, minimax reasoning, as in Chapter 7, Section 8, must be invoked. Naturally they must be consistent with the laws of probability.

In the above, we have so worded (ii) and (iii) as to make it clear that the two events involved are compatible; in (iii), we have assumed that the "conditional probability" of one event, given another, is intuitively understood. More precision is needed. From the operational definition of events, α, β, γ, etc., as experimental propositions, it is clear that each one is connected with an *observation*, which we denote by O_α, O_β, O_γ, etc. The latter symbols refer in part to the nature of the observation: to *operating* on a system as when we throw dice, experiment on an animal, echo-range on a submarine, pass an elementary particle through a system of slits or a cyclotron; or merely to *looking at* or imagining looking at some system at some epoch t. And the symbols refer to a *particular occasion* of performing the operational observation. In most of the familiar cases, O_α, O_β, O_γ, etc., can be regarded as a part or aspect of a larger and more comprehensive operation that could be denoted by $O_{\alpha, \beta, \gamma}$, etc. For example, O_α, O_β, and O_γ could refer to a single throw of a pair of dice, and α could be the statement that the sum of points shown is even; β, that is less than 7; γ, that it is divisible by 3. As another example, they may refer to three successive trials of the same type, as in tossing a coin three different times, α being the statement that the first toss gives a head, etc. Thus, we have *united the succession of three tosses into a single composite trial:* $O_{\alpha, \beta, \gamma}$ is the succession of three tosses. Again, α could be the failure to perceive the underwater sound of a submarine by a searcher on a particular occasion O_α; β could be its successful reception on another occasion O_β: $O_{\alpha, \beta}$ is simply the composite of both attempts at detection. All these cases are examples of *compatibility:* the composite trial or observation being made up of the individual ones without essential change. Further, the examples we have given so often of *incompatible* events show that their characteristic feature is that *such a combination is impossible:* although two incompatible operations may, in many cases, be performed in succession, and we may write $O_{\alpha, \beta} = (O_\alpha$ then $O_\beta)$, the examination of β in this succession is no longer the same operation as in O_β (cf. the case of an alerted observation O_β after O_α, or the position-then-momentum observation $O_{\alpha, \beta}$ in quantum mechanics: $O_{\beta\alpha} \neq O_{\alpha, \beta}$.)

It remains to make precise the concept of *conditional probability*. As mentioned at the outset of this appendix, the very notion of probability implies a body of knowledge—too incomplete to give certainty (except in trivial cases)—and which, when changed, can change the probability (a fact implying absolutely no inconsistency of principles). Now the body of knowledge bearing on an event α is usually very great, and of many different orders: general knowledge including that of the laws of nature, and the totality of experience impacting on the case; special facts and estimates; and, most concretely, that certain other events have indeed occurred (or not occurred). In simple games of chance this massive array is drastically reduced, but consider the problem facing the Allies early in 1944 in estimating the probabilities of the various possible outcomes of the Normandy invasion in operation "Overlord"! No explicit rendering by algebraic symbols of the whole body of knowledge bearing on an event α in general cases is either feasible or useful; what is present in principle is usually unprofitable to include in the symbols and has to be implied as a general background in each discussion. There is, however, a fundamentally important exception: when to the general body of knowledge is added that of the (known or hypothesized) occurrence of some particular events $(\lambda, \mu, \nu, \dots)$.

The formulation of probabilities of α, given the occurrence of $\lambda, \mu, \nu, \dots$, would be an excessively complicated matter in the absence of compatibility of the total set considered $(\alpha, \lambda, \mu, \nu, \dots)$. The conventional theory has not dealt with incompatibility: thus the set of events assumed, $\lambda, \mu, \nu, \dots$, is equivalent to a single one—the occurrence of their logical product $\gamma = \lambda\mu\nu \dots$ (viz., all of them). Then we use the symbol $P(\alpha|\gamma)$ to denote *the conditional probability of α, given γ.*

Of course γ must not be an impossible event—i.e., self-contradictory, or contradicting other items in the general body of knowledge. If we denote by 0 such an impossible event, the symbol $P(\alpha|0)$ *is not defined*. Note further that $\bar{0} = 1$, the trivially certain event.

We are now able to state the laws of probability for compatible events as follows:

(i) $0 \leqslant P(\alpha|\gamma) \leqslant 1$; $P(0|\gamma) = 0$; $P(1|\gamma) = 1$.
(ii) If $\alpha\beta\gamma = 0$, $P(\alpha + \beta|\gamma) = P(\alpha|\gamma) + P(\beta|\gamma)$.
(iii) $P(\alpha\beta|\gamma) = P(\alpha|\gamma)P(\beta|\alpha\gamma) = P(\beta|\gamma)P(\alpha|\beta\gamma)$.

It must be emphasized that an event of zero probability is not necessarily impossible; nor is one of unit probability a certainty. The last two equations in (i) have no converse.

A simplification of these laws is obtained in the case $\gamma = 1$, whereupon they reduce to the following form, which we shall use in most of the later illustrations:

(i)' $0 \leqslant P(\alpha) \leqslant 1$; $P(0) = 0$; $P(1) = 1$.
(ii)' If $\alpha\beta = 0$ (mutual exclusiveness) $P(\alpha + \beta) = P(\alpha) + P(\beta)$.
(iii)' $P(\alpha\beta) = P(\alpha)P(\beta|\alpha) = P(\beta)P(\alpha|\beta)$.

In an increasing number of publications in the mathematical literature, (iii) is not regarded as a *law* but as a *definition* of conditional probability, which would read "$P(\alpha|\gamma)$ is *defined* as $P(\alpha\gamma)/P(\gamma)$. Then the whole formal (abstractly mathematical) theory is derived from just (i)' and (ii)' (and in addition, a law of continuity, needed when the possible outcomes of a trial are infinite). This simplification—of starting with minimal assumptions—achieves theoretical elegance, and makes no difference in the resulting theorems. But in a theory to be applied to the real world by actual human operators, it ignores the fact that the concept of "the probability of α, given that γ has in fact occurred" *is already defined* (a comparable false simplification has occurred when, in the laws of Newtonian mechanics, "force" is *defined* as the product of mass times acceleration, in spite of the fact that it is measurable by other means, can be felt in static situations, and is a perfectly clear concept in itself)—with just as much or as little clarity as is the unconditional $P(\alpha)$. Of the many examples illustrating this point, we cite just one: the reasoning invoking the passive nature of observations in deriving formula (8) in Chapter 6, Section 3, and (40') in Chapter 3, Section 6.

3. DEDUCTIONS FROM THE LAWS: THEOREMS

Some immediate consequences of the laws, in combination with logically self-evident properties of sets of statements (the events), can be obtained and are constantly used. We give a few examples; for a full development of the theory, the reader is referred to any modern text on the subject. *Here and in the references it is assumed that all the events considered form a compatible set.*

Complementary probability is derived by noting the logically self-evident facts: $\alpha\bar{\alpha} = 0$, $\alpha + \bar{\alpha} = 1$, from which (i)' and (ii)' yield $1 = P(1) = P(\alpha + \bar{\alpha}) = P(\alpha) + P(\bar{\alpha})$, so that $P(\bar{\alpha}) = 1 - P(\alpha)$. Similarly for the conditional probabilities we obtain $P(\bar{\alpha}|\gamma) = 1 - P(\alpha|\gamma)$. Note also that $P(\alpha|\gamma) = P(\alpha\gamma|\gamma)$.

Implication. We say that "α implies β" ($\alpha \Rightarrow \beta$) when we know that if α occurs, β must occur—although β might occur without α necessarily occurring. (In the technical language of logic, the $\Rightarrow$ and the $=$ signs are used here in the "meta-language": statements *about* the special statements we call "events"—but not being one of them. Our "implication" is not the [useless] "material implication," the statement $\bar{\alpha} + \beta$, which is merely another event.) Then clearly $\alpha\bar{\beta} = 0$ and, applying (ii)', $P(\alpha + \bar{\beta}) = P(\alpha) + P(\bar{\beta}) = P(\alpha) + 1 - P(\beta)$, by complementary probability. Writing this in the form $P(\beta) - P(\alpha) = 1 - P(\alpha + \bar{\beta})$ and using the first equation in (i)', we see that $P(\beta) - P(\alpha) \geqslant 0$ so that $P(\alpha) \leqslant P(\beta)$. Thus the theorem: *any event that implies another cannot have a greater probability than the latter.* Similarly for conditional probabilities.

Independence. We say that "α is independent of $\beta(\neq 0)$" when $P(\alpha|\beta) = P(\alpha)$. It then follows from (iii)' that $P(\alpha\beta) = P(\beta)P(\alpha|\beta) = P(\alpha)P(\beta)$. Now suppose that $P(\alpha) \neq 0$; (iii)' shows that the last product can be written as $P(\alpha)P(\beta|\alpha)$, so that, on canceling $P(\alpha)$, we have $P(\beta|\alpha) = P(\beta)$. In other words, β is independent of α; they form a *pair of independent events*. To generalize, first note that if the probabilities of α and β are neither zero nor unity, the same will be true of their opposites $\bar{\alpha}$ and $\bar{\beta}$. Then if any pair formed by coupling one of $(\alpha, \bar{\alpha})$ with one of $(\beta, \bar{\beta})$ is a pair of independent events, the same will be true for every one of the four possible pairs so formed. These virtually self-evident statements are easily extended to the conditional probabilities.

Corresponding theorems can be formulated when instead of two events α and β, we have three: α, β, γ. While there is nothing new when each one is independent of each of the others, there is a new possibility when α is independent of β and of γ, but β and γ are not mutually independent. We must then enlarge the definition of independence, expressing it in terms of independent pairs obtained by coupling α (or $\bar{\alpha}$) with each element in the set formed by all the logical combinations of β and γ: the *Boolean algebra* generated by them. It has 16 elements (including 0 and 1) and is the sum of all possible sets of the $2^2 = 4$ mutually exclusive basic elements $(\beta\gamma, \bar{\beta}\gamma, \beta\bar{\gamma}, \bar{\beta}\bar{\gamma})$. It is not hard to show that if the four pairs obtained by coupling α with each of these basic elements is an independent pair, the same will follow when it is coupled with any of the (nontrivial) elements that they generate by addition (i.e., with every element of the Boolean algebra). Cases of elements of zero probability are excluded when necessary. Finally, two sets, $(\alpha_1, \ldots, \alpha_m)$ and $(\beta_1, \ldots, \beta_n)$ are said to be *mutually independent* if the pairs of elements formed by coupling an element of the Boolean algebra generated by the first set with one in that generated by the second always forms an independent pair. Only the 2^m and 2^n basic elements of each set need be considered. The independence of all other pairs will follow (always excluding impossible outcomes and those of probability zero).

The foregoing may seem to be an unnecessarily complicated rendering of the intuitively simple idea of two systems having 2^m and 2^n possible states and occupying them in a mutually independent way (statistically). In fact it is given little attention in most textbooks, which usually define independence by the product property. This simplification is only apparent; it merely shifts the difficulty to the point at which an *application to real* events is made.

From the foregoing, the repeated application of (iii)′ to the case of n independent events $\alpha_1, \ldots, \alpha_n$ gives $P(\alpha_1 \ldots \alpha_n) = P(\alpha_1) \ldots P(\alpha_n)$. This and complementary probability now lead to the survival probability formulas as well as to (1) and (5) of Chapter 3. We may write for the latter (noting that $\alpha_1 + \ldots + \alpha_n$ is the denial of $\bar{\alpha}_1 \ldots \bar{\alpha}_n$):

$$
\begin{aligned}
p_n = P(\alpha_1 + \ldots + \alpha_n) &= 1 - P(\bar{\alpha}_1 \ldots \bar{\alpha}_n) \\
&= 1 - [1 - P(\alpha_1)] \ldots [1 - P(\alpha_n)] \\
&= 1 - (1 - g_1) \ldots (1 - g_n).
\end{aligned}
$$

When $\alpha_1, \ldots, \alpha_n$ are mutually exclusive (i.e., $\alpha_i \alpha_j = 0$ for all $i \neq j$), the repeated application of (ii)′ gives $P(\alpha_1 + \ldots + \alpha_n)$ as $P(\alpha_1) + \ldots + P(\alpha_n)$. When they are not mutually exclusive but are independent, $P(\alpha_1 + \ldots + \alpha_n)$ is given in the preceding paragraph. There remains the case in which they are neither mutually exclusive nor independent. The result (going back to de Montmort in the seventeenth century) is easily obtained. We start with the case of $n = 2$ events, which we denote by α and β, and use the following relations, submitted as "logical truisms" (once their meaning is grasped):

$$
\alpha + \beta = \alpha + \bar{\alpha}\beta; \qquad \alpha(\bar{\alpha}\beta) = \alpha\bar{\alpha}\beta = 0
$$

$$
\beta = (\alpha + \bar{\alpha})\beta = \alpha\beta + \bar{\alpha}\beta; \qquad (\alpha\beta)(\bar{\alpha}\beta) = \alpha\bar{\alpha}\beta = 0.
$$

We may then apply (ii)′ to the sum in each line, obtaining

$$
P(\alpha + \beta) = P(\alpha + \bar{\alpha}\beta) + P(\alpha) + P(\bar{\alpha}\beta)
$$

$$
P(\beta) = P(\alpha\beta + \bar{\alpha}\beta) = P(\alpha\beta) + P(\bar{\alpha}\beta).
$$

Eliminating $P(\bar{\alpha}\beta)$ from these, we obtain the desired expression

$$
P(\alpha + \beta) = P(\alpha) + P(\beta) - P(\alpha\beta).
$$

The case $n = 3$ is handled by applying the above equation thrice: Set $\alpha = \alpha_1$, $\beta = \alpha_2 + \alpha_3$; we obtain, since $\alpha\beta = \alpha_1\alpha_2 + \alpha_1\alpha_3$,

$$
\begin{aligned}
P(\alpha_1 + \alpha_2 + \alpha_3) = P(\alpha + \beta) &= P(\alpha) + P(\beta) - P(\alpha\beta) \\
&= P(\alpha_1) + P(\alpha_2 + \alpha_3) - P(\alpha_1\alpha_2 + \alpha_1\alpha_3) \\
&= P(\alpha_1) + P(\alpha_2) + P(\alpha_3) \\
&\quad - P(\alpha_2\alpha_3) - P(\alpha_1\alpha_2) - P(\alpha_1\alpha_3) \\
&\quad + P(\alpha_1\alpha_2\alpha_3)
\end{aligned}
$$

De Montmort's theorem follows this pattern:

$$P\left(\sum \alpha_i\right) = \sum_i P(\alpha_i) - \sum_{i<j} P(\alpha_i\alpha_j) + \sum_{i<j<k} P(\alpha_i\alpha_j\alpha_k) \pm P(\alpha_1\alpha_2 \dots \alpha_n).$$

It is proved by induction: assumed true for $n-1$, it is shown to follow (by applying the case $n = 2$ enough times) for n events.

This theorem has two types of geometrical interpretation, which we illustrate in the case of $n = 3$ events, α, β, γ. The first is in terms of overlapping regions A, B, C, described, e.g., on a square of unit side; see Fig. A-1(a). Suppose that a raindrop falls at random on the square flag-stone of 1(a); and let α, β, γ, be the events of its falling within A, B, C respectively. The theorem expresses the probability that it will fall in at least one of the three regions, $P(\alpha + \beta + \gamma)$, in terms of the sum of their separate probabilities, corrected by *subtracting* the sum of the probabilities of the drop falling in the three intersections of pairs, but since this *over-corrects* the value, we compensate by *adding* the probability of the triple intersection. If "at random" means with probabilities proportional to areas, the above interpretation is even more geometrically immediate as a relation between areas.

In the circuit interpretation shown in Fig. A-1(b), A, B, C are switches, and α, β, γ, the respective events of their being closed (so a current can pass). The event of a current passing between the + and − terminals is clearly $\alpha + \beta + \gamma$. Its probability is again given by the de Montmort formula—which we might have obtained here also by the direct reasoning of the preceding sort.

The monkey and the switches. Suppose that the combination of four switches of similar appearance is made up in the "breadboard" model shown in Fig. A-2. A

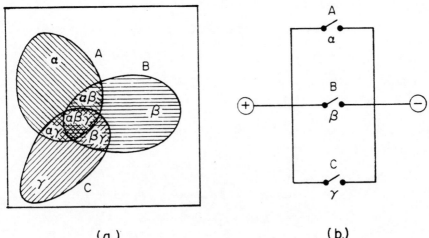

(a.)   (b.)

Fig. A-1. Two geometric interpretations of logical sums.

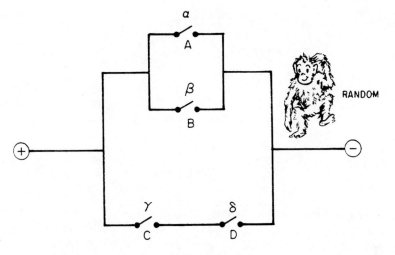

Fig. A-2. The circuit played with by the monkey.

monkey, having seen switches turned on and off, performs this operation re-peatedly with the breadboard switches—and is then driven away. What is the probability that things are so left that the current can pass between + and −? It is soon seen that this can be expressed as the event $\lambda = \alpha + \beta + \gamma\delta$. Applying de Montmort's formula, we get

$$P(\lambda) = P(\alpha) + P(\beta) + P(\gamma\delta) - P(\alpha\beta) - P(\alpha\gamma\delta) - P(\beta\gamma\delta) + P(\alpha\beta\gamma\delta).$$

Without insight into the mechanism by which the switches had assumed their final position, we could not have gone further. But our appraisal of monkey behavior strongly indicates first, that each switch has half a chance of being left closed, and second, that those events are independent. Then, by simple arithmetic, we obtain $P(\lambda) = 13/16$.

Returning to more fundamental things, we consider the totality of logical combinations of any given finite set of events (the Boolean algebra generated by the set). One can verify to oneself that any of its elements is a sum of products of the given elements and their denials. De Montmort's theorem expresses the result in terms of probabilities of sums of products. When the data (as in the above case) contain enough information to determine the probabilities of these products, the problem is solved; if not, and no further data can be found with the aid of reasonable assumptions, it is *indeterminate*. We close this section with a last theorem.

Bayes's theorem is an almost immediate consequence of (iii)'. Suppose that $\alpha_1, \ldots, \alpha_n$ are n mutually exclusive outcomes of a trial, one of which must occur ($\alpha_i\alpha_j = 0$ for $i \neq j$, and $\Sigma\alpha_i = 1$). We wish to find $P(\alpha_i | \beta)$, the conditional or a posteriori probability of α_i, given that β occurs. (ii)' gives

$$P(\alpha_i\beta) = P(\beta)P(\alpha_i | \beta) = P(\alpha_i)P(\beta | \alpha_i)$$

so that (excluding the useless case of $P(\beta) = 0$),

$$P(\alpha_i|\beta) = \frac{P(\alpha_i)P(\beta|\alpha_i)}{P(\beta)}.$$

Since $\alpha_1, \ldots, \alpha_n$ are mutually exclusive, so are $\beta\alpha_1, \ldots, \beta\alpha_n$, and furthermore, $\beta = \beta \cdot 1 = \beta(\alpha_1 + \ldots + \alpha_n) = \beta\alpha_1 + \ldots + \beta\alpha_n$. Replacing $P(\beta)$ in the above denominator by the sum of terms $P(\beta\alpha_j) = P(\alpha_j)P(\beta|\alpha_j)$, we obtain

Bayes's Formula:
$$P(\alpha_i|\beta) = \frac{P(\alpha_i)P(\beta|\alpha_i)}{\sum_j P(\alpha_j)P(\beta|\alpha_j)}.$$

Here the α_i are often termed the "causes" of the occurrence of β, $P(\alpha_i)$ are their a priori probabilities, $P(\beta|\alpha_i)$ their "productive probabilities" of β, and $P(\alpha_i|\beta)$ the a posteriori probability of the "cause" α_i, given that β has occurred.

The applications of this fundamental theorem throughout the theory of search have been amply illustrated in the present work. To point up the importance of confining its use to cases in which each item in its hypothesis is valid, we return to the monkey and the switches. Suppose that after the monkey has been driven away it is found (e.g., by an electric light in the circuit) that the current is passing. What is the probability that the lower branch CD is closed? If we were to apply Bayes's formula, we might proceed as follows: The a priori probabilities of the upper and lower branches are $P(\alpha + \beta) = 3/4$ and $P(\alpha\beta) = 1/4$. The productive probabilities (that the current will pass, given the closure of the branch in question) are each unity. Bayes's formula would then give $\frac{1/4}{3/4 + 1/4} = 1/4$. This answer is wrong: it should be $4/13$. The reason for the error is that the two "causes" α_1 and α_2 (upper and lower branch) are not mutually exclusive, as assumed in the Bayesian hypothesis. To find the correct result, let λ be the event of the current's passing; applying (iii)', we have

$$P(\lambda\alpha_2) = P(\lambda)P(\alpha_2|\lambda) = P(\alpha_2)P(\lambda|\alpha_2).$$

We have already found that $P(\lambda) = 13/16$; clearly $P(\alpha_2) = P(\gamma\delta) = 1/4$. Figure A-2 makes it evident that $P(\lambda|\alpha_2) = 1$. Hence $P(\alpha_2|\lambda) = 4/13$, as stated.

A notorious misuse of Bayes's formula has occurred in statistics. The difficulty of determining the a priori probabilities $P(\alpha_i)$ has often led to their being assumed all equal—sometimes a justifiable assumption and sometimes not, with resulting absurdities. Such abuses actually led an eminent statistician in the 1930s seriously to propose the *banning* of the teaching of Bayes's theorem in a certain great university.

What we have sought to emphasize—in these examples as throughout this whole appendix—is the importance of going back to first principles in any new or questionable application of probability. Its theorems applied as practical directions that do not need to be deeply understood can have disastrous practical results.

4. INFINITELY MANY OUTCOMES: VARIATES

There are many cases in which the natural model to use, as the simplest approximation to an actual situation, has a discrete infinitude of possible and mutually exclusive outcomes. Most often it is a sequence, and we can write the outcomes as the events $(\alpha_1, \alpha_2 \ldots)$; there are also cases of doubly infinite sequences $(\ldots, \alpha_{-1}, \alpha_0, \alpha_1, \alpha_2, \ldots)$. Not only does the subscript define the outcome of the trial, but the outcome determines the subscript: the subscript i has the probability $P(\alpha_i)$ of occurring. In this sense, the subscript is a "variable determined by chance" —the outcome of the trial or observation. Various designations are applied to such variables: *random* or *chance variables, stochastic variables, variates*. We shall adopt the latter for brevity. Of course the same concept applies to the case of trials having only a finite number of possible outcomes. The number of spots coming up in the throw of a die is a variate having integral values from 1 to 6, each with probability $1/6$. If we denote the index variate by X, and write an equation giving its value, such as $X = 3$, we are defining an event—the same event as α_3: $P(X = 3) = P(\alpha_3)$, etc.

If in any of these examples we construct a system of particles placed on the x-axis at the points of integral coordinates corresponding to the subscripts i and of mass $p_i = P(\alpha_i) = P(X = i)$, we have a (lumpy) distribution of total mass unity. The coordinate of the center of gravity is $\overline{X} = EX = \Sigma_i i p_i$, the summation being over the set of values taken by the indices (finite, or a one-way or two-way sequence). This is the *expected value* of X, (first "moment") $E(X) = \mu_1$. Theoretically it need not be finite, although in practice things can always be arranged so that it is. The *second moment* is $\mu_2 = E(X^2) = \overline{X^2}$ and is as important in statistics as in mechanics. It also may be infinite, although this is not a complication in most practical applications. The standard deviation σ is the radius of gyration of the system about its center of gravity and is determined by $\sigma^2 = E(X^2) - E(X)^2 = \mu_2 - \mu_1^2$.

A second class of cases involving observations or trials capable of infinitely many outcomes is that in which they are points in a continuum—on a line or line segment (finite or not), a plane or plane region, etc. These are among the most important cases in search theory and have already been amply illustrated. The possible outcomes are usually specified by one or more coordinates. Furthermore, in essentially all cases of interest in the experimental sciences and their applications, the probabilities of an outcome corresponding to any exactly prespecified point (or to exact values of its coordinates) is *zero* (we are excluding artifacts of certain types of approximation, or artificially constructed counterexamples). The basic form of the events in cases of a continuum of outcomes is that the state of the system belongs to a specified subregion $\mathcal{B}$ of the total possible continuum of states $\mathcal{C}$. Because of the operational requirement in the definition of "event," such subregions must be of such a nature—in regularity and simplicity of shape, etc.—that it is observationally possible to find whether the system is in state $\mathcal{B}$ or not (at least at the level of experimental accuracy). Evidently if a finite number of subregions $\mathcal{B}$ of $\mathcal{C}$ are of this observable character, so also are the regions constructed from them by taking complements $\mathcal{C} - \mathcal{B}$, set sums (unions) and intersections, but not in general the results of an infinite sequence of such processes. Furthermore, by (ii)', if a finite number of such regions are without intersections, and each has its individual probability of containing a randomly placed point, so does their union, and its probability is the sum of those of its parts. It is a *finitely additive set function*. The modern abstract theory of probability *embeds* this system of sets and set functions in a larger one, producing infinite additivity of sets (called "measurable") as well as of the set functions. See, e.g., Halmos [5], Chap. IX, Sect. 44 et seq. Since the measurable sets so obtained may not be of the nature of operationally observable events, applications to any particular natural phenomenon must be of an indirect character.

In the problems of search, as in applied mathematics in general, we are justified in assuming the order of regularity allowing the use of the methods of elementary calculus. In particular, we shall assume—as we have throughout this book—that our probability distributions in the plane have a regular density, the integral of which, over a region $\mathcal{B}$ gives its probability, and similarly for higher dimensional distributions. This is precisely what is done in considering the mechanics of material distributions, and as before, we take over the same formulas for centers of gravity: the expected position of the random point, and for the moments, etc.

5. ELEMENTARY THEOREMS ON VARIATES

In the one-dimensional case we use the function $F(x) = (X \leqslant x)$; then $F(b) - F(a) = P(a < X \leqslant b)$; for nonlumpy distributions, therefore, $f(x) = F'(x)$ is the probability density, and we have for the expected value and standard deviation σ the following integrals, to be taken over the whole x-axis:

$$EX = \int x \, dF(x) = \int x f(x) \, dx$$

$$\sigma^2 = \int (x - EX)^2 f(x) \, dx = E(X^2) - (EX)^2.$$

Now let Y be a second variate: (X, Y) is a variate point in the xy-plane of probability density that we denote by $p(x, y)$. Let us calculate the expected value of their sum:

$$E(X + Y) = \int \int p(x, y)(x + y) \, dx \, dy$$

$$= \int x \, dz \int p(x, y) \, dy + \int y \, dy \int p(x, y) \, dx.$$

Now clearly $\int p(x, y) \, dy = f(x)$ and $\int p(x, y) \, dx = g(y)$, the latter being the probability density of Y. Hence,

$$E(X + Y) = E(X) + E(Y).$$

Similarly, $E(cX) = cEX$; and indeed *the expected value of any linear combination of variates is the corresponding combination of their expected values.*

The case of products is more complicated, but when X and Y are independent in the sense of Section 2, we can show by the aid of (iii)' and the regularity assumed here that $p(x, y) = f(x)g(y)$. Then we have

$$E(X, Y) = \int \int xy\, p(x, y)\, dxdy = \int xf(x)\, dx \int yg(y)\, dy = (EX)(EY).$$

Thus *the expected value of a product of independent variates is the product of their expected values.*

The Bienaymé-Tchebychev Theorem
Let $a > 0$ be arbitrarily fixed. Then $P(|X - EX| \leqslant a) \geqslant 1 - \sigma^2/a^2$.

The proof is given by separating the integral defining σ^2 into three parts: one over the interval I_0 from $EX - a$ to $EX + a$ (in which $X - EX$ is between $-a$ and a); and the two others, I_1 where $X - EX \leqslant -a$, and I_2: $X - EX \geqslant a$. We have

$$\sigma^2 = \int_{I_0} (x - EX)^2 f(x)\, dx + \int_{I_1 + I_2} (x - EX)^2 f(x)\, dx.$$

Now we *decrease* the right-hand member if we drop the essentially positive integral over I_0. We further *decrease* it by replacing the factor $(x - EX)^2$ by the smaller quantity a^2. As a result we have

$$\sigma^2 \geqslant \int_{I_1 + I_2} a^2 f(x)\, dx = a^2 P(X \text{ in } I_1 \text{ or } I_2)$$

and this completes the proof, since $P(X \text{ in } I_0) = 1 - P(X \text{ in } I_1 \text{ or } I_2)$.

We derive the "law of large numbers," which tells us how the arithmetic mean of a succession of repeated independent trials that are (approximate) measurements of a variate comes close to its expected value as their number increases. Let the N trials to measure X (when comtemplated before knowing their results) be denoted by $X_1, \ldots, X_N$. The expected value of their mean, S, is $ES = (1/N)E\Sigma X_i = (1/N)NEX = EX$, their common expected value. The standard deviation of S is

$$E(S - EX)^2 = \frac{1}{N^2} E(X_i - EX)^2 = \frac{N\sigma^2}{N^2} = \sigma^2/N$$

Hence, by the B.T. theorem,

$$P(|S - EX| \leqslant a) \geqslant 1 - \frac{\sigma^2}{Na^2} \to 1 \text{ as } N \to \infty.$$

In other words, the probability that the mean will be closer to the expected value than arbitrarily prechosen constant a has a probability approaching unity as the sample size N increases indefinitely. This is, of course, based on the assumption of a finite EX and σ. It also assumes that the measurements are *without systematic error*—i.e., that every EX_i is the true value EX.

This theorem has recently been renamed the *weak law of large numbers*, to distinguish it from a mathematically stronger one, assigning probabilities to infinite sequences *as wholes*. Since statements about the latter do not seem to be operationally definable, any connection between the strong law of large numbers and the world of physical reality would seem to be highly indirect.

We close with the definition and properties of generating functions and characteristic functions of variates. In the case that X has only integral values, the *generating function* is the power series (or polynomial) $g(t) = \Sigma p_n x^n$. For a two-way sequence, it is a Laurent series of positive and negative powers. For a full discussion, with many important applications, see Feller [4], Vol. I.

The *characteristic function* $\phi(s)$ of a variate is more useful in the continuous case. It is

$$\phi(s) = E(e^{-isX}) = \int e^{-isx} f(x) \, dx;$$

in other words, it is the *Fourier transform* of the probability density. By formal differentiation under the integral sign (justified by the assumed regularity of $f(x)$) we find that

$$\left(\frac{d}{ds}\right)^n \phi(s) = \phi^{(n)}(s) = (-i)^n \int e^{-isX} x^n f(x) \, dx.$$

Hence,

$$\phi^{(n)}(O) = (-i)^n \int x^n f(x) \, dx = (-i)^n \mu_n,$$

and μ_n is the nth moment. Accordingly, $\phi(s)$ is called the *moment generating function*, since when expanded in a power series about $s = 0$ its coefficients are $(-i)^n/n!$ times μ_n.

Together with the former generating function, the characteristic function has a property that is largely responsible for its usefulness. Let X and Y be two *independent* variates: values known to be taken on by one do not alter the probability distribution of the other. Then evidently e^{-isX} and e^{-isY} are independent. Hence, the expected value of their product is the product of the expected values of the factors. Thus we have

$$Ee^{-is(X+Y)} = E(e^{-isX}e^{-isY}) = (Ee^{-isX})(Ee^{-isY}).$$

But this means that $\phi_{X+Y}(s) = \phi_X(s)\phi_Y(s)$. *The characteristic function of a sum of independent variates is the product of the individual characteristic function.*

In extending these concepts to more than one variate, as to the variate point (X, Y), it is more convenient to regard it as a *variate vector* having the coordinates as components. Then the new variable s introduced in the formulas above is now a *vector variable* of components (s, t), and the scalar product $sX + tY$ replaces the product used before. Here it is essential, in a distance-preserving change of coordinates (an "orthogonal" transformation), to subject the (s, t) to the corresponding change, so that $sX + tY$ remains invariant: $s'X' + t'Y' = sX + tY$. The definition of the characteristic function then becomes, in two or in n dimensions,

$$\phi(s, t) = E\{e^{-i(sX + tY)}\}, \phi(s_1, \ldots, s_n) = E\{\exp - i(s_1 X_1 + \ldots + s_n X_n)\}.$$

The proofs of all the properties for the single variate case go over unchanged.

The *normal distribution* in n-dimensional space has the form

$$p(x_1, \ldots, x_n) = K \exp(- Q(x_1, \ldots, x_n)),$$

where Q denotes a positive definite polynomial of second degree (i.e., positive except at a single point) and K is a normalizing constant (the reciprocal of the n-fold integral of exp over all n-space). The most familiar case is that of a single variate, which, together with its characteristic function, is given by

$$p(x) = \frac{1}{\sigma\sqrt{2\pi}} e^{-(x^2/2\sigma^2)}, \phi(s) = e^{-(\sigma^2 s^2)/2}.$$

The latter is found by a standard process of contour integration (for details, see Feller [4]). These formulas are written on the assumption that the variate X has been referred to its expected value as origin. A fundamental theorem in the present use of characteristic function is that (under the conditions of regularity that we assume) the latter *determines the distribution*; thus any distribution having the above characteristic function must be the normal one.

The n-variate normal distribution is reducible to the standard form. After shifting coordinate axes to the expected value of the variate vector, we *diagonalize* the resulting quadratic form Q by a rigid rotation of axes. It then becomes a sum of squares with positive coefficients, which we denote by $1/\sigma_j^2$: these are the *principal variances*. Thus the distribution takes on the form of a product of n single-variate normal densities, and the characteristic function is written down at once as the product of the single variate ones. Returning to the original axes, changing the s_i variables in the same manner, we see that the distinguishing property of the characteristic function of a normal distribution is to be of the form $\exp(-\frac{1}{2}L(s_1, \ldots, s_n))$, where L is a positive definite quadratic form in the variables s_j. When the distribution p is not centered at the expected point, a complex factor may easily be seen to appear in the characteristic function.

With these results, it is easy to show that the vector sum of any finite number of independent normal variates is normal, a fact that we have used in various places in Chapters 4 and 5.

Furthermore, the treatment of the diffusion equation outlined in Chapter 5, Sections 5 and 6, in cases in which the time does not enter into the coefficients or the boundary conditions, is directly carried out after making the appropriate passage to the characteristic function—i.e., by making a Fourier transformation.

These methods are also used in proving the *central limit theorem*, giving the normal law as an asymptotic approximation to a vector sum of a large number of random vectors—provided that as their number increases, they become increasingly "concentrated" about their mean. For precise statements, see Feller [4], Vol. II.

6. SEQUENTIAL DECISION THEORY

In Chapter 7 a study has been made of progressive search, carried out either as a sequence of operations, or as a continuous process evolving with the epoch t. In Section 1, in particular, the difference *in principle* between this conception of search and the "single try" search of Chapter 6 has been emphasized. In terms of our operational conception of events developed in this Appendix it is possible to put the matter in all clarity.

It is a truism of practical search that once the target has been detected the search stops. Or, if further action is taken, it is usually of a different kind: the lost pocketbook is picked up; the detected target if hostile and within range is attacked; the original broad type of search is followed by another type, capable of giving greater localization or surer classification; and so on. In terms of operational events, this means that the *choice of operations* to be performed at a given stage will depend on the *observed outcome* at the preceding stage. This is fundamentally different from the situation in a Markov chain, in which operations at all its epochs are predetermined, and only the conditional probabilities of the outcome of the next operation depend on the actual outcome of the one just before it, as explained in the next section.

Actually, the concepts described in the sequential search are closer to those considered in the discussion of compatibility versus incompatibility of events. In both cases, the *operation* O_α implied in the definition of the event α is at the focus of attention. But whereas incompatibility results from the effect of mutual prevention of operational observations (one destroys or essentially alters the other), sequential search changes the *choice of operation*. Thus if α and β are two searches for a target, after carrying out the operation O_α, we might have two choices of the β-operation, O_β or O_β', depending on whether α has failed or succeeded. But this is consistent with the compatibility of α and β as previously defined, viz., both composite operations $O_{\alpha, \beta}$ of O_α and O_β, and $O_{\alpha, \beta}'$ of O_α and O_β' are perfectly possible (even though the former might be practically rather pointless: why continue the same search if the target is already found?). In each case O_α and O_β (or O_β') can be regarded as defined by observing the α part and the β part of a single composite operation $O_{\alpha, \beta}$ (or $O_{\alpha, \beta}'$).

The situation illustrated by this example in search is extremely general and is at the heart of *sequential decision theory* and is implied in the various theorems and algorithms of *dynamic programming* and *differential games* as well as many similar studies. We give it the following general formulation, assuming for simplicity that all events and operations are compatible:

Let O^n be an observational operation or trial to be performed at the nth stage in a sequence, and let R^{n-1} be the totality of results that have become known to the operator in the performance of all these operations up to O^{n-1}. If he has an option regarding what O^n to perform, then his exercise of this option will lead to his making O^n depend on R^{n-1}: $O^n = \Omega(R^{n-1})$. Here the symbol Ω will often be regarded as representing a *functional* since it may depend on all the descriptors of the earlier results, themselves often functions. Of course, the integral valued n may be replaced by a continuous time t, but the results are more remote from the acts of real operators.

We shall give just one special example. Suppose that the operator will decide on his O^n according to the probability of an event α_n, and that $\alpha_1, \ldots, \alpha_{n-1}$ have occurred on the $n - 1$ earlier trials ($R^{n-1} = \alpha_1 \ldots \alpha_{n-1}$). Suppose that α_n depends on $\alpha_1, \ldots, \alpha_{n-1}$, i.e., that $P(\alpha_n)$ is different from $P(\alpha_n | \alpha_1 \ldots \alpha_{n-1})$. Then the choice of what operation O^n to perform, being determined by a conditional probability (of α_n), will be different from what it might have been had $\alpha_1, \ldots, \alpha_{n-1}$ not occurred.

The law of large numbers (weak or strong) applies to the case in which all the operations O^n ($n = 1, 2, \ldots$) are fixed in advance. The "weak" law, as shown in the last section, concerns what may be regarded as an infinite sequence of finite product spaces of increasing number of factors. The "strong" law deals with a space of infinitely many dimensions: the product of an infinite sequence of spaces. In each case the factor spaces in the products describe the outcomes of the separate trials. We have already raised the question of whether results established mathematically for the infinite product space have operational meaning—viz., express results that can be verified by a single possible act of observation. In view of the sequentially determined nature of practically all human observations of long duration, it might seem that the "strong" law is further removed from physical reality than the "weak," which supplies a useful approximation to the results of actually possible trials. The strong law would appear to have value only as an indirect instrument of thought.

7. STOCHASTIC PROCESSES*

Briefly, a stochastic process is a family of compatible variates, usually possessing certain orders of mutual dependence. When the family contains a finite number N of members it can be thought of as a *variate point* in N-space, along with a given or postulated probability density in this space. Of more interest to the physical sciences are cases in which there are infinitely many variates in the stochastic process: the variate point is in a space of infinitely many dimensions (e.g., function space) and the concept of probability density is either meaningless or at least highly obscure. Probabilistic properties in this case can be studied only after drastically restrictive assumptions are made—naturally suggested by the physical problem giving rise to the study.

In two of the most important cases, the family of variates either forms an infinite sequence (from 1 to ∞ or $-\infty$ to $+\infty$) $\{X_i\}$, or else can be identified by a single continuous variable t ranging over an interval, usually infinite in one or both directions $X(t)$. In addition to the individual probability distributions of the variate

---

*See Cox and Miller [2], Doob [3], and Feller [4].

X_i or $X(t)$ (their moments, etc.), their autocorrelations $r_n = E(X_i X_{i+n})$ and $r(s) = E[X(t)X(t + s)]$ play a vital role, especially when, as the notation suggests, they are independent of i or t: the stationary case (for one typical application, see Wiener [10]). The importance of these stochastic processes is their ability to describe so many phenomena in the physical sciences and such applications as communications engineering, meteorology, operations research and search theory, economics and the social sciences.

To indicate the basis of such applications, we must think of the individual variate X (i.e., a particular X_i or $X(t)$) as representing a *state of a system* (e.g., the variables of state) on a particular occasion (i or t). Then as i or t increases, X_i or $X(t)$ represents the *evolution* of the system in time or from occasion to occasion. This evolution could in certain cases be *determinate*; from one given state, all its future states are determined and in principle predictable, as in classical mechanics. But in the cases of present interest this is not true. Only the probabilities, or conditional ones, can be found, and it is precisely in the laws governing these that the specific nature of the stochastic process is manifested.

At the opposite pole from the determinate case is that of *independence* of all the variates in the set $\{X_i\}$ or $\{X(t)\}$. This is illustrated in the problem of independent trials, such as coin tossing, etc., but with the individual probabilities not necessarily being the same from trial to trial. Next to this is the *Markov process*; the probability distribution of X_{i+1} is determined by the given value (or point) of X_i and is unchanged by any further data concerning X_{i-1}, X_{i-2}, etc. The conditional probability distribution of X_{i+1}, given the value of X_i, is the *transition probability* $P(X_i \rightarrow X_{i+1})$ and is a function of the two sets of state variables and in general also of i. In the important case that they are independent of i, the process is called one of *stationary transition probabilities*; then there may or may not exist *steady states*, viz. distributions on the variates X_i that are independent of i. Corresponding but more exacting definitions of the Markovian property are given in the case of the continuous family $X(t)$. See Cox and Miller [2].

By far the easiest case of Markov processes to study mathematically as well as to program on computers is the stationary one. For this reason these are the ones most often used as models of the system under study. In many cases this assumption of stationary transitions has insufficient physical basis, even as an approximation. See the cases of diurnal factors that affect certain systems, ref. [5], Chapter 5.

In closing this section it must be mentioned that the set of variates in a stochastic process may require for their identification more parameters than the i or t specifying the epoch. Thus in the study of deformable media subject to turbulent motion, the variate X is the velocity and it is identified by the coordinates of position as well as by time. We have in fact seen cases of this situation in Chapter 5. And owing to the great importance of this way of envisaging turbulence, as it relates to meteorology, aviation, and disturbances of underwater propagation, it leads to a field as important as it is difficult. For introductory ideas, see Batchelor [1].

8. THE PRINCIPLE OF INCREASING ENTROPY AND THE CONDITION OF STABILITY

The numerical measure of the information in a given distribution has been introduced in Chapter 7, Section 6, through its negative, the *entropy H* defined there in (25) in the case of a system having just n states. Writing $I(p) = -H(p)$ we have (using the abbreviation log for $\log_a$, $a > 1$)

$$(1) \qquad\qquad I(p) = \sum_{i=1}^{n} p_i \log p_i;$$

and in the case of a continuum of states, corresponding to the value(s) of the variables(s) x, by its obvious generalization

$$(2) \qquad\qquad I[p] = \int p(X) \log p(X)\, dX,$$

which may involve a space of several dimensions: $(X) = (x_1, \ldots, x_m)$. Finally the *cross-entropy* (better: *cross-information*) $K(p, q)$ is defined as

$$(3) \qquad\qquad K(p, q) = \sum_{i=1}^{n} p_i \log \frac{p_i}{q_i};$$

while for continuous variates X and the two distributions $p(X)$ and $q(X)$,

$$(4) \qquad\qquad K(p, q) = \int_{\Omega} p(X) \log[\, p(X)/q(X)]\, dX.$$

Here we may of course have m dimensions, X: $(x_1, \ldots, x_m)$.

For many reasons, $I(p)$ is regarded as a numerical measure of the information concerning the state of a system contained in its probability distribution (p), and $K(p, q)$, the information concerning its state when a datum leads to the replacement of an a priori distribution (q) by an updated one (p). Cf. refs. [3–5] in Chapter 7. For this rather intuitive reason many distributions have been introduced —when a minimum of knowledge existed—on the basis of their property of minimizing $I(p)$ or $K(p, q)$, under the constraints of possible knowledge of some expected values. This method—although based on more objective physical reasoning—had led J. W. Gibbs and later J. von Neumann to the canonical distribution that occupies a central position in the statistical mechanics of reversible thermal phenomena.

In spite of many successes, there are difficulties in applying the purely subjective argument to the discovery of new distributions by this method. For one thing, an information-minimizing distribution under given constraints can exist (i.e., be free from mathematical contradictions) only under certain severe limitations of the constraints. For another thing, $I[p]$ in (2) gives values that can change under change of coordinates (variables of integration); no change occurs only when the change leaves unchanged the measure (length, area, volume, etc.), so that the

Jacobian is unity. This fact has led to an increasing use of $K(p, q)$, which is always left unchanged by the general coordinate change, but this requires for its application a knowledge of the a priori distribution (q).

The mathematical theory of the present subject is based on the *convexity inequality* (see Hardy et al. [6]). The function $f(x)$ occurring in the formulas above, defined as $x \log x$ for positive x and as its limit zero as x approaches zero through positive values, is continuous for all $x \geqslant 0$, and has a graph $y = f(x)$ always concave upward, as is shown by an elementary application of the calculus. Such a function is said to be *convex* over its interval of definition ("strictly" so when, as in the present case, the graph has no straight portions). The convexity inequality for such functions states that for any system of "weights," the weighted mean $\bar{f}(x)$ is greater than the value of the function at the similar mean of the variable $f(\bar{x})$—the case of all the weight concentrated at a single point is the only one in which $\bar{f}(x) = f(\bar{x})$; in all others, $\bar{f}(x) > f(\bar{x})$. The mechanical interpretation is that if we "load" our graph, regarding it as a material wire, its center of gravity will lie above the wire. The exceptional case is when the wire is reduced to a point. These concepts are proved by induction based on the precise definition of convexity, etc., and are extended to the case of any number of variables.

The following facts result from this inequality: $K(p, q) \geqslant 0$, and $K(p, q) = 0$ occurs if and only if the probability distributions (p) and (q) are the same. Further, the effect of a Markov states transition of (p) in (1) or (2) may increase or decrease the information, but if it has certain symmetry properties (e.g., has the same transition probability from any one state into a second as for the latter into the former) then it always either decreases the information or leaves it unchanged—the latter, when $I(p)$ is already a minimum, or when the transformation of states is *deterministic*. On the other hand, all Markov processes performed simultaneously on (p) and to (q) always decreases $K(p, q)$, but with the same two above exceptions; since its minimum is zero, this exception to the decrease means that the distributions (p) and (q) are the same. For details see Kimball et al. [7].

We shall apply the latter fact to establishing the "missing link" in the usual derivations of the Poisson distribution of an indefinite number of particles over a plain region. If $N = N(x, y)$ is as usual their density (of expected numbers) at the point (x, y), it is necessary to prove the following generalization of the formula (1) of Chapter 4, Section 1:

$$(5) \qquad P_n(u) = \frac{u^n}{n!} e^{-u}, \qquad u = \int_{\mathcal{B}} \int N(x, y) \, dx \, dy,$$

where $P_n(u)$ is the probability that the region $\mathcal{B}$ of the plane will contain precisely n targets. The usual proof assumes symmetry of the particles in the joint probability, i.e., that if $p(s_1, \ldots, s_m)$ is the probability that any set of individual particles $1, \ldots, m$ will be in the respective states $s_1, \ldots, s_m$, then this function is symmetric. It assumes further that these events are independent, i.e., that $p(s_1, \ldots, s_m) = p_1(s_1) \ldots p_m(s_m)$. With symmetry established, the latter factors are all equal. On the basis of these properties, the proof of (5) follows a familiar pattern. Let us compare the probabilities $P_n\{\mathcal{B}\}$ and $P_n\{\mathcal{B} + \Delta\mathcal{B}\}$ that there will be n particles in the region $\mathcal{B}$ and in the slightly increased one, $\mathcal{B} + \Delta\mathcal{B}$. By total and compound probability of independent events we obtain an equation from which, on dropping terms of higher order in the quantity $P_k\{\Delta\mathcal{B}\}$ for all $k > 1$, a differential equation is obtained. They form the sequence, for $n = 1, 2, \ldots$, called the equations of the *Poisson process*; see e.g., Feller [4], Vol. I, pp. 364 and 386. Their solution gives the desired (5).

The first missing link in this proof is that of symmetry, a property that is by no means self-evident and must be based on some physical conception of the phenomena involved. We shall *assume* that the forces of nature (or of the U-boat high command) deal with an even hand with the targets involved: in precise terms, that the random changes that operate on the latter form a Markovian sequence of transition probabilities that are *symmetric in the m pairs of state variables*, s_i and s_i'. From this it can easily be seen that if they act on a symmetric function $q(s_1, \ldots, s_m)$, its property of symmetry will be preserved. From any given $p(s_1, \ldots, s_m)$ we construct a symmetric one as follows. If T is a permutation that interchanges the m state variables, and $Tp(\ldots)$ the result of making this permutation on its variables, then we apply all $m!$ such permutations, take their sum, divide it by $m!$ to find our symmetric probability density (q). Applying the symmetric stochastic transformations to $K(p, q)$, it will decrease. Assuming that this process has gone on so long that quasiequilibrium has been established, and therefore that $K(p, q)$ is approximately zero, (p) and (q) are nearly equal. By this process our probability has become essentially symmetric.

The remaining link in the proof of (5) is supplied along similar lines. Now we must suppose that the stochastic changes in state act independently on the m particles, that the set of m events $s_i \rightarrow s_i'$, $i = 1, \ldots, m$ are all independent, in the carefully defined sense of Section 3. While a natural physical assumption for random particles of matter, it is very often untrue in the case of military targets. It excludes the frequent wolf-pack tactics of submarines, their mutual communication for the sake of rendezvousing or of warning. Each unit moves and acts with absolute independence of all others. When this property of random changes in state is assumed, it is easily seen that it retains the property of independence of states of any distribution. From any given $p(s_1, \ldots, s_m)$ we form the "marginal sums" or unconditional distributions of each particle $p_i(s_i)$ by integrating out all the $m - 1$ other state variables. The $q(s_1, \ldots, s_m) = p_1(s_1) \ldots p_m(s_m)$ is an independent distribution of the m particles. With the given (p) and the (q) thus defined, the decrease of $K(p, q)$ toward its lower limit, zero, establishes the independence in the quasiequilibrium state.

The most recent and comprehensive treatment of all such investigations is perhaps in the proceedings of the May 2–4, 1978, conference on the subject at the Massachusetts Institute of Technology, published under the editorship of Tribus and Levine [9]. Chapter 12, by John G. Pierce, is entitled "A New Look at the Relation between Information Theory and Search Theory," p. 339. In Chapter 13, p. 403, "Entropy Increase and Group Symmetry," the present author goes more deeply into the subjects touched on in this section, but with a particular emphasis on factors leading to entropy increase under given constraints, indicating the fundamental role of groups (sometimes of infinitely many parameters, called by Sophus Lie "infinite continuous groups").

REFERENCES

1. Batchelor, G. K. 1956. *The theory of homogeneous turbulence*. Cambridge, Eng.: Cambridge University Press.
2. Cox, D. R. and Miller, H. D. 1965. *The theory of stochastic processes*. New York: Wiley.
3. Doob, J. L. 1953. *Stochastic processes*. New York: Wiley.
4. Feller, W. 1950, 1966. *Introduction to probability theory and its applications*. vols. I, II. New York: Wiley.
5. Halmos, P. R. 1950. *Measure theory*. New York: Van Nostrand.
6. Hardy, G. H., Littlewood, J. E. and Polya, G. 1952–1973. *Inequalities*. Cambridge, Eng.: Cambridge University Press.
7. Kimball, G. E., Koopman, B. O., et al. 1959. *Notes on operations research*. Edited by P. M. Morse. Cambridge, Mass.: The Massachusetts Institute of Technology Press.
8. Koopman, B. O. 1940. The bases of probability. Bull. Amer. Math. Soc.: 46: 763–74 (and included references).
9. Tribus, M. and Levine, R. D., eds. 1978. *The maximum entropy formalism*. Cambridge, Mass.: The Massachusetts Institute of Technology Press.
10. Wiener, N. 1949. *Extrapolation, interpolation, and smoothing of stationary time series*. Cambridge, Mass.: The Massachusetts Institute of Technology Press and New York: Wiley.

Appendix B

Mathematical Supplement on Matrices

We have seen in Chapter 4, Sections 7 and 8, the application of the *method of least squares* to target localization, when more observations, subject to inevitable errors, are made than the number necessary to determine the exact position of the target, had there been no errors. We found, among other things, that the best estimate was the center of gravity of a system of *masses* placed at the points that each minimal set of observations indicated; we gave a method for estimating these masses and of describing the probable regions in which the target is located. While in principle these matters are as old as the use of least squares by Gauss, they have more applications to target localization than the ones given in Chapter 4. In fact, data from many sources and of various kinds can be combined to improve localization by least squares. This emphasizes the importance of realizing that the method of least squares can give valid results only under a set of assumptions, by no means axiomatic, and in many cases inapplicable. They are, as stated in Chapter 4, the lack of bias or systematic error, the relative smallness of the errors, their normal distribution, and the uniform a priori distribution of target positions in the region searched. The purpose of this appendix, in addition to emphasizing the facts above, is to establish a necessary algebraic tool for their implementation, sometimes called Lagrange's identity.

Lagrange's Identity. Let A and B be matrices (B_t is the transposed B), each of m rows and n columns, with $m \leqslant n$. Then the matrix AB_t, which has m rows and m columns, has a determinant equal to the sum of $C_m^n = n!/m!(n-m)!$ products of determinants $a(i_1, \ldots, i_m)b(i_1, \ldots, i_m)$, where the a-factor is the determinant formed from the columns indexed $(i_1, \ldots, i_m)$ in A, the b-factor is the corresponding determinant in B, and where all possible choices of the m integers $(i_1, \ldots, i_m)$ are made from the set $(1, \ldots, n)$—subject to the condition $i_1 < i_2 < \ldots < i_m$.

The proof is straightforward, but to avoid multiple subscripts we shall denote by symbols such as $a(i, j)$ and $b(i, j)$ the elements in the ith row and the jth column of A and B. If C is the m-by-m matrix product $C = AB_t$, by the definition of matrix product we have

$$c(\alpha, \beta) = \sum_{i=1}^{n} a(\alpha, i)b(\beta, i).$$

Hence the determinant det $C = \det[c(\alpha, \beta)]$ has each of its m^2 elements equal to a sum of n products. We shall apply the two elementary rules of determinants: if a column in a determinant is a sum of two columns (formed from any numbers whatsoever), the determinant is equal to the sum of two determinants, each having that column replaced by one of the two added columns; and the usual removal of a common factor from any column or row. Applying these processes to the βth column, we have

$$\det C = \begin{vmatrix} c(1, 1) & \cdots & \sum_i a(1, i)b(\beta, i) & \cdots & c(1, m) \\ \vdots & & \vdots & & \\ c(m, 1) & \cdots & \sum_i a(m, i)b(\beta, i) & \cdots & c(m, m) \end{vmatrix}$$

$$= \sum_i b(\beta, i) \begin{vmatrix} c(1, 1) & \cdots & a(1, i) & \cdots & c(1, m) \\ \vdots & & \vdots & & \vdots \\ c(m, 1) & \cdots & a(m, i) & \cdots & c(m, m) \end{vmatrix}.$$

We repeat this process, applying it to all columns; obtaining a result in which m different indices of summation $i_1, \ldots, i_m$ occur, each going independently from 1 to n:

$$\det C = \sum_{(i)} b(1, i_1) \ldots b(m, i_m) \begin{vmatrix} a(1, i_1) & \cdots & a(1, i_m) \\ \vdots & & \vdots \\ a(m, i_1) & \cdots & a(m, i_m) \end{vmatrix}.$$

There are m^2 expressions added, but all with the determinant on the right as a factor, and this is zero except when all $(i_1, \ldots, i_m)$ are *different*. Consider the class of terms in this sum having the same m numbers as indices: there are C_m^n such classes, and in each class, the m indices occur in all $m!$ orders. Take the member of the class for which the indices are in increasing order: $i_1 < i_2 < \ldots < i_m$: any other member of this class, e.g., with indices $(i_1', \ldots, i_m')$, differs with it only in sign, being equal to it or to its negative according as the permutation leading from $(i_1, \ldots, i_m)$ to $(i_1', \ldots, i_m')$ is even or odd. Hence, taking out the common factor determinant on the right of the equation above, it appears multiplied by the sum of $\pm$ b-products, $\pm b(1, i_1') \ldots b(m, i_m')$, the sign depending on the parity of the substitution above. But this sum, by definition of "determinant," is precisely the determinant $b(i_1, \ldots, i_m)$ of the theorem. We have indeed proved that

(28)

$$\det(AB_t) = \sum_{i_1 < \ldots < i_m}^{n} \begin{vmatrix} a(1, i_1) & \cdots & a(1, i_m) \\ \vdots & & \vdots \\ a(m, i_1) & \cdots & a(m, i_m) \end{vmatrix} \begin{vmatrix} b(1, i_1) & \cdots & b(1, i_m) \\ \vdots & & \vdots \\ b(m, i_m) & \cdots & b(m, i_m) \end{vmatrix}.$$

When $m = 2$, $n = 3$, this theorem gives us a familiar vector identity. Thinking of the two rows in each of A and B as representing the vectors $\mathbf{a}_1$, $\mathbf{a}_2$, $\mathbf{b}_1$, $\mathbf{b}_2$, having the three elements in the row in question as rectangular components, and using the notation for scalar product, we see that

$$\det(AB_t) = \begin{vmatrix} \mathbf{a}_1 \cdot \mathbf{b}_1 & \mathbf{a}_1 \cdot \mathbf{b}_2 \\ \mathbf{a}_2 \cdot \mathbf{b}_1 & \mathbf{a}_2 \cdot \mathbf{b}_2 \end{vmatrix}.$$

On the other hand, the $C_2^3 = 3$ two-rowed determinants in the matrices A and B are the components of the vector products $\mathbf{a}_1 \times \mathbf{a}_2$ and $\mathbf{b}_1 \times \mathbf{b}_2$ (apart from sign, which disappears in the product). Hence the sum in (28) is the scalar product of the latter: $\det(AB_t) = (\mathbf{a}_1 \times \mathbf{a}_2) \cdot (\mathbf{b}_1 \times \mathbf{b}_2)$.

In the case $m = n$, (28) shows that (when B is replaced by B_t so that $\det AB_t$ becomes $\det (AB)$ $\det(AB) = (\det A)(\det B_t) = (\det A)(\det B)$: i.e., it proves the law of determinant multiplication. Cf. Albert [1], Bôcher [2].

There is an important geometrical interpretation of (28), clearest in the case $B = A$. Then if the m rows of A are regarded as m vectors in n-dimensional space, and if they are drawn as directed line segments starting at the origin, they determine an m-dimensional flat space or m-plane; and in it, an m-parallelogram, bounded by m pairs of $(m - 1)$-planes, constructed as follows: From the m vectors omit one, and draw the $(m - 1)$-plane determined by the remaining vectors; and next, the m-plane parallel to the former through the tip of the omitted vector. Such pairs can evidently be constructed in m different ways. It is shown that the m-dimensional volume of this m-parallelogram is $\det A$ (if the vectors are taken in an appropriate order; zero, if the figure degenerates to a dimension lower than m). Assuming this, evidently the determinant $a(i_1, \ldots, i_m)$ is the m-volume of the projection of the original m-parallelogram on the m-plane of the axes of coordinates indexed with $(i_1, \ldots, i_m)$. Hence in this case, Lagrange's identity expresses a sort of Pythagorean theorem between m-areas. When $B \neq A$, it may be interpreted in terms of areas and angles of inclined m-planes. These relations are easy to visualize when $n = 3$ and $m = 2$. They could be proved by the transformation to standard positions and the application of the methods and results when $m = n$; they are only moderately accessible in the literature. (A good reference to these and many other related facts is Cartan [3], Chapters I and II. As that author and many others have amply shown, the simplest and most powerful tool for handling a vast variety of matters of this sort is the *exterior algebra* [introduced long ago by Grassmann].)

REFERENCES

1. Albert, A. A. 1946. *College algebra*. New York: McGraw-Hill.
2. Bocher, M. 1915. *Modern algebra*. New York: Macmillan.
3. Cartan, E. *Theory of spinors* (translated 1966). Cambridge, Mass.: The Massachusetts Institute of Technology Press.

Appendix C

The General Elementary Detection Law In Search Optimization

This appendix generalizes and deepens the analysis of the situation set forth in the first three sections of Chapter 6, where the definitions of search density $\phi(X)$ and the detection function $D(X, \phi)$ are given and the physical and operational assumptions upon which their definitions are based are considered in detail. These assumptions we shall continue to make. Recalling them, they are: that the search involves only *passive observations* (no alerting of targets or changes in the physical environment); that it is *local* in its effectiveness; that it is composed of one or more *single-tries* (no integration time is an important factor); that, as measured by $\phi(X)$ it is *subdivisible* and *additive*. These assumptions form part of the hypothesis of Theorem 1 of that chapter, but that hypothesis contained an additional assumption: that the probability of detecting the target is determined when its position is given (item (i)). When this assumption is dropped and is replaced by the more general one, that the detection probability requires for its determination in addition to its position X, k further parameters (y): $(y_1, \ldots, y_k)$, Theorem 1 is replaced by its corollary: the exponential law is still valid but in the form

$$(1) \qquad D(X, y, z) = 1 - e^{-Wz}, \qquad W = W(X, y), \quad z = \phi(X).$$

In this appendix we shall explore the effect of this more general detection law on the problem of optimal search in the case of the continuous probability distribution of the target, $p(X)$, the problem of Section 6 of Chapter 6. After obtaining the necessary condition for optimality, corresponding to that of Chapter 6, Theorem 3, but in the form of an integral equation, we identify an expression entering into the latter with the *partial detection function* $b(X, z)$, and show that it is in fact a Laplace-Stieltjès transform of a bounded monotone function. This $b(X, z)$ plays the same role as the similarly denoted function introduced in 1961 by De Guenin [1] as an ad hoc generalization of the exponential law of random search used since 1946. A result of the present appendix is that this function, being the transform as stated above, must be of a much more restricted character than the one that De Guenin and most of his successors arbitrarily assumed—if indeed it is to be consistent with the implications in its use in search optimization, either the single-try or the progressive searches described in Chapter 7.

The appendix closes with a brief discussion of two issues raised by the generalization in question. The first is the extent to which the additional assumptions of probability distributions—those involving (y)—can be established on a factual basis. The second is the question of the practical effect on the value of the search plans based on these generalizations. Could such refinements affect a search when the tracks of the searching units can only quite crudely approximate to the ideal optimum?

This appendix is essentially a condensation of the author's recent paper "An Operational Critique of Detection Laws" [4], where the various matters mentioned above are discussed in considerable detail.

1. FORMULATION AND SOLUTION OF THE PROBLEM OF OPTIMAL SINGLE-TRY SEARCH

For the sake of generality, the positional coordinates will be taken as j in number and denoted by $X: (x) = (x_1, \ldots, x_j)$; thus the full a priori probability density is a function of the $m = j + k$ variables $(x, y) = (x_1, \ldots, x_j, y_1, \ldots, y_k)$: we shall write it as $P(x, y)$. Since furthermore the detectability coefficient or "sweep width" is now assumed to depend on these m variables, we shall denote it by $W = w(x, y)$. In integration in (x), (y) etc., the abbreviations $dx = dx_1 \ldots dx_j$, $dy = dy_1 \ldots dy_k$, etc., will be used, as well as the writing of $\int \ldots dx$, $\int \ldots dy$, and $\int\int \ldots dx\, dy$ in place of j-fold, k-fold, or m-fold integrals—always taken over the full range in the space of the variables indicated. That of (x, y) will be called *system space*.

It is assumed that the a priori probability density $P(x, y) = P(x_1, \ldots, x_j, y_1, \ldots, y_k)$ of the target's positions in system space is given. In our notation we then have $\int\int P(x, y)\, dx\, dy = 1$. It is further assumed that the density of searching effort $\phi = \phi(x)$ can be so chosen as to optimize the search, under the constraints of positiveness and total amount Φ. Then the present generalization of Chapter 6, Section 2 ((5) and (6)), or Section 6 ((28) and (29)), is as follows:

Find that function $\phi(x)$ which maximizes the integral

$$(2) \qquad P[\phi] = \int \int P(x, y)[1 - \exp\{-w(x, y)\phi(x)\}]\, dx\, dy$$

*under the constraints**

$$(3) \qquad \int \phi(x)\, dx = \Phi, \qquad \phi(x) \geqslant 0.$$

---

*Assuming, as throughout this book, that the functions have the regularity (piecewise continuous differentiability etc.) of "physical" functions.

To find the necessary conditions that $\phi(x)$ must satisfy for the maximum, we begin by proceeding precisely as we did in Chapter 6, Section 6. Suppose that $\phi(x)$ actually maximizes $P[\phi]$ and that at some point x', ϕ is continuous and $\phi(x') > 0$; and let x'' be any other point where ϕ is continuous, but only $\phi(x'') \geqslant 0$. As in the earlier case, we may define two continuous functions $\psi'(x)$ and $\psi''(x)$, zero outside small neighborhoods $\mathfrak{N}'$ and $\mathfrak{N}''$ of x' and x'' respectively, and mutually congruent in the sense that their graphs can be made to coincide by a translation $x' \to x''$. Finally, we take $0 < \psi'(x) < \phi(x)$ within $\mathfrak{N}'$. Then for all $s \geqslant 0$, < 1, the function $\phi(x) - s\psi'(x) + s\psi''(x)$ will evidently satisfy (3), and hence when introduced into (2) in place of the original maximizing $\phi(x)$, will lead to a decrease (or no change) in $P[\phi]$. The nonpositive difference of the new minus the old value can easily be expanded in series of powers of s, which we take as positive, and the first power of which we then cancel. The resulting $\leqslant$ relation subsists in the limit as $s \to 0+$.

Writing for brevity

$$F(x, y) = P(x, Y) \exp[-w(x, y)\phi(x)],$$

the limiting inequality, expressing its members as iterated integrals, assumes the form

$$\int \psi'(x)\, dx \int w(x, y) F(x, y)\, dy \geqslant \int \psi''(x)\, dx \int w(x, y) F(x, y)\, dy.$$

Since $f(x) = \int w(x, y) F(x, y)\, dy$ is a continuous function of x, and since $\psi'(x)$ and $\psi''(x)$ are positive in the respective neighborhoods $\mathfrak{N}'$ and $\mathfrak{N}''$ but zero outside, the x-integrations of the products $\psi'(x)f(x)$ and $\psi''(x)f(x)$ in the expression above reduce to integrations over these respective neighborhoods. Further, the law of the mean for integrals may be applied and reduces the inequality to

$$f(\bar{x}') \int_{\mathfrak{N}'} \psi'(x)\, dx \geqslant f(\bar{x}'') \int_{\mathfrak{N}''} \psi''(x)\, dx$$

where $\bar{x}'$ is in $\mathfrak{N}'$, $\bar{x}''$ is in $\mathfrak{N}''$. Because of the congruence of $\psi'(x)$ and $\psi''(x)$, their integrals are equal and, being positive, may be canceled, leaving $f(\bar{x}') \geqslant f(\bar{x}'')$. Letting the neighborhoods shrink down to their respective centers x' and x'', $\bar{x}'$ and $\bar{x}''$ approach the latter, and by continuity, so do the functional values, and we obtain $f(x') \geqslant f(x'')$.

Returning to the original notation, we have proved that under the assumptions stated ($\phi(x)$ optimum and $\phi(x') > 0$, etc.):

(4) $\int P(x', y) w(x', y) \exp[-w(x', y)\phi(x')]\, dy$

$$\geqslant \int P(x'', y) w(x'', y) \exp[-w(x'', y)\phi(x'')]\, dy.$$

If in addition, $\phi(x'') > 0$, (4) would hold, but with the $\geqslant$ replaced by $\leqslant$; in this case the two numbers would be equal. Denoting their common value by λ, we have

Theorem 1. *Under the conditions listed at the outset of this section, for each given* $\Phi > 0$ *and optimizing* $\phi(x)$ *of* (2) *under* (3), *there exists a "discriminating" constant* λ *such that*

(i) if $\phi(x) > 0$, $\int P(x, y)w(x, y) \exp[-w(x, y)\phi(x)] \, dy = \lambda$
(ii) if $\phi(x) = 0$, $\int P(x, y)w(x, y) \, dy \leqslant \lambda$.

This can be expressed in terms of the subregion $\mathfrak{M} = \mathfrak{M}(\Phi)$ in position space $(x) = (x_1, \ldots, x_j)$ where $\phi(x) > 0$: $\mathfrak{M} = \{x: \phi(x) > 0\}$, together with its complement $\overline{\mathfrak{M}}$ where $\phi(x) = 0$. We see that the integrand in (2) vanishes throughout $\overline{\mathfrak{M}}$ and hence its maximum is

$$(5) \qquad P[\phi] = \int_{\mathfrak{M}} dx \int P(x, y)[1 - \exp\{-w(x, y)\phi(x)\}] \, dy;$$

while the determination of $\phi(x)$ is by means of the *nonlinear integral equation* (i), valid for x in $\mathfrak{M}$.

The reduction of these results to those of Chapter 6, Section 6, when the parametric variables y are absent should be obvious. In the next section we shall approach the earlier results along a different path not involving the dimensional restriction $k = 0$, i.e., with $m > j$.

2. PARTIAL DETECTION FUNCTIONS AND THEIR MATHEMATICAL LIMITATIONS

Using the same assumptions and notation as in the preceding section, it is possible to write (2) and (3) in a different form so as to introduce a further concept. We first set

$$(6) \qquad p(x) = \int P(x, y) \, dy, \qquad q(y|x) = P(x, y)/p(x),$$

thus introducing the ("marginal") probability density $p(x)$ for the distribution of position variables (x) in their j-dimensional space (given nothing concerning the values of (y)); and also, the conditional probability density $q(y|x)$ for the parametric variables (y) in their k-dimensional space (give the values (x) of the position variables). Then on writing (2) as an iterated integral, with the obvious abbreviations, we obtain

$$(7) \qquad P[\phi] = \int p(x) \, dx \int q(y|x)[1 - \exp\{-w(x, y)\phi(x)\}] \, dy$$

$$= \int p(x)b(x, \phi(x)) \, dx$$

where, for any $z \geqslant 0$,

$$(8) \qquad b(x, z) = \int q(y|x)[1 - \exp\{-w(x, y)z\}] \, dy;$$

and of course (3) remains unaltered.

Definition. *By a "partial detection function" b(x, z) shall be meant the conditional detection probability, given the values of some but in general less than all the system variables.*

As implied before, the usual case in which a partial detection function occurs is that of geographical regions that can be freely explored, whereas other system variables cannot be searched—at most their a priori distribution $q(y|x)$ at various points (x) being known. Then $b(x, z)$ is given by (8). One might then be tempted to use the term "local detection function" for such $b(x, z)$. This, however, would imply an inacceptable narrowing of the ideas, since sometimes physical variables of state can be searched (e.g., by radiation studies). Also, sometimes certain position variables cannot be searched; a detector might be so polarized that only east-west positions can be determined, not north-south. Finally the very important influence of *target aspect*, although a variable of relative position, cannot in general be individually examined in the searching process.

In these general terms, the problem of optimal search is that of maximizing, subject to (3), the value of

$$(9) \qquad P[\phi] = \int p(x)b(x, \phi(x)) \, dx,$$

there now being no discrepancy in the dimensions in the integrations in (3) and (9). In this form the original theory of optimal search of Chapters 6 and 7 has been extended, as noted before, but without qualifications beyond De Guenin's requirement of "regularity" in the sense to be examined in the following section. But the function $b(x, z)$ is mathematically restricted, as the following theorem shows.

Theorem 2. *Under the nonreactive and other hypotheses of the present appendix, every partial detection function is one minus the Laplace transform of a regular (in the sense of mathematical physics used before, not of De Guenin) nonnegative function $g(w) = g_x(w)$ having a unit integral on $0 \leqslant w < \infty$ in continuous cases, a Laplace-Stieltjès transform in general:*

$$(10) \quad b(x, z) = 1 - \int_0^\infty e^{-wz}g_x(w) \, dw, \qquad g_x(w) \geqslant 0, \qquad \int_0^\infty g_x(w) \, dW = 1$$

$$= 1 - \int_0^\infty e^{-wz} \, dG_x(w).$$

This is an almost immediate consequence of (8). First, $\int q(y|x) \, dy = 1$, as follows from (6), so that $b(x, z)$ may be written in the form $1 - \bar{b}(x, z)$, where

$$(11) \qquad \bar{b}(x, z) = \int q(y|x) \exp[-w(x, y)z] \, dy.$$

We temporarily drop the x from the notation for brevity, it being held fixed throughout the proof. It is restored in the final formulas.

For each positive value of w, we denote by $\Omega(w)$ the set of points in the space of the parameters (y) for which $w(y) < w$. (It will of course vary in general with (x), but we are holding that fast at present.) As w increases from 0 to $+\infty$, $\Omega(w)$ swells from a null set to the whole (y) space. Hence the function $G(w)$, defined as the probability that the point (y) will lie in $\Omega(w)$, viz.,

$$(12) \qquad G(w) = \int_{\Omega(w)} q(y)\, dy,$$

will increase from 0 to 1. The nature of the increase will depend on the probability distribution on the (y) space (conditioned on the given (x)). In the case of the exponential law with the fixed sweep width W, $G(w) = 0$ for w between 0 and W and will jump to 1 once w exceeds W. Then the second (Stieljès) form of (10) applies, giving the original exponential law. At the other extreme, $G(w)$ is continuously differentiable, $G'(w) = g(w)$ and $G(w) = \int_0^w g(w)\, dw$; and, as we shall show, the first form of (10) is valid. There are of course many more general possibilities—mathematically—but in the land of approximations, they need not concern us, and we shall complete the proof on the assumption of continuity.

Let the interval $[0, W]$ be subdivided into n pieces by the set of increasing points w_i, where $w_0 = 0$ and $w_n = W$, and write $\Delta\Omega_i = \Omega(w_i) - \Omega(w_{i-1})$ and $\Delta G_i = G(wi) - G(w_{i-1})$. Then

$$\int_{\Omega(W)} q(y) \exp[-w(y)z]\, dy = \sum_{i=1}^{n} \int_{\Delta\Omega_i} q(y) \exp[-w(y)z]\, dy$$

$$= \sum_{i=1}^{n} \exp[-\overline{w}_i z] \int_{\Delta\Omega i} q(y)\, dy$$

$$= \sum_{i=1}^{n} \exp[-\overline{w}_i z]\, \Delta G_i,$$

the latter two expressions, in virtue of the law of the mean for integrals: $\overline{w}_i$ is some value of $w(y)$ in $\Delta\Omega_i$, and hence is between w_{i-1} and w_i. Hence, letting the maximum length of the intervals approach zero as $n \to \infty$, the sum formula gives

$$\int_{\Omega(W)} q(y) \exp[-w(y)z]\, dy = \int_0^W e^{-wz}\, dG(w) = \int_0^W e^{-wz} g(w)\, dw.$$

From this, on letting $W \to \infty$, (11) follows, thus proving the theorem. Restoring the (x), we write the result in the form

$$(13) \qquad \bar{b}(x, z) = \int_0^\infty e^{-wz}\, dG_x(w).$$

Bernstein's Theorem (see, e.g., Widder [7], chap. IV, p. 160, where the many properties of this class of functions are given in detail) may be applied: the expression above for $\bar{b}(x, z)$, namely, that $\bar{b}(x, z)$ *must not only be nonnegative but every z derivative of even order must also be nonnegative, and every one of odd order, nonpositive.* This is formally obvious on differentiating under the integral sign. Less obvious is the converse: *that any $\bar{b}(x, z)$ having these properties is of the form* (13). Furthermore, *it is analytic in z.*

3. DE GUENIN'S "REGULAR" DETECTION FUNCTIONS IN OPTIMAL SEARCH

These functions, $b(z)$ or $b(x, z)$, were defined by De Guenin [1] as functions of the nonnegative searching effort density z at (x) that, when plotted against z, give a constantly rising curve, bounded by the horizontal one unit above the origin, always concave downward, and passing through the origin and tangent there to a line of positive slope. Examples of such functions have been encountered in Chapter 3, and, in the notation $b(x, z) = D(x, z) = D(X, \phi)$, in Chapter 6, Section 1, formulas (3) and (4). The one in (2) is only a limit of such functions. Examples of detection functions not having the De Guenin property are given in Chapter 3, Section 11, Fig. 3-15 (effect of integration time) and in Chapter 7, Section 7 (reactive targets).

Theorem 2 and Bernstein's Theorem show that all functions having the properties assumed in this appendix are *regular in the sense of De Guenin*, but *the converse is not true*. The former constitute but an extremely restricted subclass of the latter. Inasmuch as the major part of the research on optimal search is based on these De Guenin functions (see, e.g., the extensive references given by Dobbie [3] and Stone [6]) and since moreover, most of the research involves more or less implicitly the very same assumptions—and conceptions based on them (e.g., local search density, its subdivisibility, additivity without change of the form of the function $b(x, z)$, etc.)—that we have set forth here and that have formed the hypothesis of Theorem 2, it is difficult to regard such research as more general *in fact* than if it had restricted itself to the Laplace-Stieltjès transforms of the theorem above, (10).

Restricting our attention, therefore, to the detection functions (10), it is clear that they can be described as representing searches with a *variable sweep width*. They were first introduced in 1946 by the present author and his wartime colleagues in the analysis of certain operational data (see Chapter 3, Section 10), and have been applied to a number of operational investigations at the Naval Operations Evaluation Group since then. The results (not publicly available) were disappointing for the following reason: it was easy enough to select a distribution function $G(w)$ or $g(w)$, for example, a normal one, and to find values of its parameters that gave a good fit to a given set of operational data, but when another set of data—gathered under similar conditions—were studied, there was no longer a good fit until the parameter values were changed. Since there seemed no way of predicting on an objective basis what values to use in future cases, the use of such sweep width distributions *could have no predictive value* and could not be used in planning an actual future search.

As noted in Chapter 3, Section 10, we had felt early in the application of these methods that a different distribution of sweep widths, such as the Pearson Type III distribution (now usually called the gamma distribution) would be more natural as representing a picture of the phenomenon in question, but it was not used in the studies mentioned. The *theory of searches with variable sweep width* has been studied in 1969 by Stone [6] and in 1972 by Richardson and Belkin [5]. These authors have also obtained simple and beautiful mathematical formulas by using the hypothesized gamma distribution. They have not as yet published any application of these results to any searches actually made.

To anyone reading the works referenced above on optimal search using the general detection functions of the type given in (10), and a fortiori those of De Guenin, it is obvious that the theory is more complicated (we would say, by an order of magnitude) than the conventional developments based on the exponential detection law. Moreover, anyone familiar with the operational difficulties in realizing, with actual searcher tracks, an approximation to any mathematically given optimal plan—problems of the sort set forth in Chapters 8–10—may well ask whether the added complications buy any real improvement. Future research in this field can alone decide.

REFERENCES

1. De Guenin, J. 1961. Optimum distribution of effort: an extension of the Koopman basic theory. *Operations Research* 9: 1–7.
2. Dobbie, J. M. 1963. Search theory: a sequential approach. *Naval Research Logistics Quarterly* 4: 323–34.
3. Dobbie, J. M. 1968. A survey of search theory. *Operations Research* 16: 525–37.
4. Koopman, B. O. 1979. An operational critique of detection laws. *Operations Research* 27: 115–133.
5. Richardson, H. R. and Belkin, B. 1972. Optimal search with uncertain sweep width. *Operations Research* 20: 764–84.
6. Stone. L. D. 1975. *Theory of optimal search*. New York: Academic Press.
7. Widder, D. V. 1941. *The Laplace transform*. Princeton, N.J.: Princeton University Press.

Appendix D

Arrays and Lobes

The relations between received acoustic intensity and angle off the acoustic axis of an array, used in Chapter 4, Sections 3 and 6, are developed in standard texts [1 and 2]. Since these treatments are lengthened by the inclusion of technical material not used in our work and are not quite reduced to the form appropriate to our present uses, the basic facts are outlined here.

1. THE BROADSIDE PATTERN FUNCTION

Starting with an array of n elements, all of the same physical characteristics and equally spaced a units apart on a straight line of length $L = (n - 1)a$, we consider what happens when a plane sinusoidal wave is incident at an angle θ with the array axis. Our first assumption is that the electric signals produced by each array element (hydrophone) under the action of the acoustic signal arrive at the central processing point simultaneously (no "delay lines"), where their instantaneous amplitudes (i.e., at epoch t) are added. Under these conditions the *acoustic axis* of the array is perpendicular to it, so that θ is the angle between the incident ray (normal to the wave front) and the acoustic axis. We shall develop the relation between the acoustic intensity received at the central processing point and this angle θ. It is based on the space and time sequence of events diagrammed in Fig. D-1.

After a proper choice of time origin, we may suppose that the acoustic signal that reaches element B has the expression $K \cos \omega t$, where the angular frequency $\omega = 2\pi f$, f being the usual frequency, and the constant K is proportional to the mean amplitude. Clearly the same $K \cos \omega t$ also gives the acoustic signal at all points of the wave front CB. Therefore the amplitude at B', the adjacent element to B, has to travel an additional distance $b = a \sin \theta$, and therefore reaches B' a time b/c later, where c is, as usual, the sound speed. Therefore the amplitude of its contribution to the central signal-processing point is $K \cos \omega(t + b/c)$. Similarly,

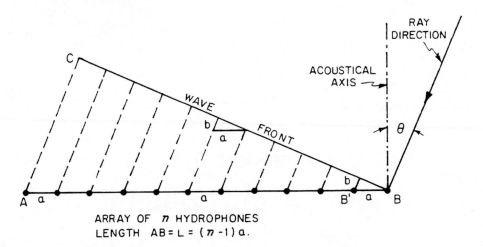

ARRAY OF n HYDROPHONES
LENGTH $AB = L = (n-1)a$.

Fig. D-1. Formation of acoustic interference lobes by an array.

the contribution of an element k spaces to the left of B is $K \cos \omega(t + kb/c)$. At the central processing point the signals from the n elements are added, giving the total signal

$$S = K\left[\cos \omega t + \cos \omega(t + b/c) + \cdots + \cos \omega(t + (n-1)b/c)\right]$$

$$= k \cos \omega(t + (n-1)b/2c) \times \frac{\sin(\omega nb/2c)}{\sin(\omega b/2c)},$$

by a standard formula of trigonometry.

However, since the *acoustic intensity* is proportional to the power of the electric signal S, we must calculate the mean square of S which is the integral of S^2 over one period $T = 1/f = 2\pi/\omega$, divided by T. Since t enters only into the cosine factor, whose mean square is $1/2$, the following result is obtained

(1)
$$\overline{S^2} = \frac{1}{2} K^2 \frac{\sin^2(\omega nb/2c)}{\sin^2(\omega b/2c)}, \qquad b = a \sin \theta.$$

The usual way in which the dependence of received acoustic intensity on angle θ is represented is by means of a polar diagram in which the ratio $\rho = \overline{S^2}/\overline{S_0^2}$ is plotted as a function of θ, where $\overline{S_0^2}$ is the maximum acoustic intensity, obtained in the present case when $\theta = 0$. (This is true, also, at $\theta = \pm \pi$, when both sides of the array are used, but because of the symmetry in AB, every result for one side is carried over by reflection in AB—rotation about AB, if all-round use were made.) To find this maximum, set $\omega b/2c = x$ and write the ratio of sines as

$$\frac{\sin nx}{\sin x} = n \cdot \frac{\sin nx}{nx} \cdot \frac{x}{\sin x}.$$

As θ approaches zero, so do b, x, and nx. Hence by an elementary property of the sine, the second and third ratio on the right approach unity. This leads to the expression $\bar{S}_0^2 = K^2 n^2/2$; and our intensity ratio is given by

$$(2) \qquad \rho = \frac{\sin^2(\omega nb/2c)}{n^2 \sin^2(\omega b/2c)}, \qquad b = a \sin \theta.$$

When plotted in polar coordinates, (2) gives a curve inscribed in the unit circle $\rho = 1$, tangent to it at the maxima ($\theta = 0$, $\pm \pi$), and symmetric in the array axis AB ($\theta = \pm \pi/2$) and in its perpendicular axis ($\theta = 0$, $\pm \pi$). The polar plot has the form of two main lobes and several side-lobes. As θ increases from 0 to the first value θ_0, for which $\omega nb/2c = \pi$, the power ratio ρ falls from 1 to 0. Replacing b by its expression in (2), this means that the value of θ_0 for which $\sin \theta_0 = 2\pi c/\omega na$ is the zero-power, half-angular width of the principal lobe(s). Replacing ω and na by $2\pi f$ and $L + a$, this becomes $\sin \theta_0 = c/f(L + a)$ or $\sin \theta_0 = c/fL$ when $n \gg 1$. Thus if $c = 1500$ m/sec., $f = 100$ Hz, and $L = 300$ m, we have $\sin \theta_0 = 1/20$, so that $\theta_0 = 1/20$ radian (to four places) or a trifle under $3°$, for the zero-power lobe half-width.

The conventional method of giving the width of a lobe is not to give its whole width as above, however, since this would include parts of the lobe too feeble to be useful. Instead one gives the "half-power" angle, $\bar{\theta}$, at which the lobe is cut by the circle $\rho = 1/2$, or equivalently, a drop of 3 db from full power at $\theta = \bar{\theta}$. The value of $\bar{\theta}$ is found by solving for θ the trigonometric equation obtained from (2) by setting $\rho = 1/2$ and replacing b by its expression in θ.

It will be noted from the above that since the important values of θ that come into play are small (as expressed in radians), it is permissible to use the approximation in which $\sin \theta$ is replaced by θ. Thereupon equation (2) becomes

$$(3) \qquad \rho = \frac{\sin^2 m\theta}{(m\theta)^2}, \qquad m = \omega na/2c.$$

This gives for the lobe half-width, $\theta_0 = \pi/m$ radians, and for the half-power angle $\bar{\theta} = u/m$, where u is the solution of the simple trigonometric equation $\sin u = u/\sqrt{2}$, so that $u = 1.392$ (all angles in radians). And, finally, $\bar{\theta}/\theta_0 = u/\pi = 0.442$. Thus $\bar{\theta} = 0.442\theta_0$, so that the lobe width measured as half-power down is proportional to the width of the full lobe.

2. THE ELECTRICALLY STEERED PATTERN FUNCTION

In the preceding derivations it has been assumed that the kth signal, once it reaches the kth hydrophone after the time delay kb/c, has its electrical signal reaching the central processing point without further delay. Now suppose that its electrical signal from the kth hydrophone passes through a circuit that imparts to it a phase delay of $\Delta t_k = kh/c$ seconds: k times the elementary delay time h/c. Then the total delay in passing from the wave-front CB to the central processing point would be kb'/c instead of kb/c, where $b' = h + b$ (the physical meaning of h is the distance in water that sound would travel in the delay time b/c introduced by the circuit). It is to be emphasized that the "delay" h/c can be negative, thus amounting to a phase *advance*. In any case, the derivation of all the formulas through (1) are the same as before, only with b replaced by the b' defined above.

REFERENCES

1. *Officer, C. B.* 1958. Sound transmission. New York: McGraw-Hill, Chapter 6.
2. *Urick, R. J.* 1967. Principles of underwater sound for engineers. New York: McGraw-Hill, Chapter III, Sections 4, 7, and 8.

Appendix E

Visual Detection

1. THE HUMAN EYE AS A DETECTING INSTRUMENT

The human eye, like a camera, has optical imaging elements and a light-sensitive surface on which an image is formed. Although the analogy suffers from oversimplification, it can serve an organizing function in discussing aspects of the human visual system that are pertinent to target detection.

A diagram showing the basic elements of the human eye is given in Fig. E-1. The transparent front surface of the eye, the *cornea*, is the primary refracting element of a compound lens system made up of the cornea and the crystalline *lens*. In a camera, which has a lens of fixed refracting power, the image is focused on a light-sensitive film by changing the distance between lens and film. In the human eye the image is made to fall on the *retina*, the light-sensitive surface, by adjusting the shape—and thus the refracting power—of the crystalline lens.

There is a point in the center of any lens such that quanta passing through that point will not be deflected in their paths. In the human eye, this point is located about 17 mm in front of the retina when the normal eye is focused on an object farther than about 3 m away. The lens is most strongly refractive when focused on a very near object, in which case the back focal distance is reduced to about 14 mm. The size of an image on the retina can be calculated by using this information. In Fig. E-2, an observer is looking at a tree 30 m high and 100 m away. When the image is in the plane of the retina, the top and bottom of the image can be located essentially by drawing paths of no deflection through point P, yielding an angle α, and determining the linear dimension of the image according to the following relationship:

$$30/100 = \text{size of image (mm)}/17$$
$$\text{size of image} = 30 \times 17/100 = 5.1 \text{ mm.}$$

It is often more convenient to refer to the size of an image in terms of the angle subtended at the nodal point P, rather than in linear dimensions on the retina, because that angle is equal to the angle α, subtended at the eye by the object in

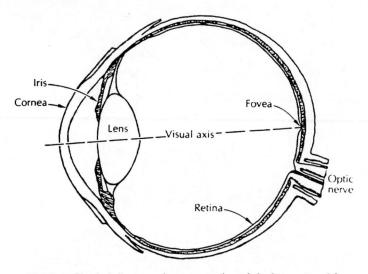

Fig. E-1. Classical diagram of a cross section of the human eye (cf. also Cornsweet).

space. In the example in Fig. E-2, the image size in terms of visual angle α, is

$$\alpha = \tan^{-1} 30/100$$
$$\alpha = 16°27'$$

Throughout the remainder of this appendix, image sizes and target sizes will be given in visual angles, because of the convenience obtained from the fact that a small object a short distance away may produce the same sized image as a larger object a longer distance away. The sizes of some familiar objects are given in visual angles in Table E-1.

Between the cornea and lens is the *iris*, the pigmented portion of the eye, which forms an aperture, the *pupil*, which is analogous to the adjustable diaphragm in a camera. In response to changes in light level, the iris is capable of contracting and

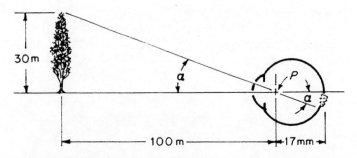

Fig. E-2. Conventional optical representation of the eye looking at a tree (cf. also Cornsweet).

Table E-1. Sizes of Selected Objects in Terms of Visual Angle, α*

Object	Size, s	Distance, d	Visual Angle, α
Sun	1.4×10^6 km	1.5×10^8 km	30'
Moon	3.5×10^3 km	3.9×10^5 km	30'
Quarter-dollar	2.4 cm	2.7 m	30'
Destroyer	120 m	13 km	30'
Submarine sail	10 m	1.1 km	30'
Aircraft carrier	300 m	35 km	30'
Quarter-dollar	2.4 cm	80 m	1'

---

*Visual angle α determined by the relation

$$\tan \alpha = \frac{s}{d}$$

where s is a linear measure of the object projected onto a plane perpendicular to the line of sight (if the object has a circular shape when projected onto a plane perpendicular to the line of sight, the appropriate measure would be the diameter of the object; for objects of other shapes, the dimension taken is a matter of choice) and d is the distance between the observer's eye and the object.

dilating, thus changing the pupil diameter within its range of about 7 mm maximum diameter to a minimum of about 2 mm. Within a small dynamic range, then, the pupil adjusts for changes in light level by allowing more or less light to enter the eye.

Light that strikes the eye is refracted by the cornea and lens to form an image on the *retina*, the thin, light-sensitive surface that lines the back of the eye. The retina is a very complex surface made up of billions of cells, more than one hundred million of which are receptor cells that are sensitive to light and the remainder of which are neural cells that connect the receptor cells in a complex processing network and eventually transmit sensory information to other parts of the brain. There are two types of receptor cells in the retina—*cones* and *rods*.

Cone cells are sensitive only to the fairly high levels of illumination encountered in daytime. Cones are responsible for color vision and for the ability to resolve fine detail. There is a small area of the retina, the *fovea*, which provides the finest spatial resolution. It is a small area, about one degree of visual angle in diameter, which is tightly packed with about 15,000 cone cells, whose center-to-center distances are approximately 0.5 min of visual angle. When an observer is "looking at" an object, the image of the object falls on the fovea, to the extent that the image is contained within a one-degree visual angle.

Rod cells are much more sensitive to light than cones and thus provide the extra sensitivity needed for night vision. Rods are not capable of distinguishing different colors, however, and the spatial resolution provided by rod vision alone is much poorer than that of foveal cones.

Table E-2. Photopic and Scotopic Vision of the Human Eye*

	Phototopic	Scotopic
Receptor	Cones (ca. 7 million)	Rods (ca. 120 million)
Retinal location	Concentrated at center, fewer in periphery	General in periphery, none in fovea
Neural processing	Discriminative	Summative
Peak wavelength	555 nm	505 nm
Luminance level	Daylight (1 to 10^7 mL)	Night (10^{-6} to 1 mL)
Color vision	Normally trichromatic	Achromatic
Dark adaptation	Rapid (ca. 7 min)	Slow (ca. 40 min)
Spatial resolution	High acuity	Low acuity
Temporal resolution	Fast reacting	Slower reacting

*From Kling and Riggs, 1971.

Some of the differences between cone-mediated (photopic) and rod-mediated (scotopic) vision are tabulated in Table E-2. Figure E-3 shows a horizontal section of an eye with the peripheral visual field indicated in degrees, and the distribution of rod and cone receptor cells as a function of peripheral visual angle.

When an image is formed on the retina, the photons comprising the image are absorbed by receptor cells (cones or rods) causing a photochemical change in a substance contained in the receptor cell, which is transformed into a change in nerve cell potential, which in turn is transmitted through a network of nerve cells to the visual cortex of the brain resulting in perception of the image—seeing.

One function of the neural network is apparently to compare the responses of nerve cells in adjacent areas of the retina. It is sufficient to be aware at this point that the effective stimulus for suprathreshold target detection is not the absolute quantity of light energy at any given point on the retina, but changes in energy level with time and differences between energy levels incident on one area of the retina relative to another area.

If a given level of light energy is incident upon a large area of the retina for more than a minute or two, the receptor cells cease to record that level as a difference, and reset, or adapt, to that light level as a new value of background, against which a new difference may be detected. The most familiar adaptation process is *dark adaptation*, a fairly complex process involving changes in the chemical equilibrium of photosensitive substances in the retinal receptor cells. When an observer who is thoroughly adapted to daylight illumination is placed in darkness, where his absolute threshold for seeing a target is measured, it is found that the threshold for detection decreases (sensitivity increases), rapidly at first, and then more slowly until dark adaptation is complete after about 40 minutes.

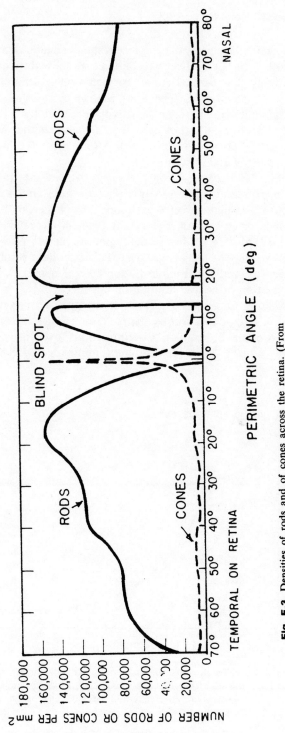

Fig. E-3. Densities of rods and of cones across the retina. (From Osterberg, *Measurements*, 1935. Compare also Pirenne, 1967.)

Figure E-4 shows three curves that represent the change in detection threshold as a function of time in the dark. The two solid curves show dark adaptation for rods and cones separately. The dashed curve represents the overall change in detection threshold with dark adaptation. The total change in threshold is approximately three orders of magnitude. The cone sensitivity increases by a factor of 10 during the first 7 or 8 minutes in the dark and then remains at that level. The rods are responsible for further changes in threshold. After about 30 minutes the rods have gained another factor of 100 in sensitivity.

Considering Figs. E-3 and E-4 together, it is evident that in the dark-adapted state the fovea is less sensitive than the peripheral retina. This is consistent with the well-known fact that at night objects are more readily seen by looking "out of the corner of one's eye" than by looking straight at them. However, the most sensitive area of the dark-adapted retina lies in the region about 10° from the fovea instead of 20° where the density of rods is greatest. This may be a result of the combined effects of rod density and the number of rod cells that make up a receptive field over which summation of neural stimulation occurs.

By the combination of differences detection, compensation with contraction and dilation of the iris, and adaptation by the receptor cells of the retina itself, the eye is marvelously capable of making discriminations over a very wide range of luminances (see Table E-3 for definition of luminance), from white objects in

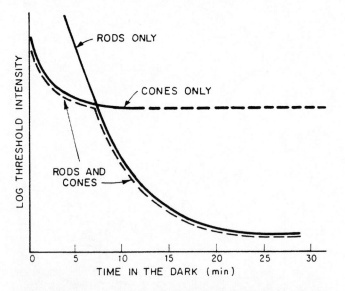

Fig. E-4. Change in visual threshold during dark adaptation. Curves are for a test flash that affects the rods only, the cones only, and when both systems are affected. (After Hecht, Schlaer, 1938; compare also Cornsweet, 1970.)

Note: The log in the scales in Figs. E-4 through E-8 are to the base 10: the "common logarithms."

Table E-3. Radiometric and Photometric Terms and Symbols

Radiometric	Symbol	Units	Photometric	Symbol	Units
Radiant flux	P	Watt	Luminous flux	F^*	lumen (lu)
Radiant intensity	J	Watt/ω	Luminous intensity	I	lu/ω
			Candlepower		candle (c)
					$1\ \mathrm{lu}/\omega = 1\ \mathrm{c}$
Irradiance	H	Watt/m^2	Illuminance	E	lu/m^2
					lux
					meter-candle (m-c)
					foot-candle (ft-c)
					$1\ \mathrm{lu}/\mathrm{m}^2 = 1\ \mathrm{lux} = 1$
					m-c $= 0.0929$ ft-c
Radiance	N	Watt/ω/m^2	Luminance	L	lu/ω/m^2
					c/m^2
					millilamberts (mL)
					foot-lamberts (ft-L)
					$1\ \mathrm{lu}/\omega/\mathrm{m}^2 =$
					$1\ \mathrm{c}/\mathrm{m}^2 = 0.3142$ mL
					$= 0.2919$ ft-L

$^*F = 685 \sum_{0}^{\infty} P_\lambda V_\lambda \, \Delta\lambda$ lumens

where V_λ = spectral luminosity function = ratio of luminous efficiency of light at wavelength λ to luminous efficiency maximum at 555 nm. The ω denotes solid angle in steradians; $\cdots/\omega$ means: $\cdots$ per solid angle. m denotes meter; $\cdots/\mathrm{m}^2$, per square meter; $\cdots/\omega/\mathrm{m}^2 = \cdots/\omega\mathrm{m}^2$ means $\cdots$ per solid angle per squ. meter.

Table E-4. Luminance Values for Typical Visual Stimuli

	Scale of luminance ft-L	
Sun's surface at noon	10^{10}	
	10^9	Damaging
	10^8	
Tungsten filament	10^7	
	10^6	
	10^5	
White paper in sunlight	10^4	Photopic
Full daylight	10^3	
Overcast day	10^2	
Comfortable reading (dark day)	10	
Twilight	1	Mixed
	10^{-1}	
White paper in moonlight	10^{-2}	
White paper in half-moonlight	10^{-3}	
White paper in starlight	10^{-4}	Scotopic
	10^{-5}	
Absolute threshold	10^{-6}	

sunlight to dark objects in moonlight—more than 10^{10} in dynamic range. Table E-4 gives luminance values for some typical visual stimuli. However, since both pupillary contraction and dilation and retinal adaptation take time, the eye cannot make use of its full dynamic range at any given time.

The retina is not a detector of absolute energy levels, but detects instead differences between energy levels. The invisibility of stars in the daytime sky is an everyday example of difference detection. Light from a star enters the eye and falls on the retina in the daytime just as it does at night, but as long as the illumination on the retina from the sky surrounding the star is nearly as great as the illuminance in the image of the star, the star image is not discriminable from the background. When the sky brightness falls at twilight, stars become visible as the difference between their luminance and the luminance of the sky increases.

Difference detection in the retina means that consideration of the detectability of objects must include not only the luminance of the object itself, but also the luminance of the area surrounding the target—the background. If the background is fairly uniform, the background luminance determines the adaptation state of the receptors. If L_t is the target luminance and L_b the background luminance, then C_t, a quantity known as *contrast*, is defined by

$$C_t = \frac{|L_t - L_b|}{L_b}.$$

It is contrast that determines the detectability of a target, not its absolute energy level (down to an absolute threshold level beyond which the eye is incapable of responding). The absolute value signs in $|L_t - L_b|$ indicate that there is contrast when $L_b > L_t$ as well as when $L_t > t_b$.

It will be evident that the intrinsic (actual) target luminance and the intrinsic background luminance are not the only factors that determine image contrast at the retina. The medium through which the light flux from the target and from the background travel—the atmosphere in most cases—modifies the contrast of the retinal image. Although absorption of light by the atmosphere reduces the total flux arriving at the retina, it does not affect the relative illuminances on the image and background areas. However, light is *scattered* by the atmosphere as well as absorbed. Thus, light from the target is scattered out of the optical path from target to eye and light from the background is scattered into the optical path. This scattering results in reduction of contrast at the image plane. A further modification of contrast may occur if the atmosphere is nonuniform.

Another variable that affects the detectability of a target is the size of the image on the retina. In a very general way, the larger the image the less the contrast need be for the target to be detected, down to an absolute minimum contrast necessary for detection. This is due in part to the fact that under certain conditions the neural network of the visual system functions as an integrator, adding responses of separate receptors over a given area. For targets of very small visual angle (1 min or so), on the other hand, image spread due to diffraction is largely responsible for the reciprocal relation between contrast and visual angle known as Ricco's law. Ricco's law describes the fact that below a minimum critical angle, reduction in the size of the target does not reduce the size of the image due to the diffraction pattern which is formed, but does reduce the total light flux available to illuminate the diffraction-limited image area. Thus the luminance of the target, and therefore contrast, must be greater for smaller targets to give the same *image* contrast.

When the observer "knows where to look" to see the target, and when the detection conditions are ideal and static, two basic factors determine the detectability of a target. Each factor is determined by several variables:

1) Effective *contrast* of the target
   a) effective luminance of the target in the direction of the observer
   b) effective luminance of the background in the direction of the observer
   c) modifying effects of the atmosphere and other intervening media
2) Effective *angular size* of the target
   a) actual size of the target
   b) distance from target to observer
   c) orientation of target with respect to image plane of observer
   d) shape of the target

2. VISUAL DETECTION UNDER SEARCH CONDITIONS (TARGET MOTION IGNORED*)

Since the primary interest in this book is on acquisition of targets under search conditions, it must be assumed that the observer in such a case does not "know where to look" to see the target. Determining the detectability of a target under search conditions involves consideration of some additional factors. If the observer is not "looking at" the target, the image of the target will fall on the retina in a location outside of the highly sensitive fovea (considering daylight conditions only, for the moment). The distribution of receptor cells in the retina is not uniform, as seen in Fig. E-3. The density of cone cells decreases rapidly with distance from the fovea. Very generally, under daylight illumination, this results in an increase in the amount of contrast required to detect an image the farther the image is from the fovea. In terms of target space, the farther the target is from the fixation point (the place where the observer is looking), the greater its contrast must be in order to be detected. Alternatively, if the target contrast remains the same, the target image must be larger for detection to occur, meaning in general that the target must be closer to the observer in order to be detected by peripheral vision.

The eye is not fixed in its socket, however, nor does it look in any one place for very long. The eye typically scans the visual world making several stationary *fixations* per second, separated by rapid jumps—*saccades*—to the next fixation. Little if any visual information is perceived during a saccade, which may last from 30 to 100 msec, depending on the visual angle traversed. All useful visual information is obtained during the fixation periods, which may last for 200 msec to as much as a second, but rarely for longer than a second. A high degree of training is required for an observer to be able to suppress saccades for longer than a few seconds.

For search conditions, then, two *additional* factors affect the detectability of a target:

1) The *location* of the target relative to the fixation point
2) The number and distribution of fixations

Laboratory Data on Visual Detection Thresholds

The human visual system has probably been studied more extensively by psychophysicists and physiologists than any other sensory system. There is an abundance of laboratory data recording many aspects of the visual process obtained from controlled and precise experiments. Unfortunately, because of the multiplicity of variables that affect visual *target detection*, even without the added complication of the search situation, it is not always possible to extrapolate from laboratory data to actual field conditions to obtain predictions of detection performance with useful precision.

---

*See end of text for reason.

In addition to the plentiful laboratory measurements, there are also a smaller number of data from applied or operational experiments where data are taken from either real or simulated situations matched as closely as possible to the situation in which predictions are desired. Such data are useful for limited application to directly relevant predictions, but again, extrapolations cannot always be made without risk of introducing unacceptable levels of error.

S. Q. Duntley and fellow workers at the Visibility Laboratory at Scripps Institution of Oceanography have done more than any other workers in the field to identify the variables that are important in the prediction of the visibility of objects, and to make extensive field and simulation measurements of many of these variables, most notably in the areas of atmospheric transmissivity and the luminance and reflectance of many different types of targets and backgrounds. The Duntley et al. (1964) paper is highly recommended as a comprehensive compendium of the status of visibility prediction capability at that time. Two additional papers from the same laboratory (Duntley 1948b; Gordon et al. 1975) contain very useful nomograms for use in predicting the visibility of various objects. No attempt will be made to reproduce these nomograms, since the original papers are so easily obtainable in the open literature. It is worth noting that, with the exception of some additional data published by Taylor in 1964 (Duntley et al. 1964), very little data applicable to the visual search problem have been published since the burst of data generated by the needs of World War II.

The data available for prediction of the detectability of targets are laboratory measurements of the threshold for detection of visual stimuli as a function of target contrast, target size (area of target in angular dimensions), and adaptation level of the observer's eyes (background luminance). The available data in general are from situations requiring little if any search for the target.

The largest body of data on contrast thresholds was generated by Blackwell (1946), often referred to as the Tiffany data. This was a very thorough study measuring the detection threshold for circular targets. The contrast necessary to just see the target (the 50% detection threshold) was measured for five target sizes whose diameters ranged from 3.6 to 121 min of arc at background luminances ranging from 10^2 ft-L (daylight) to 10^{-6} ft-L (dark night). Targets were presented for 6 sec in a situation that required search over a 6° area. The responses were a forced choice of one stimulus location of a possible eight positions. Time to detect was not reported. Several hundred thousand measurements were taken using nine practiced observers.

Lamar et al. (1947) reported measurements of contrast thresholds (62.5%) for rectangular targets presented for 3 sec whose length-to-width ratios ranged from 2 to 200, with areas ranging from 0.5 to 800 sq. min of visual angle, for two background luminances, very bright daylight (2950 ft-L) and very dark daylight (17.5 ft-L).

Taylor (in Duntley et al. 1964) reported contrast thresholds (50%) for various sized targets with a 0.33 sec exposure time (corresponding to a typical fixation length) for a background luminance of 75 ft-L (approximating overcast daylight).

Lamar (1946) reported data taken by Craik for contrast thresholds (57%) with a daylight background for targets of various sizes, and including detection by the peripheral portion of the retina. Unfortunately, only the curve fitted to the data is presented by Lamar, so some of the details of the experimental design are not available.

The data from Blackwell (1946), Lamar et al. (1947), Taylor (1964) and Craik (in Lamar, 1946) show remarkable agreement on the contrast thresholds required for roughly 50% detection of circular or relatively symmetrical targets under full daylight conditions. Some additional data published by Blackwell in 1969 and reported in Dunipace (1974) for contrast thresholds at 10^3 ft-L (full daylight) and 10 ft-L (very dark daylight) are also in excellent agreement. It is clear from a comparison of these data that contrast thresholds are essentially the same for background luminances ranging from very bright, sunlit sand and water down to the brightness of an overcast day or sunset.

Figure E-5 shows a smooth curve fitted to the data from the five experiments described above. It should be remembered that these data represent the 50% threshold of detection under ideal, static conditions in a laboratory setting in which very little if any search is required. Figure E-5 gives the contrast necessary for detection as a function of the angular area of the target, or its equivalent circular diameter, for full daylight (ranging from 75 to 3000 ft-L) background conditions.

The major perturbation on this curve is the effect of changes in background luminance, as can be seen in Fig. E-6. When the background luminance falls below the sunset or twilight level (around 10 ft-L), the threshold changes so much as to

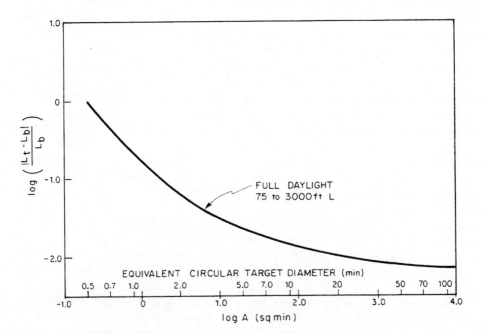

Fig. E-5. Threshold contrast for 50% probability of detection as function of target area.

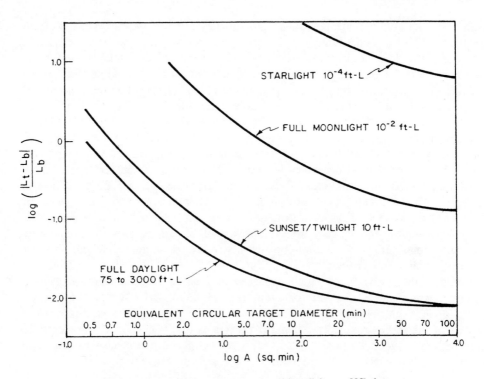

Fig. E-6. Effect of different degrees of ambient light on 50% detection probability threshold.

make it virtually impossible to determine the threshold contrast unless the adaptation luminance is known quite precisely. Background luminance has a far greater effect on threshold contrast than target area for backgrounds darker than an overcast day. Unless the observer's adaptation level can be measured accurately under field conditions, it would seem that very little can be said about the contrast necessary for detection.

In daylight conditions the peripheral retina is increasingly less sensitive to contrast as the image falls farther away from the fovea. This becomes another major variable when the detectability of a target under search conditions is desired. A high contrast target might be detected anywhere on the retina but a target at about threshold contrast could only be detected if the image fell on the fovea.

There is not an abundance of data on detection thresholds as a function of *image location* as well as size and contrast. However, Tanner (1954) published peripheral threshold contrasts for 5 targets ranging in size between 1 and 120 minutes of visual angle. Targets were so arranged that the images fell at various locations between the fovea and 12 degrees away from the fovea, and included measurements taken with the image at the fovea. The adaptation level was 75 ft-L (moderate daylight) and targets were presented for 0.33 seconds, approximating a typical fixation duration. Lamar et al. (1947) also included some peripheral detection data at two image positions, 1.25 and 10 degrees from the fovea for bright daylight (2950 ft-L) and twilight (17.5 ft-L) conditions using asymmetric targets. The curve fitted to Craik's data by Lamar (1946) is another source of peripheral detection data. These data were converted to the ratios of threshold contrast at the peripheral location to threshold contrast at the fovea. These ratios were computed for two peripheral locations, 2 and 10 degrees from the fovea. The ratios appeared to be a little varying function of target area; they were plotted and a best fit curve was drawn through the points for the two locations. The smoothed ratios were then applied to the daylight foveal contrast threshold curve to obtain two curves representing the contrast necessary for threshold detection when the target falls 2 or 10 degrees off the visual axis. These curves are presented in Fig. E-7. There is probably a factor of 2 of uncertainty inherent in these curves, for the data were not as consistent as the foveal detection data, and the sensitivity of the peripheral retina does not necessarily vary the same way in all directions. However, the curves give an estimate of the additional contrast needed for detection when the observer "doesn't know where to look."

Shape is another variable which has been manipulated by Lamar et al. (1947). Briefly, their results show that for asymmetrical targets with a ratio of length : width of less than 50 : 1 threshold contrasts are very close to those for circular targets of the same area. Even when the ratio is as much as 200 : 1, the threshold contrast increases only a factor of 2 over circular targets of the same area. Data are available only for relatively small targets. These data are not shown in a figure

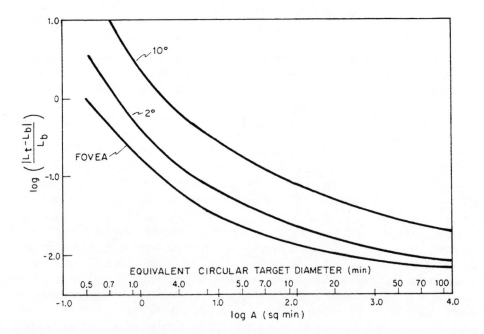

Fig. E-7. Threshold contrast for targets 2° and 10° from the fovea.

because, for most ordinary targets, shape makes very little difference in contrast thresholds.

Krendel and Wodinsky (1960a, b) have made measurements to determine whether visual search in an unstructured field is consistent with the model of *repeated independent trials* described in Chapter 3. In their experiments, observers were presented with a small target in a large, unstructured visual field. Four different target sizes were used, all small, and each was presented at four different contrasts on four different background luminances in four different size search areas. In each of the 256 conditions, the combination of contrast and size was sufficient to make the target indisputably and unambiguously detectable if the observer fixated upon it. One purpose of the experiment was to determine whether the exponential relation between probability of detection $p(t)$ and search time t conforms to the relation

$$(1) \qquad\qquad p(t) = 1 - e^{-\gamma t}$$

(equation (3) or (40), Chapter 3). Another purpose was to test whether the coefficient γ is inversely proportional to the solid angle of the field to be searched or, alternatively stated, whether the time required to reach a particular level of detection probability is strictly proportional to the solid angle searched. In both respects, the experimental results are consistent with the model predictions. As expected, the coefficient γ varies with size and contrast. This prevents pooling of results to test equation (1). However, when the observations for the two largest search areas are subdivided into 128 groups within each of which all variables except p and t are kept constant, the fit to the exponential curve in equation (1) is statistically satisfactory in 112 out of the 128 groups. Observations on the two smallest search areas could not be used for evaluation because detection times were too short. The degree of linearity of γ with t^{-1} can be tested with pooled data and is very high (Fig. E-8). This means that an unambiguous visual search rate with units of steradians per second could be established for each target for each observer. In fact, the paper includes pooled data from four observers sufficient to compute those search rates for 64 combinations of target size and contrast, although the computations have not been carried out.

Bloomfield (1970) also reports an exponential distribution of search times for a task where the target is to be located in a background of similar nontarget stimuli.

The curves representing contrast thresholds for detection of targets as a function of target size (Figs. E-5 to E-7) give the contrast necessary to detect a given size target 50 percent of the time. Blackwell (1946) points out that his observers were not confident of seeing the target when they responded unless the probability of seeing was greater than 0.90. The slope of the average frequency of seeing curve for Blackwell's subjects was such that multiplying the $P = 0.50$ threshold contrast by 1.6 gives the contrast necessary for detection to occur 90% of the time. This is a more realistic detection criterion for field application. If a higher probability of detection ($P = 0.99$) is desired, the $P = 0.50$ threshold contrast should be multiplied by 2.0.

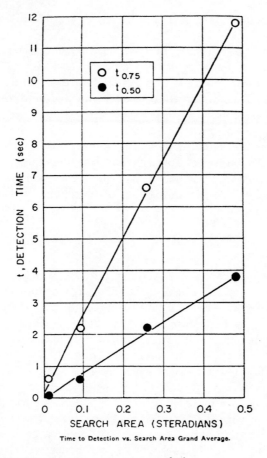

Time to Detection vs. Search Area Grand Average.

Fig. E-8. Detection time versus area searched.

There are several other variables that have a general impact on detection performance in the field but which are not present in the laboratory situation. Since these variables are not a function of target size, contrast, or adaptation luminance, estimates have been made of field factors that can be used as contrast multipliers to make the laboratory data predict more closely what the detection performance would be under field conditions. The $P = 0.50$ contrast threshold can be multiplied by one or more of these field factors.

In the field, the observer's response is generally of the yes-no variety, whereas most of the laboratory data are based on a forced choice response, which gives a somewhat more sensitive measure of threshold. To convert from forced-choice to yes-no response, multiply contrast by 1.2. In the laboratory, the subjects are generally notified when the target is presented and they may know what size target to look for. If the time of occurrence and target size are unknown in the field, multiply contrast by 1.5. If the target is present only infrequently in the field, the vigilance of the observers may be less than the vigilance of subjects in the laboratory where stimulus presentations are frequent. For lack of vigilance multiply by 2.0. It is emphasized that these field factors are merely estimates. Actual differences between laboratory and field performances should be determined for each field situation.

Atmospheric transmission must be taken into account for field detections. This is a much more complex variable and depends heavily on the particular conditions under which the field search is made. A rough estimate may be obtained from the meteorological visibility measured in the field. *Meteorological visibility V* is defined as the horizontal range at which the contrast transmittance is 2 percent. Visibility is generally agreed to be the range at which a large distant black object is just recognizable against the horizon sky. With reference to Fig. E-5, it can be seen that if the contrast required for 50% probability of detection of a large target is multiplied by the field factors necessary to convert 50% laboratory detection to nearly certain detection (factor of 2.0) with a yes-no response (factor of 1.2) and an estimated factor to represent the difference between yes-no detection and recognition, the required contrast is very close to 2 percent. The combined effects of atmospheric absorption and scattering are expressed by the following approximate formula, in which R/V is the (dimensionless) ratio of ranges, C_0 the intrinsic contrast at the target, C that at range R.

$$(2) \qquad\qquad C = C_0 \exp(-3.912\, R/V).$$

Atmospheric transmission can be a very complicated factor. Some other independent measure of the transmission properties of the actual field location at the time of search is highly desirable. Reference to the sources listed under atmospheric transmission in Table E-5 should make the desirability of such a measure clear.

Table E-5 lists some of the variables, other than target size and contrast and adaptation level, which affect visual detection. Where estimates have been made of the approximate effect on the contrast required for detection, these estimates are given in the column labeled "contrast factor." When no numerical estimates have been made, an indication of the probable impact of the variable on detectability is given. References are given for the convenience of readers concerned with particular variables and how they may affect detectability of targets.

It is apparent that although much work in visual detection has been done, especially by the group at Scripps, much more data, particularly on field variables, and a better understanding of variables, such as alerting, training, and search strategy, are required before very accurate estimates can be made of target detectability under field search conditions.

When V, C_0, and target size are known, R (at different levels of probability) can be found from (2) (plotted logarithmically) and Fig. E-5, etc. (using Table E-5 when appropriate). The R of the point of intersection of these two graphs is the required range. To obtain lateral range curves and sweep widths more accurately, Table E-5 must be extended to a more detailed contrast factor versus probability relationship. Then Figure E-5 can be used to give probabilities other than 50%. See Chapter 3, Section 4.

Table E-5. Some Factors Affecting Visual Detection

Variable	Contrast Factor	Reference
Detection probability > 0.50		Blackwell 1946
0.90	1.6	Taylor 1964
0.99	2.0	
Alerting (time of occurrence & target size)	1.5	Taylor 1964
Response: yes-no vs. forced choice	1.2	Taylor 1964
Vigilance	1.2	Jerison & Pickett 1963
		Taylor 1964
Naive vs. trained observer	2.0	Taylor 1964
Fixation pattern and search strategy	moderate	Ford, White & Lichtenstein 1959
		Grether 1963
		Harris 1960
		Miller & Ludvigh 1960
		White & Ford 1960
Payoff for detection	slight	Jerison & Pickett 1963
		Tanner & Jones 1960
		Tanner & Swets 1954
Optical devices	slight	Coleman & Verplanck 1948
		Hardy 1946
		Horman 1967
		Overington 1973
		Smith 1960
Target shape & orientation	slight	Fry 1947
		Lamar et al. 1947
		Lamar et al. 1948
Target & background uniformity, illumination & reflectance	moderate to great	Boileau & Gordon 1966
		Gordon & Church 1966
Atmospheric absorption & scattering	great	Boileau & Gordon 1966
		Duntley 1948a
		Duntley et al. 1957
		Duntley et al. 1963
		Duntley et al. 1964
		Gordon et al. 1973

3. TARGET MOTION

Throughout this treatment of visual detection, the effect of target motion has not been examined. Yet in even the most primitive warfare—even in the animal kingdom—targets are often revealed by their motion, and concealment may be achieved by not moving. The principal reason for the present omission of this factor is that most of the work is concerned with very distant targets, as those in naval warfare. For these the angular change in direction due to their motion is too slight to influence their detectability.

The effect of target motion on visual detectability in, e.g., land or guerrilla warfare, hunting game, etc., while highly worthy of quantitative study, has received very little.

BIBLIOGRAPHY

AGARD Conference Proceedings no. 41, 1968.

Baker, C. H., ed. 1963. Special issue: Visual capabilities in the operation of manned space systems. *Human Factors*: 5 (June).

Baker, Howard D. 1963. Initial stages of dark and light adaptation. *J. Opt. Soc. Am.* 53: 98–103.

Baron, W. S. and Westheimer, G. 1973. Visual acuity as a function of exposure duration. *J. Opt. Soc. Am.* 63: 212–19.

Blackwell, H. Richard. 1946. Contrast thresholds of the human eye. *J. Opt. Soc. Am.* 36: 624–43.

_____. 1963. Neural theories of simple visual discriminations. *J. Opt. Soc. Am.* 53: 129–60.

_____. 1972. Luminance difference thresholds. In *Handbook of Sensory Physiology*, Vol. VII/4, *Visual Psychophysics*, eds. D. Jameson, and L. M. Hurvich. Berlin: Springer-Verlag.

Blackwell, H. R., Ohmart, J. G., and Harcum, E. R. 1960. Field and simulator studies of air-to-ground visibility distances. In *Visual Search Techniques*, Symposium, 1959, eds. A. Morris and E. P. Horne. NAS-NRC Committee on Vision, Washington.

Bloomfield, J. R. 1973. Experiments in visual search. In *Visual Search*, Symposium 1970, NAS-NRC Committee on Vision, Washington.

Boileau, A. R. and Gordon, J. I. 1966. Atmospheric properties and reflectances of ocean water and other surfaces for a Low Sun. *Applied Optics* 5: 803–13.

Broadbent, D. E. 1958. The general nature of vigilance. In *Perception and Communication*, ed. D. E. Broadbent. Oxford: Pergamon Press.

Brody, H. R., Corbin, H. H. and Volkmann, J. 1960. Stimulus relations and methods of visual search. In *Visual Search Techniques*, Symposium 1959, eds. A. Morris and E. P. Horne. NAS-NRC Committee on Vision, Washington.

Cohn, T. E. and Lasley, D. J. 1974. Detectability of a luminance increment: effect of spatial uncertainty. *J. Opt. Soc. Am.* 64: 1715–19.

Cohn, T. E., Thibos, L. N., and Kleinstein, R. N. 1974. Detectability of a luminance increment. *J. Opt. Soc. Am.* 64: 1321–27.

Coleman, H. S. and Verplanck, W. S. 1948. A comparison of computed and experimental detection ranges of objects viewed with telescopic systems from aboard ship. *J. Opt. Soc. Am.* 38: 250–53.

Cornsweet, T. N. 1970. *Visual perception*. New York: Academic Press.

Ditchburn, R. W. 1973. *Eye movements and visual perception*. Oxford: Clarendon Press.

Dunipace, D. W., Strong, J., and Huizinga, M. 1974. Prediction of nighttime driving visibility from laboratory data. *Applied Optics* 13: 2723–34.

Duntley, S. Q. 1948. The reduction of apparent contrast by the atmosphere. *J. Opt. Soc. Am.* 38: 179–91.

_____. 1948. The visibility of distant objects. *J. Opt. Soc. Am.* 38: 237–49.

_____. 1963. Light in the sea. *J. Opt. Soc. Am.* 53: 214–33.

Duntley, S. Q., Boileau, A. R., and Preisendorfer, W. 1957. Image transmission by the troposphere I. *J. Opt. Soc. Am.* 47: 499–506.

Duntley, S. Q., Culver, W. H., Richey, F., and Preisendorfer, R. W. 1963. Reduction of contrast by atmospheric boil. *J. Opt. Soc. Am.* 53: 351–58.

Duntley, S. Q., Gordon, J. I., Taylor, J. H., White, C. I., Boileau, A. R., Tyler, J. E., Austin, R. W., and Harris, J. L. 1964. Visibility. *Applied Optics* 3: 549–97.

Ford, A., White, C. T., and Lichtenstein, M. 1959. Analysis of eye movements during free search. *J. Opt. Soc. Am.* 49: 287–92.

Fry, G. A. 1947. The relation of the configuration of a brightness contrast border to its visibility. *J. Opt. Soc. Am.* 37: 166–75.

Fuchs, Albert F., The saccadic system. 1971. In *The control of eye movements*, eds. P. Bach-y-Rita, and C. C. Collins, pp. 343–362. New York: Academic Press.

Gordon, J. I., and Church, P. V. 1966. Sky luminances and the directional luminous reflectances of objects and backgrounds for a moderately high sun. *Applied Optics* 5: 793–801.

Gordon, J. I., Edgerton, C. F., and Duntley, S. Q. 1975. Signal-light nomogram, *J. Opt. Soc. Am.* 65: 111–18.

Gordon, J. I., Harris, J. L., Sr., and Duntley, S. Q. 1973. Measuring earth-to-space contrast transmittance from ground stations. *Applied Optics* 12: 1317–24.

Graham, C. H., ed. 1965. *Vision and visual perception.* New York: Wiley.

Grether, W. F. 1963. Visual search in the space environment. *Human Factors* 5: 203–09.

Harcum, E. R. 1960. Detection versus localization errors on various radii of the visual field. In *Visual Search Techniques*, Symposium 1959, eds. A. Morris and E. P. Horne. NAS-NRC Committee on Vision, Washington.

Hardy, A. C. 1946. Atmospheric limitations on the performance of telescopes. *J. Opt. Soc. Am.* 36: 283–87.

_____. 1967. How large is a point source? *J. Opt. Soc. Am.* 57: 44–47.

Harris, J. L. 1960. Factors to be considered in developing optimum visual search. In *Visual Search Techniques*, Symposium 1959, eds. A. Morris and E. P. Horne. NAS-NRC, Committee on Vision, Washington.

Hecht, S. 1947. Visual thresholds of steady point sources of light in fields of brightness from dark to daylight. *J. Opt. Soc. Am.* 37: 59 (letter).

Hecht, S., Ross, S., and Mueller, C. G. 1947. The visibility of lines and squares at high brightnesses. *J. Opt. Soc. Am.* 37: 500–07.

Hecht, S., Shlaer, S., and Pirenne, M. H. 1942. Energy, quanta, and vision. *J. Gen. Physiol.* 25: 819–40. Also, Hecht, S., and Shlaer, S., 1938.

Horman, M. H. 1967. Visibility of light sources against a background of uniform luminance. *J. Opt. Soc. Am.* 57: 1516–21.

Howarth, C. I., and Bloomfield, J. R. 1969. A rational equation for predicting search times in simple inspection tasks. *Psychonomic Sci.* 17: 225–26.

Jerison, H. J., and Pickett, R. M. 1963. Vigilance: a review and re-evaluation. *Human Factors* 5: 211–38.

Kelly, D. H. 1974. Effects of the cone-cell distribution on pattern-detection experiments. *J. Opt. Soc. Am.* 64: 1523–25.

Kling, J. W., and Riggs, L. A. eds. 1971. *Woodworth and Schlosberg's experimental psychology* (3rd ed.). New York: Holt, Rinehart & Winston.

Kornfeld, G. H., and Lawson, W. R. 1971. Visual-perception models. *J. Opt. Soc. Am.* 61: 811–20.

Krendel, E. S., and Wodinsky, J. 1960a. Search in an unstructured visual field. *J. Opt. Soc. Am.* 50: 562–68.

Krendel, E. S., and Wodinsky, J. 1960b. Search in an unstructured visual field. In *Visual Search Techniques*, Symposium 1959, eds. A. Morris and E. P. Horne. NAS-NRC Committee on Vision, Washington.

Lamar, E. S. 1960. Operational background and physical considerations relative to visual search problems. In *Visual Search Techniques*, Symposium 1959, eds. A. Morris and E. P. Horne. NAS-NRC Committee on Vision, Washington.

Lamar, E. S., Hecht, S., Shlaer, S., and Hendley, C. D. 1947. Size, shape, and contrast in detection of targets by daylight vision. I. Data and analytical description. *J. Opt. Soc. Am.* 37: 531–45.

Lamar, E. S., Hecht, S., Hendley, C. D., and Shlaer, S. 1948. Size, shape, and contrast in detection of targets by daylight vision. II. Frequency of seeing and the quantum theory of cone vision. *J. Opt. Soc. Am.* 38: 741–55.

Low, F. N. 1951. Peripheral visual acuity. *Arch. Ophthalmol.* 45: 80–99.

Mackworth, N. H., Llewellyn-Thomas, E., and Holmquist, S. 1960. The television eye marker on a changing visual world. In *Visual Search Techniques*, Symposium 1959, eds. A. Morris and E. P. Horne. NAS-NRC Committee on Vision, Washington.

Miller, J. W., and Ludvigh, E. 1960. Time required for detection of stationary and moving objects as a function of size in homogeneous and partially structured visual fields. In *Visual Search Techniques*, Symposium 1959, eds. A. Morris and E. P. Horne. NAS-NRC Committee on Vision, Washington.

Morris, A., and Horne, E. P., eds. 1960. *Visual Search Techniques*, Symposium 1959, NAS-NRC Committee on Vision, Washington.

Nachmias, Jacob, and Kocher, E. C. 1970. Visual detection and discrimination of luminance increments. *J. Opt. Soc. Am.* 60: 382–89.

Overington, I. 1973. Interaction of vision with optical aids. *J. Opt. Soc. Am.* 63: 1043–49.

Overington, I., and Lavin, F. P. 1971. A model of threshold detection performance for the cental fovea. *Optica Acta* 18: 341–57.

Pirenne, M. H. 1967. *Vision and the eye*. London: Chapman Hall.

Schnitzler, A. D. 1973. Image-detector model and parameters of the human visual system. *J. Opt. Soc. Am.* 63: 1357–68.

Shapley, R. 1974. Gaussian bars and rectangular bars: the influence of width and gradient on visibility. *Vision Research* 14: 1457–62.

Sloan, L. L. 1961. Area and luminance of test object as variables in examination of the visual field by projection perimetry. *Vision Research* 1: 121–38.

Smith, R. P. 1960. Use of binoculars in search for submarines. In *Visual Search Techniques*, Symposium 1959, eds. A. Morris and E. P. Horne. NAS-NRC Committee on Vision, Washington.

Smith, S. W., and Louttit, R. T. 1960. Some effects of target microstructure on visual detection. In *Visual Search Techniques*, Symposium 1959, eds. A. Morris and E. P. Horne. NAS-NRC Committee on Vision, Washington.

Symposium on Physiologica Optics, 1963. eds. A. Morris and E. P. Horne. *J. Opt. Soc. Am.* 53: no. 1.

Tanner, W. P., Jr., and Jones, R. C. 1960. The ideal sensor system as approached through statistical decision theory and the theory of signal detectability. In *Visual Search Techniques*, Symposium 1959, eds. A. Morris and E. P. Horne. NAS-NRC Committee on Vision, Washington.

Tanner, W. P., and Swets, I. A. 1954. A decision-making theory of visual detection. *Psych. Review* 61: 401–09.

Visual Search. 1973. Symposium 1970, NAS-NRC Committee on Vision, Washington.

Westheimer, G., and McKee, S. P. 1975. Visual acuity in the presence of retinal-image matron. *J. Opt. Soc. Am.* 65: 847–50.

White, C. T., and Ford, A. 1960. Eye movements during simulated radar search. *J. Opt. Soc. Am.* 50: 909–13.

White, C. T., and Ford, A. 1960. Ocular activity in visual search. In *Visual Search Techniques*, Symposium 1959, eds. A. Morris and E. P. Horne. NAS-NRC Committee on Vision, Washington.

Appendix F:
Radar and Electromagnetic Detection

Radar is a device for detecting and locating objects at a distance with electromagnetic waves. Electromagnetic radiation from a transmitter is emitted from a transmitter and scattered (or reflected) from a target. Some of the scattered energy from the target returns as an electromagnetic echo to a receiver, where it is detected and compared with the transmitted energy. Information about the presence, location, velocity, and sometimes other characteristics of the target can be deduced from the comparison.

Radar can be and has been studied from many points of view. Fortunately a leading treatise [1] elects to introduce the subject by examining the way in which laws of nature, engineering design parameters, and practical limitations determine, limit, and degrade the performance of radar as a detection device. The two introductory chapters of that book cover in considerable detail exactly those aspects of radar that are relevant to its use as a sensor system for search and screening, without engineering details that would obscure the issues of importance. The fundamentals of the subject were firmly established and well understood by 1962, and except for clearly identified references to contemporary applications and the engineering limitations of these existing electronic devices, the treatment can be considered up to date at the level of detail treated there.

A very important quality of radar is that the electromagnetic waves on which it depends travel freely through the atmosphere and space, and through smoke and clouds that block ordinary vision. At some frequencies (wavelengths), electromagnetic radiation passes moderately well through rainfall, foliage, and nonmetallic structures such as light wooden buildings. At other frequencies, useful amounts are diffracted around the curvature of the earth beyond the visible horizon.

In a common form of radar, a short burst—say one microsecond long (give or take a factor of 10 or more; see Skolnik [1])—is emitted at a frequency around 1000 megahertz (give or take a factor of 10 or more; Skolnik discusses radar using transmission other than single-frequency bursts, and at other frequencies [1]) through a directional antenna. The energy propagates radially from the transmitting antenna, and the energy intensity of the transmitted wave packet diminishes in proportion to the square of the distance from the transmitter.

A portion of the radiated energy is intercepted by a target, and reradiated as scattered energy. The amount reradiated in the direction of the receiver is described by a radar cross section of the target. (The radar cross section is the projected area of a hypothetical object that reradiates isotropically and returns the same amount of energy as the actual target. The radar cross section is often much larger or much smaller than the geometric cross section.)

The scattered energy of interest is that reradiated toward the receiver, usually near the transmitter. The scattered energy is also attenuated in proportion to the square of the distance to the transmitter, and a portion of the energy is intercepted by a receiving antenna and processed, displayed, and detected with an electronic receiver.

Thus the inverse square of range enters twice as a factor.

Inasmuch as light travels at a finite speed (300 meters per microsecond) the time delay Δt between the transmitted pulse and the received pulse is a measure of range to the target. If Δt is measured in microseconds and the range R in meters, then

(1) $$R = 150\Delta t.$$

This provides *range information* about the target.

If the target is moving relative to the transmitter, the frequency of the scattered signal will be shifted by an amount called the Doppler shift, which is proportional to the component of relative target velocity in the direction of the transmitter and receiver. This provides *velocity information* about the target.

The transmitted energy is confined to a narrow beam by a directional radiating antenna. In general terms, the angular size of the beam in radians is of the order of magnitude of the wavelength of the radiation divided by the antenna size. Thus a circular parabolic antenna three meters in diameter would focus 3-centimeter-wavelength radiation in a beam about one one-hundredth of a radian, or half a degree, in diameter. The size and directional pattern of the receiving antenna can be matched to that of the transmitter, so that only targets within this beam are detected. This provides *directional information* about the targets detected.

By concentrating the radiated energy in a small cone, the transmitting antenna increases the energy density within that cone relative to the density that would be achieved if the energy were radiated uniformly in all directions. The ratio is called the antenna gain. The same phenomenon is found in the receiving antenna, where the amount of energy collected is proportional to the area of the receiving antenna. But because of the relation between radiation wavelength λ, beam pattern, and effective area A_e, the antenna gain G is the same whether it is used as a transmitting antenna or a receiving antenna. For a planar antenna the relation is

(2) $$G = \frac{4\pi A_e}{\lambda^2}.$$

If (as is common) a single antenna is used for both transmitting and receiving, the relation between transmitted and received power can be expressed as

(3)
$$P_r = \frac{P_t A^2 \sigma}{4\pi\lambda^2 R^4} = \frac{P_t GA\sigma}{(4\pi R^2)^2} = \frac{P_t G^2 \lambda^2 \sigma}{(4\pi)^3 R^4}$$

where

> P_r is the power received by the antenna
> P_t is the power transmitted
> A is the antenna area
> σ is the effective scattering area of the target
> λ is the wavelength of the radiation
> R is the range from antenna to target
> G is the antenna gain (dimensionless).

If the minimum signal level detectable at the receiver is S_{min}, then we can set P_r equal to S_{min} and solve for the maximum detection range R_{max}

(4)
$$R_{max} = \left[\frac{P_t GA\sigma}{(4\pi)^2 S_{min}} \right]^{1/4}$$

or two equivalent forms.

Obviously, the range of detection varies with the fourth root of the transmitter power and the fourth root of the target scattering area. Because of the relation between area and gain, it varies with the square root of the product of antenna area and antenna gain. It is proportional to the inverse fourth root of the minimum detectable signal level.

The minimum detectable signal is determined by the amount and statistical character of background interference and noise and receiver noise. One irreducible source of noise is thermal or Johnson noise. The available thermal noise power is

(5)
$$kTB_n$$

where k is Boltzman's constant (1.38×10^{-23} joule/degree), T is the absolute temperature, and B_n is the receiver bandwidth in Hertz. At a temperature around 290° Kelvin (around 62°F), the factor kT has the value 4×10^{-21} watts per Hertz of bandwidth. If, for instance, an aircraft radar is looking down toward the earth, thermal noise received by the receiving antenna is an irreducible physical constraint. The thermal noise received from space is much lower, and scattered energy from real matter other than a target—say from the ground to an aircraft radar—is commonly much higher. The internal electronic noise of the receiver can easily be reduced to the level of thermal noise of several hundred degrees entering the receiving antenna and can be made as low as a few tens of degrees of thermal noise or less, at some expense, if such performance is needed. When all performance constraints are balanced against the cost of overcoming them, it is rarely practical to use such a quiet receiver. In most search applications of radar to search other than in space, echoes from unwanted scatterers other than the desired target will limit the minimum detectable signal at a higher level.

To illustrate formulas (2)–(5), suppose we have a circular antenna 1 meter in diameter so that

$$A = \pi/4 = 0.785 \text{ sq. m.}$$

and that

$$\lambda = 3 \text{ cm} = 0.03 \text{ m.}$$

Then

$$G = 1.10 \cdot 10^4.$$

Suppose further that

$T = 290°K,$

$B_n = 10^6$ Hz (bandwidth required to pass a one-microsecond pulse),

then

$$kTB_n = 4 \cdot 10^{-15} \text{ watts.}$$

The effective noise temperature T is often expressed as the product of the actual temperature T_0 and a dimensionless noise figure F_n, or expressed in terms of the noise figure F_n alone, with the ambient temperature 290°K understood. Suppose, for the sake of argument, that the minimum reliably detected signal is 13 decibels above, or twenty times stronger than, the mean thermal noise, i.e.,

$$S_{\min} = 20 \cdot 4 \cdot 10^{-15} = 8 \cdot 10^{-14} \text{ watts.}$$

Suppose further that

$$P_t = 10,000,$$
$$\sigma = 1 \text{ square meter.}$$

Then, from eq. (4),

$$R_{\max} = 51,100 \text{ meters} = 51.1 \text{ kilometers.}$$

Because of noise and interference fluctuations, the minimum detectable signal fluctuates. Detection must therefore be described in statistical terms. As the decision threshold for detection is lowered, the probability that a signal from a particular target will be detected increases, but the probability of a false alarm due to noise or interference also increases. The performance of a search system depends on false alarms as well as on target detections, so both are considered. The relation expressing the quantitative trade between false-alarm probability and target-detection probability is called the receiver operating characteristic (ROC).

The probability of false alarm can be lowered and the probability of target detection can be increased by observing several pulses and integrating the results, either incoherently at the receiver output or coherently before the carrier phase information has been lost. This takes time and transmitter energy, and must be traded against the necessity to point or sweep the directional beam to search in other directions. The number of pulses necessary to scan a particular solid angle is inversely proportional to the antenna beam solid angle, and thus is directly proportional to antenna gain. The time between pulses must be made long enough so that all echoes are received before the following transmitted pulse, otherwise there will be ambiguity in associating an echo with the transmitted pulse that generates it, and the range determination is no longer unique. If targets are few and widely spaced, as in space tracking or enroute air traffic control, this ambiguity can be resolved by various means, so shorter interpulse intervals can be used.

The actual performance of radar departs from the ideal outlined above for many reasons besides interference. The scattering cross section of targets fluctuates with direction and is often much less than the geometrical cross section. The antenna pattern is not a perfect cone, and there are power losses in the antennas and feeds, so the antenna gains are less than theory predicts and fall off if the target is not in the exact beam center. Also, any loss in the antenna and feed hardware is seen by the receiver as a thermal source, and contributes to evaluating the noise figure. The diplexer inserted in the antenna feed to divert transmitter energy away from the transmitter toward the antenna and energy received by the antenna away from the transmitter and into the receiver has losses and raises the overall receiving noise figure further. A loss of sensitivity called *collapsing loss* is experienced when several potentially discriminable search cells are combined before detection on a single display—say signals of a wide range of Doppler shifts but a single range on a range display, or signals with several antenna elevation angles but a common range and bearing on a geographic position display. All equipment differs from the ideal in small respects that collectively degrade its performance. The operator fails through inattention, lack of training, fatigue, or poor motivation, to perform as an ideal detector. Antenna sidelobes cause energy to return to the receiver from directions other than the target. Variation in atmospheric density and particulate matter like rain cause distortion and scattering in the propagating waves. Depending on the degree of precision sought, this list of departures from the ideal can be augmented almost without end.

However, the qualitative relation between detection range and major system parameters is well represented by equation (4), and the actual performance of many radars differs from that by a factor between 0.5 and 1.0, which can be estimated within a few percent from careful consideration of the significant sources of performance degradation.

REFERENCES

1. Skolnik, M. I. 1962. *Introduction to radar systems*. New York: McGraw-Hill.

Appendix G
Sonar Detection

SONAR SEARCH—GENERAL

The only form of energy that propagates over substantial distances in sea water is sound. For example, in clear waters one can see to a distance of about 50–100 feet, and it has been estimated that the output of a blue-green laser with peak power of one megawatt will travel only about 2000 yards in the sea before its level is virtually undetectable. The hull of a submerged submarine can cause a small, localized anomaly in the earth's magnetic field. This fact is the basis for a magnetic detection system that, because of its short range, is used primarily for localization. On the other hand underwater acoustic propagation measurements have been made over distances of thousands of miles.

Sonar is used to search for submerged submarines, torpedoes, mines, and other underwater objects. Sonar equipment falls into two general categories: passive and active. Passive sonar equipment is designed to detect the sounds made by the target, e.g., propellor noise. Active sonar equipment forms a pulse of sound energy that propagates through the water, is reflected off the target, and propagates back to a receiver. Active sonar is sometimes called echo-ranging sonar because one half the product of the propagation time and the average speed of sound gives an estimate of the range or distance between the sonar and the target.

Passive sonar can give substantial detection ranges on many targets, but it can be defeated by slow, quiet submarines. It can determine the bearing to a target, but the range can only be estimated with difficulty and sometimes these estimates can be erroneous. Classification (being able to tell that a target is indeed a submarine) is usually accomplished quite easily with a passive system because of the distinctive sounds emitted by submarines, surface ships, whales, etc.

Active systems have the advantage that they cannot be defeated by a quiet, slow-moving target. One can obtain range and bearing information and, because of Doppler shifts in frequency, relative speed information. Classification of targets with active sonar is usually more difficult than with passive sonar; however, all active sonar systems necessarily have at least a limited passive capability. Active systems have the disadvantage of having an additional form of interference that does not exist for passive systems. This interference is called reverberation and is caused by the backscattering of the transmitted sound from inhomogeneities in the sea water and its surfaces. Furthermore, it may alert the enemy.

Whether or not a target is detected by sonar depends ultimately on a human operator. Regardless of whether a spot appears on a scope or a sound in a pair of headphones, there is no detection if the operator does not call it. Therefore, the performance of a sonar system depends not only on equipment characteristics and environmental factors, but also on psychological ones.

In this chapter examples of both active and passive sonar detection will be discussed, but only as examples to illustrate the type of problems involved. The aim of the operational analysis of sonar search is to determine how search equipment or search craft should be used in any particular situation to give the best result. This result may be expressed as a lateral range curve or a sweep rate in accordance with Chapter 3. There are a great many factors that determine the lateral range curve, involving characteristics of the equipment, its operation, the target, its behavior, and sound transmission in the ocean. Some variables such as own ship speed can be determined easily by the searcher and controlled to some extent, whereas others, such as sound conditions, are beyond his control. The values of these uncontrollable variables often determine how the values of the others should be chosen. In any particular case, the various factors must be considered in detail, and the lateral range curve obtained in accordance with estimates of the physical situation. Before analyzing any typical problems, however, it is worthwhile giving a general outline of the factors that come into play. In the following we will discuss four types of factors: environmental, target, equipment and displays, and psychological. These factors will be discussed in two columns, one for active and one for passive sonar so that direct comparisons can be made. When identical considerations refer to both active and passive cases, the two-column division will be temporarily abandoned.

Active	*Passive*
The scheme of echo-ranging is shown in Figure G-1.	The scheme of listening detection is shown in Figure G-2.

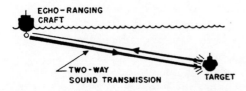

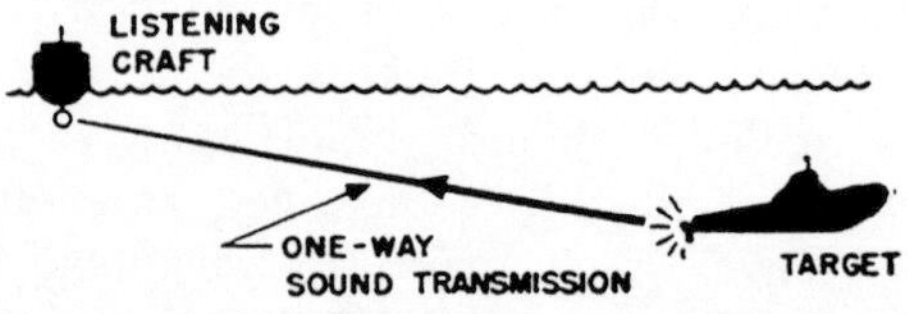

Fig. G-1. Two-way sound transmission. (Source: Bernard Osgood Koopman, *Search and Screening*, OEG Report No. 56, 1946.)

Fig. G-2. One-way sound transmission. (Source: Bernard Osgood Koopman, *Search and Screening*, OEG Report No. 56, 1946.)

ENVIRONMENTAL FACTORS

1. Propagation Loss

The reduction in intensity of the sound as it travels through the ocean is called propagation loss. For an active system the sound experiences a two-way propagation loss, whereas for passive systems, the loss is half of this. In an infinite isotropic medium the propagation loss would be composed of a geometrical spreading term (inverse square law) and an energy absorption term. For this case, the intensity I, in decibels db, can be expressed as a function of range r in yards as

$$(1) \qquad\qquad I = I_0 - 20 \log_{10} r - ar$$

The term I_0 represents the acoustic intensity at a distance one yard from and on the acoustic axis of the source, and a is an absorption coefficient in db/yard.

The ocean is neither infinite nor isotropic. This makes the estimation of propagation loss considerably more difficult and sometimes permits detections to be made at ranges where the simple approach of Eq. (1) would say they should not be possible, and vice versa. The ocean surface and bottom scatter and absorb energy on reflection, and the speed of sound is a function of depth, which varies from place to place. An example of measured propagation loss is given in Fig. G-3. The data were obtained in deep water with a hydrophone at a depth of 1801 meters using explosives as sources detonated at a depth of 91 meters with a horizontal spacing of 0.2 nautical mile. The most outstanding feature of Fig. G-3 is the

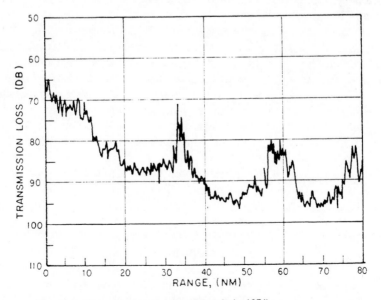

Fig. G-3. (from some measurements made in 1974).

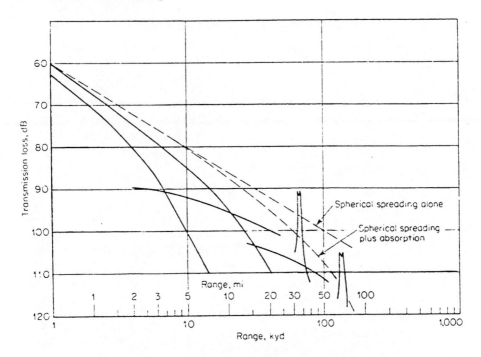

Fig. G-4. Transmission loss versus range for different propagation paths. (Source: Robert J. Urick, *Principles of Underwater Sound for Engineers* [New York: McGraw-Hill, 1967], Fig. 6.26.)

convergence zones exhibited at ranges of about 34 and 58 miles. These are caused by refraction of the acoustic energy.

Figure G-3 is presented here merely to give the reader a feeling for real propagation loss in the ocean as opposed to curves computed from analytical expressions. A simplified and more useful (for our purposes) form of propagation loss is given in Fig. G-4. The dashed curves for spherical (inverse square law) spreading, and spherical spreading plus absorption, are shown for comparison. The heavy curve starting at the left is a direct path with some refraction effects. The other two heavy curves show what can be obtained if the sound reflects off the bottom. Finally, two convergence zones can be seen at about the 35- and 70-mile ranges.

Propagation in shallow water is more complex than for deep water and is considered beyond the scope of this chapter. The curves of Fig. G-4 will be used later in this chapter in the discussion of sonar performance and lateral range curves.

2. Ambient Noise

The noise existing in the ocean that tends to interfere with the detection of sonar signals is called ambient noise. This noise is caused by many different types of

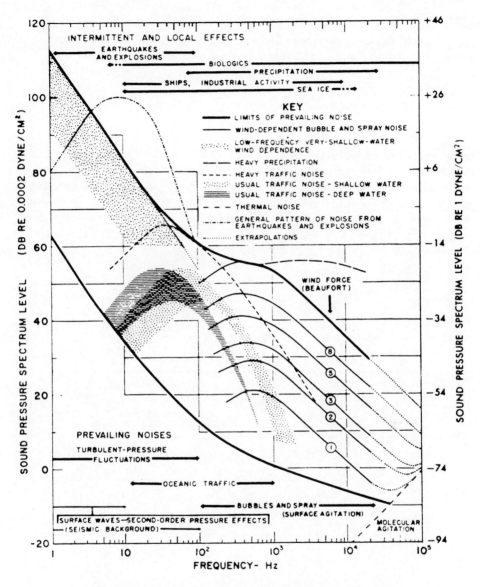

Fig. G-5. A summary of ambient noise sources. (Source: "Oceanography and Underwater Sound for Naval Applications" U.S. Naval Oceanographic Office Special Publication SP-84, October 1965 Fig. 79.)

sources, some of which are given in Fig. G-5. In this figure, the noise spectrum level is plotted against frequency. The spectrum level is the noise pressure in a one-hertz bandwidth centered at a particular frequency, expressed in db.

3. Self-Noise

The interfering noise generated by one's own ship or the sonar equipment itself is called self-noise. Self-noise includes electrical noise that gets into the system. A sonar system should never be limited by electrical noise unless there is a malfunction. Self-noise also includes noise generated by the machinery on the vessel and noise caused by the flow of water. Both of these latter types are speed-dependent. Examples of submarine and destroyer self-noise spectra are given in Figs. G-6 and G-7 respectively.

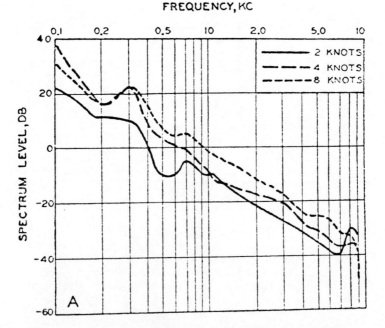

Fig. G-6. Spectra of sonic self-noise of a submarine at various speeds, submerged at periscope depth. (Source: "Principles of Underwater Sound," div. 6, vol. 7, NDRC Summary Technical Reports, National Research Council, 1946, Fig. 4A of Chapter 13.)

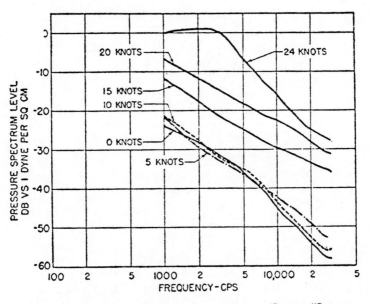

Fig. G-7. Self-noise versus speed for a destroyer. (Source: "Sonar Listening Systems," div. 6, vol. 14, NDRC Summary Technical Reports, 1946, Fig. 10 of Chapter 13.)

4. Reverberation

Reverberation is the backscattering of transmitted sound into the receiving system. As such it pertains only to active systems. The scattering is caused by acoustic reflections off the ocean surface and bottom and off inhomogeneities in the water column. The reverberation level depends on the horizontal and vertical beamwidths of the transmitting and receiving systems and the pulse length, since these determine the volume or area insonified. Reverberation level can be reduced by reducing pulse length or beamwidth (if possible) or both. In general, the limiting form of interference for active sonars is reverberation at short range and noise at long range. Reverberation is extremely variable and has been studied to a con-

siderable extent. A detailed discussion of reverberation and scattering is beyond the scope of this chapter.

TARGET FACTORS

1. Radiated Noise

The radiated noise of surface vessels and submarines is used by passive systems to make detections. The spectra of these craft depend on the type, size, speed, and—for any particular ship—on its state of maintenance and operating conditions. For submarines, the spectra also depend on the operating depth. At low speed the spectra are dominated by machinery noise and at high speed the dominant factor is cavitation. Figures G-8 and G-9 give some smoothed

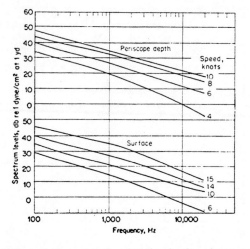

Fig. G-8. Smoothed spectra of conventional submarines on electric drive. (Source: Robert J. Urick, *Principles of Underwater Sound for Engineers* (New York: McGraw-Hill, 1967), Fig. 10.16.)

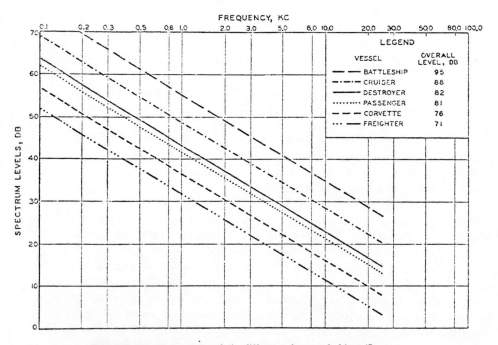

Fig. G-9. Average spectra of six different classes of ships. (Source: "Principles of Underwater Sound," div. 6, vol. 7, NDRC Summary Technical Reports, National Research Council, Chap. 12, Fig. 15.)

spectra for submarines and surface ships respectively.

2. Target Strength

Target strength refers to the reflecting power of the target and is analogous to the term effective radar cross section used in radar.

When the sound beam strikes the target, the amount reflected depends on the size and shape of the target, the nature of the target material, and also its orientation. The frequency and ping length of the sound being reflected are also of importance. These various factors determine the "target strength," which gives the intensity of the echo (reduced to 1 yard from the target) relative to the intensity of the outgoing ping when it hits the target. For a submarine, typical values would be

Bow aspect	16 db
Beam aspect	25 db
Stern aspect	8 db

3. Target Speed

Target speed affects both active and passive system performance. The radiated noise spectrum of the target is speed-dependent as shown in Fig. G-8. Certain distinctive operating noises and cavitation noise become more apparent at higher speeds. These factors influence passive sonar performance. Doppler frequency shifting depends on the speed of the target relative to that of the sonar. This is an important factor for active sonar systems, because if the Doppler shift is great enough the sonar may operate under noise-limited conditions rather than reverberation-limited conditions.

4. Target Aspect

Target aspect of a submarine is the angle of viewing of the target by the sonar, e.g., bow on, stern on, beam on, etc. It is important to active systems because it determines the target strength as mentioned above. Its importance to passive systems lies in the fact that the target is not a uniform radiator of sound.

5. Target Depth

The target operating depth affects the signals received by both active and passive systems. If the target is operating near the water surface there may be a direct acoustic path from target to sonar and a surface-reflected path of almost equal strength. Under these conditions acoustic interference can occur, causing reinforcement and cancellation in the echo received by active systems or in the radiated signal received by passive systems. If the target is deep, the paths may be separated in time and level to the point where the interference is trivial. Also, if the target is deep, propellor cavitation will be suppressed and passive detection may be more difficult.

EQUIPMENT FACTORS

1. Beamforming

In order to obtain directional discrimination in both transmission and reception, sonar systems use acoustic apertures that are several wavelengths in dimension. Use of these apertures results in diffraction patterns familiar from optics; in sonar work they are called beam patterns. In general, the patterns have a major lobe or beam defining an angular region of enhanced sensitivity or response surrounded by a region of reduced sensitivity that contains many minor or side lobes. For details, see Appendix D.

Modern sonar systems fill the acoustic aperture with a number of transducers that are used for both transmission and reception if the system is active, or hydrophones if the system is passive. The outputs of the array elements are combined in a beamformer that generally adds these voltages. If the array elements all lie in a plane, the beam pattern obtained by addition has the major lobe pointed normal to the plane. If the elements lie on a curved surface, the element outputs must be phase-shifted (narrowband system) or time-delayed (broadband system) to make the signals add in phase. Beamformers can also be used to steer the beam to a given direction without physically turning the array and also to form several beams simultaneously. Because of power limitations, active systems usually form only one transmitting beam but may rotate this beam during transmission. They may scan or monitor a number of preformed beams on reception. The formation of several simultaneous beams is usually accomplished by use of digital circuitry, which causes about one db reduction in signal-to-noise ratio.

2. Array Gain

The array gain of an array is the amount in db by which the signal-to-noise ratio at the beamformer output is greater than that obtained at the terminals of a single, omnidirectional hydrophone under the same acoustic conditions. The only restriction in this definition is that the coherence and directionality of the signal and noise fields must be the same for both hydrophone and array. If the coherence and directionality of the signal and noise fields are known, the array gain can be computed as the difference between the array signal gain and the array noise gain, all quantities in db.

For the special case of a plane wave signal and isotropic noise the array gain is called directivity index. A completely filled array is one in which the sensing elements are spaced no farther apart than one-half wavelength. For this type of linear array the approximate directivity index is given by $10 \log_{10}(2L/\lambda)$ where L is the length of the array and λ is the wavelength of the sound. Under the same conditions the approximate directivity index for an area array is given by $10 \log_{10}(4\pi A/\lambda^2)$ where A is the area of the array.

3. Source Level

Source level is a measure in decibels of the intensity of the transmitted pulse of an active system. It is determined for a position on the axis of the major lobe of the projector beam pattern at a given distance from the projector, usually one yard or one meter. Source level consists of two parts, one due to the total power radiated, and the other due to the directivity index of the projector array. Directivity in a projector array concentrates the radiated power in the major lobe of the beam pattern. Therefore, for a given power output, the more directive the array, the higher the source level. A typical value for source level is 110 db relative to one microbar at one yard.

4. Signals and Signal Processing

Several different types of signals are used by active sonar systems for various reasons. The most prevalent are pulsed sinusoids (called pulsed CW), pulsed frequency-modulated (FM) and explosives. Explosives are used primarily from aircraft because they yield a high source level from a small, lightweight package. Pulsed FM has certain advantages when the sonar is reverberation-limited.

The purpose of signal processing is to enhance the signal-to-noise ratio before it is presented to an operator. The more common types of signal processing are filtering, energy detection, and correlation. Filtering is a technique for dividing the receiving frequency band of a sonar into relatively small increments and observing each one individually. This process eliminates all the interference except for a small amount that exists at approximately the same frequency as the signal. Energy detection is a technique that makes it possible to observe relatively sudden changes in incoming energy as a function of frequency, bearing, or time. Correlation techniques are used to exploit the coherence of signals and incoherence of most forms of interference. For active systems the received waveform is compared electronically with a replica of the transmitted waveform. For passive systems the waveforms received by sensors separated in space are compared.

DISPLAYS AND PSYCHOLOGICAL FACTORS

The sonar displays in common usage today are headphones, several types of cathode ray tubes (CRT), and chemical paper rolls. A well-trained and experienced operator can still do a very creditable job of detection and classification using his aural faculties. He can detect echoes in noise and reverberation backgrounds and, many times, can determine if the Doppler shift is up (closing range) or down (opening range). When listening passively he is able to classify targets by their distinctive sounds. Many of these feats are accomplished through the use of what the psychological acousticians call the aural critical bands. The operator's auditory faculty functions as a bank of juxtaposed band pass filters of varying width, which can be sampled selectively. Through the use of this mechanism the operator is able to extract clues and use them to detect and classify.

The CRT displays are usually used with active systems and are of the plan-position-indicator (PPI) type. On this type of display the target shows up as a light spot, and the range and either true or relative bearing to the target can be read.

The paper displays are usually used with passive systems. The most common ones are frequency-time recorders and bearing-time recorders. These display energy as a function of frequency or bearing across the paper roll vs. time along the length of the paper. The use of this type of display allows the operator to perform a visual integration of the signal, which enhances the signal-to-noise ratio.

Associated with each of these displays there is a quantity called recognition differential. This is simply the signal-to-noise ratio at the input to the processing-display subsystem (or output of the beamformer) required for the operator to make a detection with a probability of 50%. Put another way, when the recognition differential is obtained at the beamformer output, it is just as likely that the operator will miss the detection as that he will make it. The recognition differential is a fixed number of decibels for any particular sonar in proper operating condition.

Most of the time the signal-to-noise ratio existing at the beamformer output will be either greater than or less than the recognition differential. The difference between the existing signal-to-noise ratio and the recognition differential is called signal excess. Positive signal excess indicates that the probability of detection is greater than 50% and negative that it is less than 50%. In the following we will explain how sonar range can be related to probability of detection by using signal excess.

Signal excess E in decibels can be computed from the following relationships.

(2) $$E = L - H - N + G - \Delta \quad \text{(passive)},$$
(3) $$E = L - 2H - I + T + G - \Delta \quad \text{(active)},$$

where L = source level of sonar projector (active) or radiated noise of target (passive), H = one-way propagation loss, N = noise level, G = array gain, Δ = recognition differential, I = interference level for active system (either noise or reverberation or the energy sum of both), and T = target strength.

Two assumptions are made that are usually fairly good: (1) signal excess is normally distributed in decibels, and (2) the terms in the signal excess equations are statistically independent. The second assumption permits the computation of the variance of signal excess as the sum of the variances of the terms in the equation if they are known. Knowing the signal excess and its variance permits one to use the normal distribution assumption to estimate probability of detection.

SONAR DETECTION EXAMPLES

Passive Detection

For illustrative purposes we will consider the detection of a submarine by use of a passive radio sonobuoy. The sonobuoy system is usually deployed and monitored from an aircraft. As such it is small and lightweight and so uses a single hydrophone as the sensing element, which is omni-directional ($G = 0$ db). It will be assumed that the recognition differential for this system is -8 db.

For a target we will take a periscope-depth submarine traveling at 6 knots. From Fig. G-8 we find that the source level L of this target is 27 db re 1 dyne/an^2 at 1 yard at an assumed frequency of 1 kHz. It will be further assumed that the Beaufort wind force is 1 so the ambient noise is -55 db and there is no self-noise.

To find the allowable transmission loss for 50% probability of detection we use Eq. (2), set $E = 0$ and solve for H:

(4) $$H = L - N + G - \Delta.$$

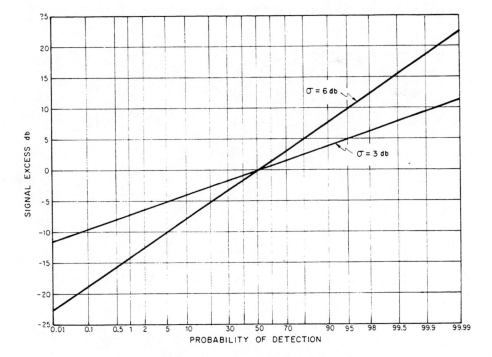

Fig. G-10. Signal excess vs. probability of detection for two standard deviation values (σ).

Substituting values from above one obtains

$$H = 27 + 55 + 0 + 8 = 90 \text{ db.}$$

Using Fig. G-4, we find that this transmission loss corresponds to a range of 15 kiloyards, i.e., the range at which the probability of detection is 50%.

There are several ways of finding the ranges that correspond to other probabilities of detection. The way to be described here uses a plot of signal excess vs. probability of detection on arithmetic (normal) probability graph paper. On this paper a normal distribution plots as a straight line passing through the points signal excess = 0, probability = 50%, and signal excess = one standard deviation (σ), probability = 84%. Such a plot is given in Fig. G-10, where the assumed values for σ mentioned earlier are used. One uses this plot by reading the value of signal excess corresponding to the desired probability of detection. This value of signal excess is substituted in (2) which is then solved for propagation loss H. The range corresponding to this loss is read from Fig. G-4 as before. This has been done for the passive detection case considered here, and the results are given in Fig. G-11. In addition to showing how the probability of detection varies with range, this figure clearly illustrates the effects of the standard deviation of signal excess on the lateral range curves. The smaller σ leads to a curve whose shape approaches that expected from a definite range law. The probability of detection remains quite high out to a range of about 10 kiloyards and then drops quite sharply. The curve with

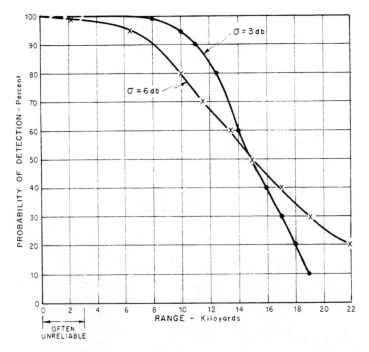

Fig. G-11. Probability of detection vs. range for a passive sonar.

the larger σ maintains a more gentle slope over most of the range. This illustrates the point that definite range law assumptions are dangerous under conditions where the standard deviation is substantial.

Active Detection

Next let us consider the detection of a submarine by use of active sonar. We assume a sonar system with a source level of 110 db *re* 1 dyne/cm² at 1 yard (including directivity index) and operating at a frequency of 5 kHz. Further assume the directivity index is 20 db. This corresponds to a beamwidth of about 20° between -3 db points if the aperture has the shape of a circular piston. The searching ship's speed is assumed to be 10 knots, and the self-noise spectrum level is -35 db (Fig. G-7). Assume the Beaufort wind force is 5 so the ambient noise level is -47 db. Since the self-noise dominates, the ambient noise can be ignored. In most cases where self-noise dominates, the sonar directivity will not help to increase the signal-to-noise ratio. If detailed information about the self-noise is available, such as what it is and whether or not it is located in the near field (Fresnel region) of the sonar, a decision can be made as to the validity of including directivity index or array gain in the performance prediction calculations. Generally the prediction will have to be based on only the kind of information available here so for the self-noise-limited sonar, the value to be used for array gain in Eq. (3) is 0 db.

For this example we will consider the simple case of an active sonar that uses a pulsed sinusoid as its signal. To a first approximation we can consider the energy in the pulse as existing at a single frequency (there is some spectral spreading caused by the finite length of the pulse). The reflected pulse will also consist of energy at a single frequency, which may be different from the transmitted frequency due to the relative motion of sonar and target (Doppler shift). It can be seen that because of the possibility of Doppler shifts, the frequency bandwidth of the receiver must be wider than required to just accommodate the transmitted pulse. For the purposes of our example we will assume the bandwidth of the receiver is 50 Hz, which will accommodate ± 7.5 knots of Doppler shift at 5 kHz. The required added bandwidth has the deleterious effect of allowing extra noise into the system. The noise spectra given in Figs. G-5 and G-7 are values for a 1-Hz bandwidth. Assuming that over a 50-Hz bandwidth the noise spectrum is linear, one can see that the total noise allowed into the receiver is 50 times the values obtained from the spectral plots. This means that the noise values to be used in Eq. (3) are the spectrum levels plus 10 log (receiver bandwidth). In this example the receiver bandwidth is 50 Hz, and so the spectrum levels are increased by 17 db.

Before proceeding with the lateral range curve calculation we must make two more assumptions: the target is presenting bow aspect so the target strength is 16 db, and the recognition differential for the sonar is -7 db.

The foregoing values are substituted in Eq. (3), E is set equal to zero, and the equation is solved for the transmission loss H, yielding $H = 75.5$ db. From Fig. G-4

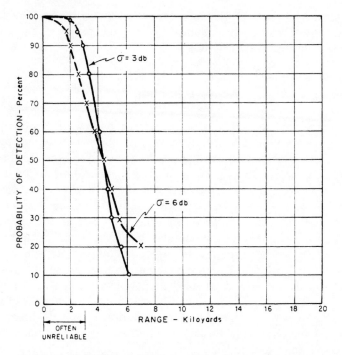

Fig. G-12. Probability of detection vs. range for an active sonar.

we find that this corresponds to a range of 4.5 kiloyards for a detection probability of 50%. From here on the computations are the same as for the passive case. Figure G-10 is used to obtain the signal excess values for the probabilities of interest. These values are substituted in Eq. (3), which is solved for propagation loss H, and the corresponding range values are obtained from Fig. G-4. The results of this work are shown in Fig. G-12.

Once again, the effect of the standard deviation can be seen, but the contrast in the curves does not appear to be as great as in the passive case. This is probably due to the shorter ranges involved.

Authors Cited

Albert A. A., 302
Andrews, F. A., 171
Batcheler, G. K., 298
Belkin, B., 310
Blackwell, H. R., 333
Bloomfield, J. R., 333
Bôcher, Maxime, 302
Bourbaki, N., 170
Bridgman, P. W., 7
Cartan, Elie, 302
Chew, M. D., 193
Cornsweet, T. N., 333
Courant, R., and Hilbert, D., 137
Cox, D. R., and Miller, H. D., 298
Craik, K. J. W., 325
De Guenin, J., 171, 310
Dobbie, J. M., 7, 45, 170, 171, 193, 310
Doetsh, G., 137
Doob, J. L., 298
Duntly, S. Q., 333
Everett, H., III, 171
Fano, R. M., 193
Feller, W., 137, 298
Gelb, A., 137
Gibbs, J. Willard, 171
Gordon, J. I., 334
Halmos, P. R., 298
Hardy G. E., Littlewood, J. E., and
   Polya, G., 298
Hecht, Selig, 334
Hellman, O., 193
Hilbert, D., 137
Kimball, G. E., 193, 298

Kolesar, P., 23
Koopman, B. O., 7, 90, 137, 171, 193, 298,
   310
Krendel, E. S., 334
Kullback, S., 193
Lamar, E. S., 334
Levine, R. D., 298
Littlewood, J. E., 298
Miller, H. D., 298
Morse, P. M., 7, 298
National Research Council, 333, 334, 335
Osgood, W. F., 137
Persinger, C. A., 193
Pirenne, M. H., 335
Pollock, S. M., 193
Polya, G., 298
Richardson, H. R., 90, 171, 310
Ross, S., 193
Sanshine, J. A., 193
Scripps Institute, 325
Shlaer, S., 334
Skolnik, M. J., 7, 337
Stone, L. D., 7, 90, 171, 193, 310
Taylor, J. E., 333
Tribus, M., and Levine, R. D., 298
U.S. Naval Oceanographic Lab., 347
Urick, R. J., 314, 346
Watson, G. H., 137
Whittaker, E. T., 137
Widder, D. V., 310
Wiener, Norbert, 298
Wodinsky, J., 334

For a bibliographical survey and digest of search theory up to 1968, see Dobbie, J. M., A Survey of Search Theory, *Oper. Res.* 16:525–37.

For a more complete list of works on vision in connection with visual search, see the bibliography at the end of Appendix E.

Index

About the Author

BERNARD OSGOOD KOOPMAN (Ph.D.–Harvard) is Adrain Professor of Mathematics Emeritus of Columbia University from which he retired in 1968 after 41 years in the Department of Mathematics (Department Chairman for five years). He discovered the connection between Hamiltonian systems and Hilbert space, which led Von Neumann and G. D. Birkhoff to the Ergodic theory and thence led to a modern revival in theoretical dynamics. With Dr. Kimball, he founded the modern theory of search and applied it in World War II to the design of many naval operating plans. Analysis of search and various methods of detection has continued to the present time and has recently led him, in cooperation with Dr. Gordon Raisbeck, to develop new methods for the study of hydro-acoustic propagation. His study of war games and combat simulation has led him to uncover the role of the underlying stochastic process.